Title: Space Elevators: An Assessment of the Technological Feasibility and the Way Forward

Editors: Peter A. Swan, David I. Raitt, Cathy W. Swan, Robert E. Penny, John M. Knapman

Printing of this Study was sponsored by The Virginia Edition Publishing Company

International Academy of Astronautics
6 rue Galilée, Po Box 1268-16,
75766 Paris Cedex 16, France
www.iaaweb.org

ISBN/EAN IAA : 9782917761311

9 782917 761311

Cover Illustration: chasedesignstudios.com

Space Elevators: An Assessment of the Technological Feasibility and the Way Forward

Editors

Peter A. Swan
David I. Raitt
Cathy W. Swan
Robert E. Penny
John M. Knapman

4

Table of Contents

Acknowledgements

This study was conducted under the auspices of Commission III (Space Technology & System Development) of the International Academy of Astronautics (IAA) and benefited from review and comments by numerous members of the Academy, as well as members of the Commission and the International Space Elevator Consortium.

The study could not have been completed to this level of detail without the timely and invaluable efforts of a diverse collection of experts from around the world who contributed not only their time and knowledge, but also provided material as well as their technical expertise for the study. These experts included the members of the study group, the chapter authors to whom significant recognition should go, and especially the editors of the study (all names are provided in Appendix A). The diverse contributors included individuals (as well as former staff now retired) from space agencies, commercial firms, universities and non-profit organizations.

Thanks are also due to the members of the International Academy of Astronautics review committees who provided highly useful comments on the final draft of this study report.

For a number of years the IAA has sponsored sessions on space elevators, encouraging research towards the cosmic study, at the yearly International Astronautical Congresses - held under the auspices of the International Astronautical Federation (IAF), the International Academy of Astronautics (IAA) and the International Institute of Space Law (IISL) - in Vancouver (2004), Fukuoka (2005), Valencia (2006), Hyderabad (2007), Glasgow (2008), Daejeon (2009), Prague (2010), Cape Town (2011), Naples (2012) and Beijing (2013). Thanks are due to the organizers of these sessions and all those contributing papers at the sessions together with the attendees whose questions and lively participation helped clarify and solidify concepts and ideas.

In addition, special thanks are made to the International Space Elevator Consortium (ISEC) for co-hosting and supporting the series of workshops held at the yearly ISEC conference in Seattle which again brought minds together to focus on the issues.

The Editors

Preface

I am pleased to acknowledge the present International Academy of Astronautics (IAA) cosmic study entitled "Space Elevators: An Assessment of the Technological Feasibility and the Way Forward." I should like to thank the Study Group members who have prepared this study, the peer reviewers, and also the Trustees of the Academy who have reviewed it. I would particularly like to thank the Editors Peter A. Swan, David I. Raitt, Robert E. Penny, Cathy W. Swan and John M. Knapman for their dedication to the work.

The study is a timely input to the Heads of Space Agencies Summit in Washington in January 2014, organized by the IAA, the subject of which is Space Exploration - Planetary Robotic and Human Spaceflight Exploration. No doubt all the space agencies of the world will welcome such a definitive study that investigates new ways of transportation with major changes associated with inexpensive routine access to GEO and beyond.

After 50 years of existence, the International Academy of Astronautics is recognized by space agencies as a unique and elite body that can help in advancing international cooperation. There is no doubt that the Academy, due to this study, will contribute to advancing international consensus and awareness on the need to search and develop new ways of transportation in conducting space exploration while preserving our universe in the same way we are now trying to preserve our planet Earth. Many newcomers joining the club of emerging space countries will also benefit from this study in their future international space cooperation.

The IAA, with members from all over the world, is engaged in extending the frontiers of knowledge in space exploration and also in finding applications to solve the everyday problems of humankind. Academicians are working in unison to achieve the set goals of the Academy and it is inspiring to note the many emerging topics of global importance, such as the present study on space elevators.

Gopalan Madhavan Nair
President
International Academy of Astronautics

Executive Summary

"Don't undertake a project unless it is manifestly important and nearly impossible[1]."

What are the questions for this study report?

This report addresses the simple and complex issues that have been identified through the development of space elevator concepts over the last decade. The report begins with a summary of those ideas in Edwards' and Westling's book "The Space Elevator" (2003). Out of these beginnings has risen a worldwide cadre focused upon their areas of expertise as applied to space elevator development and operational infrastructure. The report answers some basic questions about the feasibility of a space elevator infrastructure. A preview of the main questions and answers shows the depth and breadth of this Cosmic Study.

- Why a space elevator?
- Can it be done?
- How would all the elements fit together to create a system of systems?
- What are the technical feasibilities of each major space elevator element?

What is a space elevator?

A space elevator is a system for lifting payloads, and eventually people, from the Earth's surface into space. The one under consideration in this report consists of a tether 100,000km long balanced about a node in geosynchronous orbit (GEO) and reaching down to an anchor point on Earth. Electrically powered spacecraft, called tether climbers, travel up or down the tether at far lower costs [currently projected at $500/kg] than using rockets. In addition, the service the space elevator provides is a cargo capacity/throughput of two orders of magnitude larger than present rockets, with tremendously kinder environmental effects, and a miniscule potential for future space debris. Tether climbers can continue to the apex anchor – the point at 100,000km altitude – where their speed is sufficient for direct interplanetary travel.

Why a space elevator?

The value and benefit of developing a space elevator infrastructure is even greater than earlier estimates, as it will change our approach to operations in space. Low cost, safe, reliable and flexible delivery of payloads to Geosynchronous Earth Orbit (GEO) and beyond could create an "off-planet" environment filled with opportunities ranging from commercial space systems to exploration of the solar system. Daily initiation of 20 metric ton climbers, safe delivery to GEO and beyond, and a projected price of $500 per kg, will open up the solar system and lead to many new commercial ventures. In addition, the radical change from chemical rockets and the low risk approach of climbing vertically at reasonable speeds will greatly reduce two major hazards that are dominant today: 1) the environmentally friendly, electrically driven, motors will have almost no hazardous material polluting the atmosphere, and 2) this delivery technique does not create orbital debris, especially in Low Earth Orbit (LEO).

Another major benefit will be in supporting human exploration. The first ten years will enable massive movement of equipment to GEO and beyond. Human exploration can leverage this

---

[1] Edwin Land, quoted in the Coral Reef Alliance letter, March 30, 2011. www.coral.org

tremendous capability by assembling large spacecraft at GEO with massive fuel loads delivered at $500/kg. After ten years of operations, humans should also be riding to GEO.

The benefits for humanity on Earth can be phenomenal. The ability to inexpensively deliver large quantities to orbit will enable capabilities stimulating an Earth renaissance. The facility to provide power to any location on the surface [space solar power satellites] will enable development across the world. Several examples are that Africa could skip the 20th century of wires while the outback of countries like India or China would not have to burn coal and the Amazon region could retain more of its rain forests. In addition, the increase in communications and Earth resource satellites will remake the emergency warning systems of the world. Some intractable problems on the Earth's surface would also have solutions, such as the safe and secure delivery – and thus disposal - of nuclear waste to solar orbit.

Can it be done?
The authors recognize that the whole project, especially the projected price per kilo, is dependent upon a strong, lightweight material that will enable the space elevator tether. The principal issue is material produceability at the strength, length and perfection needed to enable a 100,000km long tether. Almost all other issues surrounding each of the major segments have either been resolved in space before or are close to being space ready today. Only the tether material is at a high technological risk at this time. Chapter 3 goes into projections of material growth and increase in capabilities showing their potential with a good prospect of suitable material becoming available by the 2020s.

How would all the elements fit together to create a system of systems? Each of the early chapters addresses one of the major elements of space elevator infrastructure. As the study progresses, the reader moves from tether material to individual segments to systems level analyses. This sequence illustrates the parts of a space elevator infrastructure and then shows the operational view as it all fits together. In addition, in the market and financial chapters, the development of future space markets are projected with their funding profiles for the next 40 years.

What are the technical feasibilities of major space elevator elements?
Each of the individual chapters describes major segments of the space elevator and discusses NASA Technical Readiness Levels and Risk Management trades to ensure the technical feasibilities can be assessed. The space elevator roadmaps show the approach from the current year [2013] to operational time periods. A factor for the future of space elevator infrastructure is the majority of components, subsystems, and segments have been developed before as components of other space systems [except for the tether material]. This leverage of 50 years' experience is invaluable and will enable development of space elevator segments in a timely manner.

The conclusions from this study fall into a few distinct categories:

- **Legal:** The space elevator can be accomplished within today's arena

- **Technology:** Its inherent strengths will improve the environment and reduce space debris in LEO and beyond. It can be accomplished with today's projection of where materials science and solar array efficiencies are headed. The critical capability improvement is in the space elevator tether materials, currently projected to achieve the necessary strength to weight ratio in the next 20 years. The space elevator will open up human spaceflight and decrease space debris and environmental impacts.

- **Business:** This mega-project will be successful for investors with a positive return on investment within 10 years after erection is complete.

- **Cultural:** This project will drive a renaissance on the surface of the Earth with its solutions to key problems, stimulation of travel throughout the solar system, with inexpensive and routine access to GEO and beyond.

Potential Role for the International Academy of Astronautics
The authors believe that the IAA will have a significant role in future space development with their global reach inside National Space Agencies. As such, it is proposed that:

- The Academy establishes a Space Elevator Permanent Committee to coordinate efforts in space elevator research and development projects within National Space Agencies. Initially, the efforts would be centered around follow-up activities resulting from the distribution of this report to some 300 locations inside the world-wide space arena. This focus would ensure a global enterprise.

- The Academy assists Space Elevator activities in understanding the developing space markets, such as the Space Solar Power or Asteroid Mining ventures.

Cosmic Study Result
The authors have come to believe that the operation of a space elevator infrastructure will lead to a "game changing" experience in the space world. Each of the authors considers that the space elevator can be developed when the tether material is mature enough. Our final assessments are:

**A Space Elevator appears feasible, with the realization
that risks must be mitigated through technological progress.**
and
**A Space Elevator infrastructure will be achievable
through a major global enterprise.**

Introduction

Background

Today's rocket launches have improved dramatically from the early days when two out of three rockets exploded. While complete failures and explosions are less frequent, delivery to incorrect orbits occurs more often than desired. However, improvements in rocket technology have made them more reliable, not significantly more economical or less dangerous to the payload or the environment. The world needs a routine, safe, affordable, and easy method of gaining orbit. As far as the authors of this study are concerned, the Star Trek options of gravity alterations or dilithium crystals are not available in the near future. However, the authors truly believe that there is a potential for space elevators to provide such routine, safe, daily, inexpensive and quiet access to orbit. Two of the key advantages need to be illuminated: a) an environmentally friendly approach; and, b) a significant decrease in space debris growth. As such, this study has been undertaken to pursue risk reduction technology development and present a systems engineering look at how to accomplish the goal of a space elevator transportation infrastructure to Earth orbit and beyond.

The initial question is "What is a space elevator?" A space elevator is a system for lifting payloads, and eventually people, from the Earth's surface into space. The system considered here consists of a 100,000km long tether balanced about a node in geosynchronous orbit (GEO) and reaching down to an anchor point on Earth. Electrically powered spacecraft, called tether climbers, travel up or down the tether to reach GEO at far lower cost than using rockets. This lower cost is currently estimated to be in the order of $500/kg. In addition, the cargo capacity/throughput service is two orders of magnitude larger than current rockets, the environmental effects are significantly kinder, and the potential for future space debris is minuscule. Tether climbers can continue to the apex anchor – the point at 100,000km altitude – where their speed is sufficient for direct interplanetary travel.

This study report is centered around the first ten years of operations with robotic tether climbers and non-human payloads. Once the concept has been validated, and the proper support for human transportation is refined [radiation hardening, one week duration compatibility, and low-g levels], the movement of humanity can begin in earnest towards the solar system. This concept is shown in Figure 1 as a Nodal Layout for a space elevator transportation infrastructure. Tether climbers are shown both below and above the GEO Node to illustrate the approach; and, the Marine Node is expanded to show an Earth terminus that supports the infrastructure. There will be many potential variations [concept options] for each of the segments of a space elevator – as there should be for any major engineering study conducted 20 + years before operations.

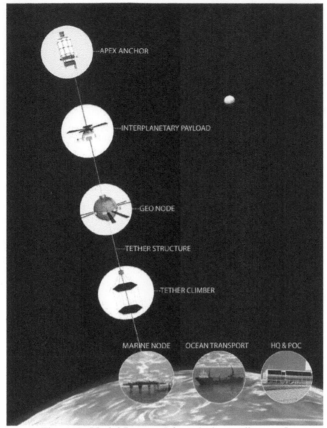
Figure 1. Nodal Layout [chasedesignstudios.com]

Why this study report?
Key to this tremendous global study effort is a realization by the International Academy of Astronautics (IAA) that if significant growth in global space enterprises is to occur, access to space MUST become more economical. Many options have been proposed – re-usable launch vehicles, magnetic levitation, rail guns and gravity adaptations. The authors of this study believe in a figure of $500/kg to Geosynchronous Earth Orbit (GEO) and are working on one approach towards this end. This reduction in cost, by two orders of magnitude, will make space accessible for anyone sufficiently motivated. It is too early in the development cycle to declare success; however, this report will show a path that could succeed. There are many engineering, social, legal and financial challenges yet to be solved; however, this document addresses solutions to most of them. In addition, the rewards to the global environment would be remarkable – not least the safe disposal of nuclear waste. It is very difficult to predict the future; but, the potential for space elevator success is tangible. At the 2nd Space Elevator Conference in Santa Fe, Sir Arthur C. Clarke (2003) stated:

"The space elevator will be built ten years after they stop laughing....
And they have stopped laughing!"

Why a Space Elevator?

To understand <u>why</u> a space elevator is needed, three components of the discussion must be present:

- **The human spirit needs no restrictions:** Once the Apollo 8 picture of the Earthrise from lunar orbit was broadcast, the world was sensitized to our limitations and realized that we were on a fragile planet. We must soar beyond our boundaries and expand into the solar system and beyond. Figure 2 shows the image that illustrated the fragility of Mother Earth.

Figure 2. First View of the Fragile Earth Credit: NASA

- **The realization that chemical rockets cannot get us to and beyond Low Earth Orbit economically:** The rocket equation requires that approximately 80% of the mass on the launch pad is fuel and 14% is structure, control equipment and other essential elements of a launch vehicle. This leaves roughly 6% for payload [mission satellite]. Taking mass with you to consume [fuel] and throw away [structures] is economically catastrophic when you must reach 300km altitude and 7.9km/sec to be in Low Earth Orbit. The tyranny of this rocket equation, driven by the pwerful gravity well, must be broken to enable commercial expansion into space.

- **The recognition that the "*Space Option*" will enable solutions to some of Earth's current limitations:** The space option is an alternative that will open access to space to humanity. Resources, expansion area and future hopes ride with the launch of each satellite and exploration activity. By lowering the price to orbit, ensuring an infrastructure that does not throw away 94% of its mass every time it launches, and by making spaceflight respond to a daily or weekly schedule will ensure that expansion beyond Earth can be real.

These driving desires will enable the space elevator to be constructed and will result in a new paradigm that is closer to a train schedule than anything so far achieved in space. A premise is that when the space elevator infrastructure is completed and daily operations are refined, tremendous demands from new businesses, in addition to regular or old space customers, will surface. The key changes that will revolutionize the space environment are:

- **Routine:** Space will become routine with lift-offs occurring every day with 20-ton tether climbers.

- **Price:**   The price for a payload to be delivered to GEO will be below $500/kg. This change from the current figure of around $20,000/kg will alter the clientele for space liftoff and open businesses by entrepreneurs that are not even considered today.
- **Safety:**   Elevators have inherent safety vs. the dangerous practice of mounting valuable payloads on top of huge tanks of high explosives.
- **Delivery Dynamics:**   Space elevators will have vibrations in the region of cycles per day and shock loads equivalent to petals dropping into a pond instead of the explosive potential and violent rock and roll experienced during rocket lift off.
- **Good for the Environment:**   Operations of a space elevator will decrease environmental damage and almost eliminate creation of new space debris.

The beauty of this situation is that the remarkable routine, inexpensive trip to space can be safe. The dreams of humanity and the desires of space travel can ensure that the motivation to build a space elevator will flourish once the feasibility has been proven. This future end state of routine, inexpensive, and safe operations on a space elevator infrastructure will lead to a tremendous community established at the unique region around each space elevator longitude and GEO altitude [approx. 42,000km radius]. A key is that the physical attributes of a space elevator results in a remarkable coincidence – proven space location for commercial and government mission successes and an easy environment to conduct operations within a free fall [zero weight/zero stress] environment. This space elevator optimization of location occurs where the space elevator meets the GEO altitude and leads to the following three sets of future missions and activities.

- Space Transportation Post [refueling, assembly, variable velocity "kicks", recovery/refurbishment/repair, command posts, communications]
- Assembly station for satellites in free fall environment [Interplanetary, Communications, Navigation, Earth Resources, Space Based Solar Power, Scientific investigations, Commercial Initiatives]
- Human Station [Hotel growing to Colony]

Initial Space Elevator Vision
We have all heard of the problems in our world. Our toughest challenges include: energy, climate, health, fresh water, natural disasters, conflicts and global collapse. Issues such as AIDS, war, terrorism, globalism, and weakening economies are more immediate but pale in comparison to the larger, unstoppable threats that will face us and our children in the coming decades, or millennia.

- Population: Earth may not be able to support the increasing number of people.
- Energy: We are running out of the fossil fuels that are the cornerstone of modern societies, and the nuclear power option has been discredited in major countries like Japan and Germany.
- Pollution: Our various activities are affecting the Earth and are creating massive climate change.
- Global Catastrophe: An asteroid hitting the Earth or a tectonic plate movement could be a small disaster, a city killer or a global transformation.

Hence the focus on space exploration, the main drivers of which are:
- The quest for scientific knowledge
- Technological innovation, development and transfer
- Enhancing a strong, competitive industrial base and economy
- Ensuring strategic independence and security
- Strengthening of national identities and cultural development through cooperation
- Inspiration, awareness and education

On the other hand, there are a number of constraints to be taken into account:
- Geopolitical – national policies and increasing globalization
- The foreseeable budget for space exploration activities
- The current costs of space exploration
- The key interests of individual nations
- The available national and international competencies

Having a basic vision for a space elevator is a critical beginning to help provide some solutions to world issues. However, the vision is valuable only if it can be made real, if it is clearly articulated and if a detailed plan for moving from the current state to the goal exists. The space elevator concept has existed in various forms for decades, even centuries, but only with recent efforts has it become a project that can indeed be realized. [See Appendix D for space elevator history]. The vision needs to fit the current culture and shown below is a proposal put forward called a the "Space Elevator Vision." The authors see this as a starting point for the global effort of developing a space elevator infrastructure. The future team responsible for actually building the space elevator should create their own perception as soon as possible. A simple vision that can change the world is proposed here as:

Space Elevator Vision:

The space elevator gives us the road to limitless opportunities while opening up the solar system.

Recently, Scientific American published an article entitled, "Starship Humanity" (Smith, 2013). Early in the introduction, interesting words popped up that parallel our vision, ".. we are entering the early stages of the migration of our species away from Earth..." In addition, in the summary of the article, "...we must re-engage the proactive approach that has made human survival possible up to the present and use that capacity to shape our own evolution beyond our home planet. We must be immensely bolder than our bureaucracies. Failing that, in time we will become extinct, like everything else on Earth. As H. G. Wells wrote about the human future in 1936, it is 'all the universe or nothing.'"

Chapter 1
Study Approach

1.1 Background

During the 3rd annual Space Elevator Conference in Washington, D.C. George Whitesides (Whitesides, 2004) stated:

"Until you build an infrastructure, you are not serious."

This first chapter summarizes Dr. Bradley Edwards' (Edwards and Westling, 2003) space elevator baseline and sets the stage for the rest of the study to illustrate the growth from this historic understanding. In addition, the chapter answers in more detail the question "why now?" It also describes the approach of the International Academy of Astronautics [IAA] for a Cosmic Study. The last part of this chapter lays out the book's structure with a summary of each chapter. This report posits that a global transportation infrastructure could be real in the near term and that the space community has stopped laughing and is being serious. The time is now to address the potential of a space elevator infrastructure to geosynchronous orbit and beyond. As a major stimulus to thinking about the space elevator, Arthur C. Clarke's work reflected the future and where humankind was headed. Throughout his writing career, he summarized three laws that are applicable to the space elevator. They will be reflected during this report in various locations. The first law is:

> Sir Arthur C. Clarke's First Law:
> When a distinguished but elderly scientist states that something is possible, he is almost certainly right. When he states that something is impossible, he is very probably wrong.

1.1.1 Dr. Edwards' Standard

As noted, the current space elevator approach is an outgrowth of the work of Dr. Bradley Edwards resulting in his seminal book "The Space Elevator" (Edwards and Westling, 2003). The initial work was conducted in two phases funded by NIAC – the NASA Institute for Advanced Concepts. Phase I ran from May-October 2000 (Edwards NAIC Phase I) while Phase II ran from March 2001-January 2003 (Edwards NAIC Phase II). This publication changed the landscape from one where the space elevator was an idea in science fiction to one of potential execution in the foreseeable future. Edwards' engineering analyses and savvy insight into what was possible started a ground swell of innovation across the globe. The public embraced the idea and has pursued it in many arenas (newspapers, journals, popular magazines, and TV shows). Over the next ten years the Edwards concept was a baseline for the modern-day space elevator. This was focused around the belief that the materials industry would deliver a tether material of sufficient strength to enable the system of systems called a space elevator. Like our forefathers who pioneered trains, steam engines, airplanes and rockets, the small community of space elevator pioneers are inspired by the possibility and potential of an operational transportation infrastructure going beyond geosynchronous orbit prior to 2040.

For the purpose of this report, and so that engineers can trade against a conceptual design, the general characteristics for the first few space elevators were established in 2003 by Dr. Edwards as:

- Length: 100,000km, anchored on the Earth with a large mass floating in the ocean and a large counterweight at the top end, called an Apex Anchor.
- Width: One meter
- Design: Woven with multiple strands to absorb localized damage and curved to ensure edge-on small size hits do not sever the tether.
- External Power: The power must be external as the gravity well is extreme and lifting your own power is a non-starter. Dr. Edwards' approach was to use large lasers pointing up to the climber with a "solar panel like" receiver on its nadir position.
- Cargo: The first few years will enable 20ton payloads without humans [radiation tolerance an issue for the two week trip] with five concurrent payloads on the tether for the two-week trip to GEO. [Currently, the plan is seven concurrent payloads for one-week travel.]
- Construction Strategy: The first space elevator will be built the tough and only way – down from GEO; then, once the gravity well has been overcome, it will be replicated from the ground up leading to multiple elevators around the globe. This redundancy will reduce the magnitude of catastrophe if one is lost.

1.1.2 Why Now?

Dr. Edwards published his approach in 2003 and showed the world that a space elevator could be built. The present study is a "ten year look" at the development of ideas and concepts that have strengthened belief in a space elevator. It can, and should, be built to improve the quality of life of the Earth's population. Here are some of the innovative ideas that will be addressed in the various chapters.

- Deployment complexity – New "bootstrapping" approach [Chapter 6]
- Solar power only option [Chapter 4] Replace laser source with traditional space power, ubiquitous solar [see Appendix E-2 for details].
- 25-30 MYuri[1] tether design as part of a Feasibility Condition [Chapter 3]
- Space debris concern – Extremely low probability of collision [Chapter 8]
- Roadmap to Reality [Chapter 11]
- Robust Operations Concept [Chapter 9]
- High Stage One to move above atmosphere and open up the option of using only solar arrays for electrical power [Chapter 5]
- Dynamics of ribbon, especially at GEO altitude [Chapter 6]
- A melding of legal regimes [terrestrial, Law of Sea, Aeronautics Law and Space Law] [Chapter 12]
- An update on the financial approach with a preliminary business plan [Chapters 13/14]

These advances in innovative approaches to engineering challenges have surfaced because there is a tremendous demand to have a cost of $500/kg to GEO. This report will present current thinking on an achievable space elevator; and, hopefully, lower the level of risk perception by more in-depth research. In addition, it will enhance understanding of a viable

---

[1] Definition of MYuri is in Appendix E-1.

approach to an infrastructure for space that could be routine, inexpensive, safe, reliable, and possible within 30 years.

1.1.3 Conferences

Since the publication of "The Space Elevator" (Edwards and Westling, 2003), a small community of space elevator enthusiasts has discussed various approaches and analyzed engineering trades. As of the end of 2013, there have been tens of conferences in the United States and around the world focusing on the development of a space elevator concept. The extensive conference activities associated with the community are:

- Annual International Space Elevator Conferences: 1st (2002) Seattle, 2nd (2003) Santa Fe and 3rd (2004) Washington DC.
- Space Exploration 2005 and 2007: Space Elevator Workshops - Albuquerque
- International Astronautical Congress Sessions: 55th Vancouver (2004), 56th Fukuoka (2005), 57th Valencia (2006), 58th Hyderabad (2007), 59th Glasgow (2008), 60th Daejeon (2009), 61st Prague (2010), 62nd Cape Town (2011), 63rd Naples (2012), 64th Beijing (2013).
- International Space Elevator Conference (August in Seattle): 2008, 2009, 2010, 2011, 2012, 2013.
- Japanese Space Elevator Conferences: 2010, 2011, 2012.
- European Space Elevator Conferences: 2007, 2008, 2009, 2010, 2011, 2012.

In addition, NASA's Centennial Challenges have been pointed towards space elevator development along with their parallel activities: the Tether Strength Challenge and the Power Beaming Challenge.

1.2 Cosmic Study Approach

The International Academy of Astronautics is looking at a future space elevator in as many aspects as possible whilst assessing the technological feasibility and debating in parallel the challenges facing the project. This approach consists of professional experts discussing their fields of endeavor and making projections into the future. The combination of the Academy and professionals from around the world is a multiplication of expertise and leveraging of cross discipline skills to discuss and consolidate a future engineering mega-project [see Appendix B for the list of authors]. The forty authors and five editors were as diverse as the space faring nations of today. There were significant contributions from the 21 Japanese authors plus European, Canadian, Australian and American authors and editors.

In the present document, Part I presents the foundation for the study group report. This introductory chapter lays out the report and describes the sponsor and the approach. The second chapter allows the reader to see the "big picture." This infrastructure view of a future space elevator system enables the reader to place the various components together and ensure the system of systems architectural approach is shown.

Part II is a direct look at the issues of the major elements and a description of how to assess these challenges at the systems level while demonstrating success criteria. There are chapters covering individual challenges such as tether material, tether climber design, power to ascend, and anchor characteristics. During each of the major challenges, the discussions start with a baseline, with reasonable alternatives, and analyze their readiness for space implementation. Each of the chapters discusses the basic designs, maturity level of the various parts, risk/consequence levels of each and, finally, shows a path toward implementation. The technological readiness levels [TRL] are assessed along with discussions of our conclusions in the format of findings.

Part III provides a systems look at the basic transportation to space (GEO and beyond) infrastructure. As this is a mega-project that will cross many borders [physical, engineering discipline, political, social and financial], the approach will step through major aspects of a space elevator. In addition, this systems approach includes: how to operate, a cross discipline look at engineering options, requirements based engineering, probable schedule, potential stakeholders, risk assessment, and financial needs across dynamics of the space elevator structure, location of the base node and threats to the tether.

Figure 1-1. Technology Readiness Levels

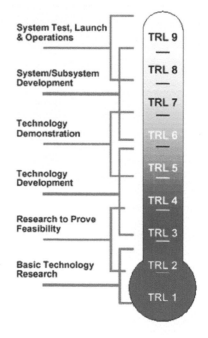

Part IV lays out the roadmap for space elevator development to illustrate that the major components of the infrastructure could come together in a timely manner. This provides an assessment of the status of a space elevator transportation infrastructure with a projection of when, how, and IF the project proceeds. It also looks at the global issues [both financial and legal] while closing the study with final conclusions and recommendations.

The final portion, Part V of the study report, summarizes these conclusions, makes some recommendations, and proposes the next steps to keep the momentum building towards an operational system. During the many chapters and across the many disciplines, two topics are addressed consistently – maturity measure of technology and risk/consequence assessment. The maturity comparison is conducted with a consistent scale of "Technology Readiness Levels (TRL's)," as shown in Figure 1-1. A supporting aspect of a space elevator design is the overall maturity of the components, subsystems, systems and materials. In fact, many items that will make up the elements of a space elevator have already been qualified for space. Other components range from needing scientific refinement through technological demonstration to engineering development.

These three categories of maturity (Westling, 2005) are defined as:

- **Scientific Refinement: TRL 1-3** The ability of mankind to discover how things work.
- **Technological Demonstration: TRL 4-6** Applies science to useful projects by experimentation and testing.
- **Engineering Development: TRL 7-9** Implements knowledge into repeatable and beneficial components, subsystems and systems.

The reality of developing a mega-project is that components of the design fall within all three categories and different levels of development and refinement must be applied. Can you imagine what the developers had to accomplish when producing the following products?

- Gas lamps were placed throughout London
- Electricity was provided around Washington, D.C.
- Telephones were installed across Canada
- Airplanes started carrying paying passengers around the Pacific
- The tunnel was drilled under the English Channel.
- The bridge was built between Denmark and Sweden.

A look at the elements of a space elevator with respect to risk is presented in the space systems engineering approach of risk vs. consequence. The chart below (Figure 1-2) shows a generic state, where the likelihood of a risk occurring is in the vertical axis and consequence of such risk is in the horizontal axis. By placing the appropriate item of concern in a square, the manager can understand the importance or need to respond to a specific engineering risk. The top ten risks of a project are identified and placed inside the risk matrix.

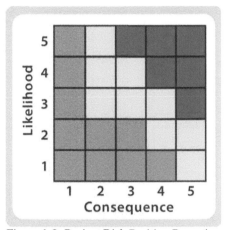

Figure 1-2. Project Risk Position Reporting

1.3   Layout of the Cosmic Study
The following paragraphs show the flow of the study report. For each chapter below a brief abstract is presented.

Part I – Introductory

Chapter 1: Study Approach
This first chapter establishes Brad Edwards' space elevator baseline in 2003, and sets the stage for the rest of the study to grow from this historic baseline. In addition, the chapter describes "why a space elevator," suggests a comprehensive vision, and indicates the IAA's approach for their cosmic studies.

Chapter 2: Systems Infrastructure View

This chapter presents the "big picture" of the design of a space elevator from the operational concept of a High Stage One to multiple space elevators in the Eastern Pacific. The idea of this chapter, placed early in the study report, is to enable the reader to place all the major components together and help fathom the complexity of the system of systems, called a Space Elevator Transportation Infrastructure.

Part II – Major Elements

Chapter 3: Tether Material

A space elevator tether must be made of a material that can withstand both its environment and operational stresses. A feasibility condition is identified which establishes goals for the tether material. Materials currently being tested in the laboratory have surpassed that level and promise a tether that can withstand the environmental and operational stresses necessary.

Chapter 4: Spacecraft: Deployment, Buildup, Operational

The variety of climbers will surprise even the early believers in a space elevator. There will be tether weavers, repairers, safety inspectors along with logistical trams, commercial climbers, human rated climbers, hotels, launch ports, etc. However, key to their success will be the requirement to have an open standard so that all manner of climbers can work on the space elevator. The analogy would be the railroad's standard width of its rails. Power will be supplied through various mechanisms leading to electrical motors that move the climbers. Design trades will lay out options. The current concept for operational climbers is to launch at dawn using solar energy only from above the atmosphere and to rest during the short eclipses. This chapter is broken down into:

- Operational Climbers: Defined as the commercial version of a spacecraft taking customer payloads to altitudes such as GEO, LEO and Solar System trajectories.
- Deployment Spacecraft: Defined as the massive space system assembled in LEO and then rocketed to GEO for initial operations. The deployment spacecraft would then deploy the tether in the downward direction towards the surface of the ocean while raising itself in the opposite direction, keeping the whole system at the allocated GEO node.
- Buildup Climber: Defined as the small system that would ride up the initial "seed" tether and weave [or attach with epoxy] additional strands of the tether. Approximately 200 trips would be necessary to reach operational status of the space elevator.
- GEO Node Spacecraft: Defined as a massive space system for the operational space elevator located at the geosynchronous altitude to enable the off-loading, loading, fueling and handling of space elevator climbers and customer payload spacecraft.

Chapter 5: End Station Infrastructures (Marine Node & Apex Anchor)

The two ends of a space elevator have many possible engineering paths. It turns out that one of the biggest issues is the location of the Marine Node terminus. The trades for Earth attachment reach across political, investment, engineering, weather, and operational issues. A simple solution could be that a heavy ship(s) would act as a base for operations as well as moving the tether out of harm's way by initiating a resonance motion. Much more will be discussed during the chapter on location and technologies. In addition, the benefits of elevating the base station to a high altitude will be discussed with a relatively new technological concept that can provide that capability. Trades are presented to show the reason for elevating the base station to an altitude above the atmosphere. The counterweight, or apex anchor, will be the mechanism that allows the tether to maintain tension and perceived rigidity. The makeup of the apex anchor and its components must be discussed to ensure a consistent design with simple engineering solution.

Part III – Systems Approach

Chapter 6: Dynamics and Deployment
An operational tether will provide challenges across many areas. A 100,000km space elevator will have new and exciting dynamics that can only be predicted as there is no equivalent experimental model. Many of the traditional space issues [such as the influence of the Sun and the Moon] will exist with new ones surfacing as the development goes forward. At present, there are two distinct and attractive approaches for the deployment of a space elevator. Each starts at GEO and deploys a single strand of tether to be built upon. Approaches vary at this point with one building from the ground up [Edwards approach] and the other lifting itself up from the counterweight reel [reference the Gassend concept shown in Appendix E-5].

Chapter 7: Systems Design for Environment
A complexity for the systems approach to a space elevator infrastructure is that it crosses so many environments. This chapter addresses environments [except space debris – see Chapter 8] from the surface [ocean or land], through the winds and storms of our atmosphere, across multiple layers of complex particles, and crossing magnetic fields from the lower reaches of space, to GEO and beyond.

Chapter 8: Systems Design for Space Debris
The International Space Elevator Consortium recently studied the issue of space debris, its probability of collision for the space elevator [with the debris density as of April 2010], and mitigation techniques. This chapter lays out systems design issues and proposed solutions for this problem and recommends operational, technical, and policy approaches.

Chapter 9: Operations Concept
Operations of a space elevator infrastructure will cross many traditional arenas including: space operations, logistical support of remote locations, maritime delivery, personnel support for remote operations and future on-orbit operations. This chapter presents an operations view of the infrastructure, provide estimates for operations and maintenance costs, and show a "Day in the Life" of an operator.

Chapter 10: Assessment of Technology
Each chapter has addressed the technological readiness of specific elements of a space elevator and the risk probability vs. consequence assessment. These are summarized in this chapter with a layout of the difficulties expected for the future of this mega-project. In addition, there is a list of potential studies that should be initiated as soon as possible.

Part IV – Architectural and Policy Considerations

Chapter 11: Developmental Roadmaps
Organizations which take on monumental tasks require a vision with roadmaps that lays out the major thrusts, hurdles, and engineering paths. Roadmaps have historically been a useful tool. They allow everyone involved to help lay out the path for development of a mega-project such as the space elevator infrastructure. This chapter proposes a series of technology

prototype developments to be conducted in parallel. This would culminate in an "in-orbit" space elevator prototype test [1,000km long tether with climbers and apex anchors at roughly 3,000km altitude]. This chapter then presents baseline roadmaps which can be matured towards operations.

Chapter 12: Legal and Regulatory Perspective
A significant aspect of the legal world is that this transportation infrastructure will cross four major disciplines of law; space, terrestrial, maritime, and aeronautical. Which will dominate? Who will own a space elevator and where will it be registered and located? These are major questions that must be considered early in development. At least two legal regimes are proposed for developing a future space elevator.

Chapter 13: Market Projections
To place the project in perspective, the projected market must be laid out for both the traditional GEO, LEO market and innovative future markets. It turns out the market projection is very supportive of rapid development of space elevator infrastructures, enabling many critical future businesses to support its development. Such issues are discussed in this chapter.

Chapter 14: Financial Perspective
Numerous mega-projects have experienced difficulties because of a lack of understanding of the financial environment or political maneuvering across competing jurisdictions. The reality of a space elevator systems development is that it will not occur until two things happen: 1) the tether material is proven out and 2) investors will finance the creation of an infrastructure to space. This chapter presents a preliminary business plan, lays out a set of financial assumptions, and provides a "first look" market projection, which exceeds the criteria to go forward with investments.

Part V – Recommendations and Conclusions

Chapter 15: Study Conclusions and Recommendations
This chapter brings the study to its end with recommended actions and a list of important conclusions. Each of these is supported during the presentation of the report and can be traced back to an important contribution of one of the writers or a key reference.

Appendices
A. Contributors
B. Glossary of Acronyms
C. Study Terms of Reference
D. Space Elevator History
E. Technical Appendices
   1. Definition of Mega-Yuri
   2. Complexities of Laser Power Projection
   3. Summary of Space Tethers
   4. Safety Factor
   5. Tether Substantiation Methods
F. International Space Elevator Organizations
G. Consolidated Findings
H. IAA in brief

1.4   Finding

Finding 1-1: The space elevator will improve the human environment. The characteristics of a routine, on schedule (7 times a week), $500/kg fee, non-explosive service, without major pollution or launch shake-rattle-roll and without major restrictions on packaging of the payload, will lead to robust demand for space elevators.

Chapter 2
Architectural Vision of Space Elevators

2.1 Background

The mature arena of space elevators will be a robust environment with routine, safe, inexpensive and environmentally friendly movement of cargo to geosynchronous orbit and beyond. The following presentation of ideas and concepts is to prepare the reader for the various chapters to follow. Each of the concepts and statements below is supported in one or more of the other chapters. The purpose of this chapter is to establish the "big picture" and propose a future for the space elevator businesses and user community.

This new view of the future space elevator infrastructure will expand upon the innovative concept and reach beyond the starter space elevator of Dr. Edwards. Space elevator concepts have circulated around the globe as an idea that would work if material developments proceed as projected in chapter 3. The single item that is high risk is the tether material development as it is dependent upon high strength material such as carbon nano-tubes. For the last 13 years, the space elevator has been seen as a very possible approach to revolutionize access to space. Two of the benefits of the space elevator infrastructure revolve around the high demand for cargo to GEO as well as the unique aspects of the transportation complex. The real strength of a space elevator, which no one talks about, is the change in delivery technique. Low cost is definitely THE issue; but, its other characteristics, listed below, also excite the user community.

The major strengths of a space elevator based space transportation infrastructure would be:
- Revolutionarily inexpensive to GEO [$500/kg to GEO]
- Commercial Development similar to bridge building
- Financial Numbers that are infrastructure enabling
- Routine [daily launches]
- Safe [no chemical explosions from propulsion]
- Permanent infrastructure (no throw-aways)
- Multiple paths when infrastructure matures
- 24/7/365/50 yrs. [bridge similarities]
- Massive loads multi-times per week [7 tether climbers per elevator]
- Cargo segments of 14 metric tons each
- Opening up design options for space systems
- No shake-rattle-roll during launch
- Fewer volumetric restrictions for launch
- Easy delivery to GEO location within a week
- Recovery and repair of satellites
- Minimum stressers with slow accelerations
- Little impact upon the global environment
- No consumption of fuel [solar cells will drive the motors for lift]
- Does not leave space debris in orbit, and
- Co-orbiting [floating] at GEO for easy delivery and assembly.

2.2 Unique Delivery to Space

The space elevator is very similar to riding an elevator in a high rise building such as in London, New York or Dubai. As you go up you are reaching different floors. In the case of the space elevator, the levels are related to orbital regions that have historic values. These are:

- Geosynchronous Orbit: This is a spot that is stationary above a location on the equator; but, actually traveling at approximately 3.1km/second to maintain its circular orbit at 42,164km radius in the equatorial plane [or zero inclination].
- Interplanetary Insertion: This location on the space elevator varies as the altitudes relate to the energy levels that will enable the spacecraft to release itself and initiate a flight beyond Earth's orbit, such as to the Moon, Mars, Venus or even out of the solar system.
- Middle Earth Orbit: This region is populated with navigation satellites and is a smaller circular orbit than GEO.
- Low Earth Orbit: LEO is the location of choice by Earth resources management missions and is extremely valuable. As such, the energy required to gain a LEO orbit necessitates significant energy beyond what is gained through the space elevator climb and release. The extra energy required would be for circularization and inclination change.

The concept is simple to understand. As you climb on the elevator, the location carries an inherent energy equivalency. The first is the rotational energy. At the surface of the ocean, the Marine Node has a rotation of one revolution per day, roughly 0.45km/sec. At this point the climber has an energy equivalent of standing on the surface of the Earth with a similar velocity [kinetic energy] and with a height of zero [potential energy]. As the elevator climber transfers its electrical energy into height and circular velocity, it changes the tether climber energy with respect to potential and kinetic energies. As the climber ascends, the horizontal velocity increases [as well as the potential energy] because the space elevator has a constant rotation rate [Earth's rotation] with an increasing radius. As horizontal velocity is related to the rate of rotation [which is constant] and the radius from the center of the Earth, the energy is increasing rapidly.

The easy case to understand is the GEO altitude. At this location [our GEO node] the space elevator climber has added enough energy to be in an equivalent orbit to GEO. This leads to a simple conclusion: Delivery to GEO altitude on a space elevator allows the climber to release the payload into a stable location which would be perceived as floating in a GEO orbit.

The next concept is delivery to an interplanetary orbit. This requires more energy, a rocket motor for inclination changes as well as trajectory corrections, but not for the majority of the required energy to leave the Earth and venture towards other bodies in our solar system. Once the climber has risen above the GEO altitude, the energy increases. It grows rapidly to a velocity that "sling-shots" the payload into a trajectory that leaves the Earth's influence and starts on an elliptical flight around the sun towards another solar system body. As our equator and the Sun's ecliptic plane are not the same, the spacecraft, once it has left the space elevator, will require guidance rockets to reach the proper trajectory/orbit.

Dropping off the space elevator prior to the GEO altitude enables spacecraft to reach additional orbits such as MEO and LEO. The complexity is two-fold:
- Complexity 1 – The energy gained for orbital insertion requires an altitude of at least 23,390km, so the kinetic and potential energy combination is sufficient to have an elliptical orbit with a perigee greater than the radius of the Earth which then misses the surface on the opposite side of the orbit.

- Complexity 2 – Once dropped off the space elevator, the natural inclination is zero or equatorial. If the desired orbit has inclination requirements, energy must be applied to change from zero inclination to the desired orbital tilt.

2.3 Mega-Project Parallel

The mega-project approach to developmental programs verifies the concept of being successful with big ideas and major expenses. A mega-project is defined as taking more than ten years to complete and more than one billion dollars investment. Huge projects such as this have been accomplished many times. It turns out that the evolution of the space elevator started within the engineering fields [Pearson, Artsutanov, Edwards] and then moved into the science fiction arena [Clarke, and others]. During those various engineering projects, major issues were addressed and in some cases the main theme of the project was shown. One wonders about the thinking process of those major project champions when reading about the historic feats of construction such as our major bridges in all parts of the world [e.g. between Sweden and Denmark; Florida Keys; Japanese Island hopping; and now from Gibraltar to Morocco]; canals [Suez, Panama, Erie, Dutch, etc.]; tall buildings [Dubai, Kuala Lumpur, London, Eiffel Tower, Chicago, etc.]; and tunnels [e.g. the Channel Tunnel between England and France]. David Raitt was the first to compare the space elevator with some of these mega-projects almost ten years ago (Raitt and Edwards, 2004).

When we put these projects into perspective, think of the architects drawing up the plans, realize engineers provide remarkable materials, understand builders pull it all together, recognize program managers keep on schedule, and visualize machine drivers assemble the parts; we must marvel at the courage it takes and knowledge and experience necessary to embark on these projects. Each of these individuals "knew in their hearts" that there were threats to the design. However, they ensured nothing happened to their projects. Some recent summaries of mega-projects show the tremendous scope of these transportation infrastructures, committed to by countries, states and corporations. The following chart (Table 2-1) shows the latest estimate of the top 10 mega-projects that are underway (Gale, 2011). Although the space elevator is a ground-breaking mega-project with benefits that are hard to predict reliably, it is helpful to compare and draw inspiration from the work and achievements of these others.

Professor Bent Flyvbjerg, of the Said Business School at Oxford University, stated in his book (Flyvbjerg, 2003):
> "Today infrastructure plays a key role in nothing less than the creation of what many see as a new world order where people, goods, energy, information and money move about with unprecedented ease. Here the politics of distance is the elimination of distance. Megaprojects are central to the new politics of distance because infrastructure is increasingly being built as megaprojects. Thus the past decade has seen a sharp increase in the magnitude and frequency of major infrastructure projects, supported by a mixture of national and supra-national government, private capital and development banks."

In addition Edward Merrow (2011) observes that:
> "successful megaproject managers typically share three qualities: they are generalists, politically savvy within their own organizations, and good communicators, "especially good at communicating upward," he notes. Most importantly, he says that project leadership depends on the ability to protect the team from external pressures."

Name	Amount [US $B]	Information
High Speed 2, England	45.6	The United Kingdom plans to create a high-speed railway connecting London and the West Midlands and linking London, northern England and Scotland.
Gorgon Liquefied Natural Gas, Australia	37	The megaproject will provide gas and liquefied natural gas through the creation of a series of pipelines and a domestic gas plant.
South Stream Pipeline, Russia	20	A gas pipeline stretching from Russia, through the Black Sea, to the coast of Bulgaria will supply natural gas to the region.
London Crossrail, England	25.5	This railway system under central London will connect existing routes and provide additional transport for the commuter rail.
GCC Rail, United Arab Emirates	25	This high speed Gulf Cooperation Council rail system runs from Kuwait to Oman, linking six nations.
Masdar City, United Arab Emirates	22	Abu Dhabi's project to create a city reliant entirely on renewable energy will also include a focus on clean technologies.
NextGen Air Traffic Control System, USA	20	Tweaks to the national air transportation system include reducing environmental impact and increasing national security.
Rio-Sao Paulo-Campinas High Speed Rail, Brazil	2	Brazil plans to build a high-speed rail system to connect Sao Paulo and Rio de Janeiro, its two biggest cities.
Round 3 Wind Farm Zone, England	18	The United Kingdom has begun an effort to use offshore wind power to deliver electricity to nearly a quarter of the country.
Port of Qingdao, China Expansion	15	Located on the Yellow Sea, this seaport is China's second largest. The megaproject involves a new dock and renovations to the existing port.

Table 2-I. Mega-Project Descriptions

In the original book by Dr. Edwards (Edwards. 2003), the estimate for space elevator costs ranged greatly; from $6B to greater than $10B. At the 2004 International Astronautical Congress, Dr. Edwards and Dr. Raitt (Raitt, 2004) presented a paper estimating the costs of mega-projects and the space elevator.

"... initial estimates for the Space Elevator – which can lift over 5000kg - give a lift cost for the first simplistic system to any desired orbit of $150- $1100/kg depending on financing, with the ultimate lift cost being eventually reduced to a mere $10/kg." In addition, they predicted "the Space Elevator will have a tremendous impact upon society and industry when launch-to-orbit costs are reduced to around an anticipated $100/kg." [Raitt, 2004]

This study report, in the financial chapter [14], presents the current estimates for space elevator construction and operations. In this report, we picked a "mid-point" in the trade between expectation of business growth and future costs. The rationale was to have a baseline price for comparison across the chapters that was calculated for this study with the latest information. The result of the analysis in chapter 14 showed an initial operating price of $500/kg.

2.4 Operations View

After thinking about the great achievements of our predecessors, the scale of the space elevator does not seem beyond belief. The space elevator infrastructure certainly qualifies as a mega-project. Each of the past chief designers and chief builders of mega-projects ensured that their dreams were fulfilled after much work and savvy relationship building. To visualize this complex interaction, Chapter 9 has been put together to show the relationship between major elements of the space elevator and its major operations centers. Table 2-II lists the primary components included inside the scope of a space elevator business and Figure 2-1 shows the overall operations view of a space elevator infrastructure.

Function	Location
Enterprise Operations Center	HQ & Primary Ops Center
Transportation Operations Center	HQ & POC
Payload (Satellite) Operations Center	HQ & POC and Owner's Ops Center
Climber Operations Center	HQ & POC
Tether Operations Center	HQ & POC
GEO Node Operations Center	HQ & POC
Marine Node Operations Center	Marine Node

Table 2-II. Operations Centers of the Space Elevator

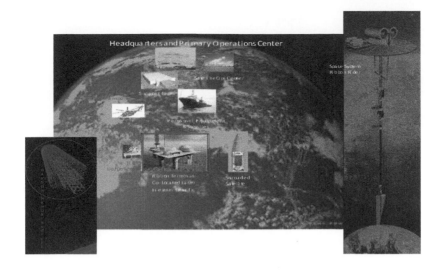

Figure 2-1. Space Elevator OV-1

If one were to trace a cargo for the space elevator from the customer facility [assume Denver, Colorado] to the GEO arc, it would take the following steps:

1. Contract and planning with Headquarters
2. Delivery to base support station
3. Transportation on ocean going cargo vessel
4. Delivery at floating operations platform
5. Loading onto stage one platform
6. Loading onto the tether climber
7. Climbing on the tether for seven days
8. Delivery at GEO orbital station [or MEO, LEO, & beyond]
9. Robotic off-loading
10. Preparation for mission
11. Release to mission orbit

It would seem that the business vision of this revolutionary capability would be:
> To develop a workhorse transportation infrastructure that moves cargo routinely and safely to orbit [LEO, MEO, GEO and beyond] with a return on investment that correlates with the low risks.

Historic successes of mega-projects are everywhere, to include some bridges that are over 2,000 years old [e.g. water aqueducts in Rome], some cathedrals that are over 1,000 years old [e.g. Trier, Aachen, Sofia, Bolnisi, etc.], and some canals that are expanding after 140 years of operations [e.g. Suez and Panama Canals]. The threats and issues that the space elevator team encounters will be real and must be addressed during the planning and construction projects; however, architects, engineers and builders know that they can be successful with good planning, calculations and a little bit of luck.

Arthur C. Clarke's Second Law:
… the only way of discovering the limits of the possible is to venture a little past them into the impossible.

2.5 Concepts Discussed

The space elevator project has some issues which are addressed and discussed extensively in the chapters to follow. Here are a few of those issues:

Tether Characteristics [Chapter 3 and many more]
This cosmic study understands that there will be many variables during development. Flexibility is required for the formulation of the concept of a space elevator infrastructure. As such, this cosmic study has standardized on a series of engineering numbers about the tether that can be used throughout the many chapters. An example is that the rated tether will be 38 MYuri; thus, you could order that from a supplier and satisfy system requirements. Table 2-III gives an overview of the numbers discussed inside the Cosmic Study.

Tether Characteristics	
Rated Tether:	38 MYuri [49.4 GPa @ 1.3 gm/cm^3]
Density of Material:	1.3 gm/cm^3
Operational capacity:	35.2 GPa or 27 MYuri [maximum]
Taper Ratio:	6
Safety Factor:	1.4 or 40%
Cross Section:	62.8 mm^2 - GEO node -1m x 62.8 mirometers
10.5 mm^2 - Earth terminus -1m x 10.5micrometers	
Standard Climber:	20 Metric ton [6MT structure + 14 MT payload]
Number of Climbers:	7 if spread with each having varying weights
Equivalent mass of 29 metric tons	
Tether Mass:	6,300 metric tons
Apex Anchor:	1,900 metric tons [30% of tether mass]
Tether Length:	100,000 km radius

Table 2-III. Cosmic Study Tether Standards

Loading and Speed of Tether Climbers [Chapter 4]
Each operations company expects to have seven tether climbers on each ribbon taking seven days to reach GEO with a capacity of 14 metric tons [MT] of cargo each. If the system is working 50 weeks a year, the throughput would be 9,800 MT per year per pair [2 space elevators x 7 cargos per week x 14 MT of cargo x 50 weeks = 9,800 Mt per year]. Chapter 4 describes how the tether climber is designed and the carrying capacity of each. The estimate at this time is that the tether climber will have a mass of 20 MT with 14 MT of that being paying cargo delivered to GEO and beyond. Table 2-IV shows the variation in weight of the space elevator climber when one realizes that the mass is the same all the way to GEO while the gravitational pull decreases and the weight reduces proportionally. The table shows a fully loaded space elevator with seven 20 MT climbers and an elevator with returning empty carriers [seven 6 MT equivalents].

For a 20 MT Tether Carrier - radius	Contributing Forces [g & cf] Factor	20 MT Weight Equivalent	6 MT Weight Equivalent
Earth's surface - 6,378 km	1.0	20 MT	6 MT
12,756 km	0.25	5.0	1.5
19,134 km	0.1	2.0	.6
MEO (GPS orbit) 26,600 km	0.043	0.8	.24
27,000 km	.041	0.8	.24
34,000 km	.014	0.3	0.08
GEO at 42,160 km	0.00	Zero "G"	zero
Total Equivalent Mass on Ribbon of seven tether climbers		28.9	8.66

Table 2-IV. Equivalent Weight of Tether Carrier

A space elevator tether is described as a 30 MT space elevator when it can suspend a 30 MT load at the bottom with all the factors accounted for; such as safety factor, dynamics effects, and tension in the tether. As such, if the space elevator was called 30 MT, it could hold up to seven climbers distributed as shown in the 20 MT weight equivalent column; but, many more climbers if they were empty and coming down the space elevator. Figure 2-3 shows a drawing of a tether climber with solar arrays deployed.

Figure 2-3. Tether Climber(upper left) , Dwarfed by
Deployed Solar Arrays [Frank Chase Image 2012]

The velocity of the tether climbers will vary with many factors, but the average should match the needs of the operator and the customer. The current numbers estimate seven days travel time to go from the Earth's surface to geosynchronous altitude. The numbers are shown in Table 2-V.

GEO Radius	42,160 km
Earth Radius	6,378 km
Altitude to GEO	35,782 km
hours in 7 days	168 hr
seconds in 7 days	604,800 sec
velocity	213 km/hr
velocity	59 m/sec
maximum power	11.8 MWatts

Table 2-V. Estimated Speeds for Seven day trip

Among the factors affecting the velocity will be the angle to the sun for efficient conversion of energy to drive the wheel configuration and the weight equivalent of the climber vs. altitude. When the tether climber is high, solar illumination will be almost constant and the weight will be lighter so the motor will not work as hard as it does near the surface of the Earth. This is discussed in Chapter 4 on the tether climber.

Space Debris [Chapter 8]
The threat from space debris, especially in LEO, is real. The numbers are not intimidating as there is a lot of room in orbit and only 16,000 tracked objects flying around. Chapter 8 shows the breakout of where and how many of these objects have the potential to interfere with the space elevator. The conclusion from a study conducted by the International Space Elevator Consortium, entitled "Space Elevator Survivability; Space Debris Mitigation" (Penny *et al*, 2011) , stated:

> "This study represents the culmination of efforts by the contributors and answers the question: Will space debris be a "show stopper" for the development of the Space Elevator Infrastructure? The answer is a resounding NO!

> The recognition of space debris risk with reasonable probabilities of impact is an engineering problem. The proposed mitigation concepts change the issue from a perceived problem to a concern; but, by no means is it a significant threat. This study illustrates how the development office for a future space elevator infrastructure can attack this problem and convert it into another manageable engineering problem."

Dynamics of Tether [Chapter 6]
The dynamics have been studied extensively because there are many factors that influence the motion of a tether. The issue revolves about the gravitational forces of the sun, moon and the non-homogeneity of the Earth. The addition of a massive Apex Anchor at the top end enables sufficient tether tension to help create the "stiffness" and stabilization of tether motion. The Marine Node enables the bottom end to be stationary when desired and moved when needed. Each of these dynamics puzzles is addressed inside the chapter on dynamics and deployment (Chapter 6). However, the conclusion is that the space elevator is dynamically stable.

Deployment [Chapter 6]

The phenomenal distances to be dealt with on deployment are of a concern for many people as they study the concept. Indeed there are some major issues of transfer of angular momentum as the space elevator is deployed and center of mass loses altitude as the forces interact. Each of the issues is dealt with in the deployment and dynamics chapter (6) as well as presenting a "how to" deployment scenario in Chapter 4.

Severance [Chapter 6]

The issue of severance is of special concern as it could be catastrophic. There is a special section dealing with this potential and a discussion of the probabilities, mitigations and "fixes." One idea is that the most probable cause would be space debris at 800km altitude [highest density; however, not a significant threat – as discussed in Chapter 4]. This would lay down the lower 800km of the space elevator [perhaps with a tether climber]; however, it would not lie along the equator due to Coriolis effects. In addition, a quick reaction deployment of ribbon from above could assist in saving the rest of the space elevator. All these items are discussed in Chapter 6 Dynamics .

Stage One [Chapter 5]

To simplify the design of tether climbers, the concept of "solar only" became the baseline. The elimination of laser power as the principal [or even just nighttime] energy enables the tether climber to work with a single set of power cells converting energy to electricity. This simplicity drove the decision to eliminate the deployment of solar arrays inside the atmosphere. This mandated the first stage on the ocean to reach above the atmosphere. There are three designs in Chapter 5 that show a High Stage One, a surface option, and a spring forward approach. These three alternatives lay out solutions which allow the climbers to be deployed above the atmosphere and initiated towards GEO with very fragile solar arrays distributed around the tether carrier.

Space Elevator Deployment Satellite [Chapter 4]

One challenge for the initiation of the space elevator system is "starter" ribbon deployment. The mass of the initial ribbon must be taken to GEO location and then released down and up with control to ensure stability. Once the ribbon has been deployed down to the Marine Node and up to the Apex Anchor, the Deployment Satellite must support the build-up of the tether and the initiation of the operations. Chapter 4 discusses these issues along with a preliminary design for the spacecraft.

Legal [Chapter 12]

Who can own a space elevator and within which set of precedents will the legal arena reside? Both of these questions will be addressed inside Chapter 12, which deals with the Law of the Sea, Aeronautical Law and Space Law. All of these agreements are international in nature and support the environment of the space elevator as it crosses all of those regimes. With the sponsorship of a nation and the Earth terminal located in international waters, the space elevator is achievable within current international laws.

2.6 Mature Space Elevator Businesses [Chapter 13]

If one jumps to the time period when the space elevator infrastructure is mature [let's estimate 2035], competition exists between various companies supplying the services as well as general recognition that GEO arc business opportunities are remarkable. Figure 2-4 illustrates a series of space elevators positioned in the Eastern Pacific going towards the stars.

Figure 2-4. Space Elevator in the Pacific [chasedesignstudios.com]

The concept is simple: each operational company buys the space elevators from a construction firm and has two operational elevators within their business model. The picture shows the initial space elevator [closest] that is the basis for all construction and will be called the "replicator space elevator." That business line is for a firm that builds mega-projects and creates space elevator pairs. The business plan [see Chapter 14 for financial breakouts] shows the existence of four companies in the years of operational space elevator infrastructures. The first is the company that builds space elevators and is called "Carbon Space-Way Inc." The next three companies are in business to supply cargo to the GEO arc and beyond, as shown in Table 2-VI.

Business Line	Company Name	# Of Space Elevators
Construction	Carbon Space-Way Inc.	Replicator
Transportation	Space-Way Operations Company	2
	West Space-Way Operations Company	2
	East Space-Way Operations Company	2

Table 2-VI. Companies of the Space Elevator Infrastructure

Each one is owned by a different set of investors that have various expectations to be fulfilled. One concept is that a government organization, such as JAXA, owns one of the space elevators; one is owned by an international organization, such as INTELSAT; and one is owned by a commercial venture. Figure 2-4 illustrates the replicator space elevator of Carbon Space-Way and then one of the two space elevators directly west of the original site [Space-Way Operations Company] with a combination of two space elevators for mostly up, but some down business.

Each of the transportation companies, such as the Space-Way Operations Company, expects to have seven tether climbers on each ribbon taking seven days to reach GEO with a capacity of 14 MT of cargo. If one has the system working 50 weeks a year, the through-put would be 4,900 MT per year per space elevator. If one were to take the estimate of price for a kilogram of cargo to GEO, $500/kg, then the revenue for one year would be $2.45 billion per tether. Some interesting aspects of this calculation go back to the assumptions of cargo carriers per week and how much they can carry. Chapter 4 describes how the tether carrier is designed and the carrying capacity of each.

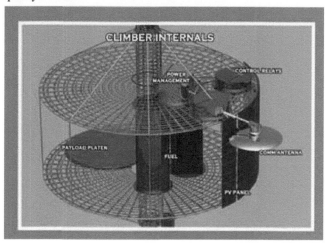

Figure 2-5. Climber [chasedesignstudios.com]

A pair of space elevators, with the Replicator in the foreground, is shown in Figure 2-4. As can be seen from this image, there are three space elevators spaced about 500km apart along the equator. The discussion of where and why in the Pacific is handled during chapter 5's study of the two end structures of the space elevator. After understanding the vision and the concept of multiple space elevators, an architectural view of the big picture should fall into place. This is accomplished with three images: (1) Replicator and a pair of space elevators in the Pacific [Figure 2-4], (2) a conception of the tether carrier with six metric tons of mass carrying 14 metric tons of cargo [Figure 2-5], and (3) an operational view of a single space elevator infrastructure [Figure 2-6].

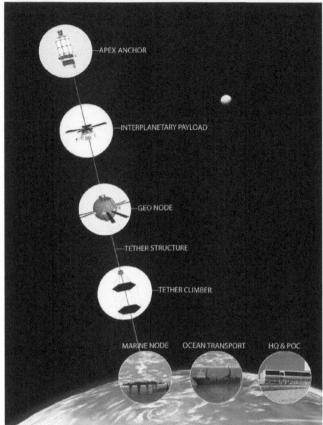

Figure 2-6. Nodal Operations [chasedesignstudios.com]

2.7 Market Projection (Chapter 13)

The owners of two commercial space elevators are expecting to have the through-put necessary to have a decent return on investment while opening up space from GEO to beyond. This vision is important if one is to ensure a business success and mega-project completion. In the Financial Chapter (14), the details of the income and expenses are laid out so the investors have a feel for the value equations necessary to have success. In addition, the Financial Chapter shows how the space elevator community consists of three corporations, each operating two space elevators. The first tether is designed to conduct business in only the "up" direction with the second designed to handle mostly up for the business case, but periodically handle "down" cargo and, in the future, human cargo. This basic principle of having two space elevators per commercial company enables robust space elevator infrastructure to handle its customers and still have a viable return on investment.

The market projection is sized through three customer bases;
1. GEO communications satellites [traditional business at $300M per satellite to GEO total cost: $100M launch, $200M spacecraft],
2. LEO satellites being dropped off above 22,000km altitude with a space-tug to change from elliptical equatorial orbits to circular polar orbits, and

3. Innovative Future Businesses, especially Space Solar Power (SSP).

It is always exciting to look at the future of the global need for access to space. However, the current methodology does NOT encourage businesses to expand into space at a toll of $20,000/kg to GEO. As a result of major reductions in price barriers to get into space, the space elevator will ENABLE innovative businesses to excel by charging in the region of $500/kg to orbit.

2.8 Finding
This chapter has shown the big picture so the reader can look at individual study topics inside each chapter and place them in context. Findings are developed inside each chapter and summarized at the end of the book.

Chapter 3
Tether Material

3.1   Background

The tether must be made of a material that can withstand its environment and operational stresses. This would include all of the threats to the system as well as tensile stress inherent to support itself. It turns out that if the tether's strength is between 27 and 45 MYuri[1], a space elevator can not only support itself, but seven tether climbers [at 20 MT each including 14 MT payloads] at one time. The materials currently being tested in the laboratory have surpassed that level and promise a tether that can withstand the environmental and operational stresses necessary. Will it end up being carbon nanotubes, or boron nitrite materials, or something else? The current tether design is of a one meter wide woven tether, paper thin, consistent in shape [curved to defeat a single small piece of space debris from severing it] from the anchor to the counterweight with some tapering. This chapter discusses the Feasibility Condition which describes the relationships of design driving the tether characteristics with a basic summary of tether material requirements. The authors then discuss the current status of the carbon nanotube (CNT) tether material expected to grow to the necessary strength, resilience in space, and endurance for a commercial project.

3.2   Feasibility Condition

3.2.1 Motivation

As is well known, there is no hard minimum requirement on the specific strength of a space elevator tether. Specific strength is defined as the level at which the material breaks in tension. The lower the specific strength, the higher the tether taper ratio, and the heavier the tether gets for a given climber mass. A taper ratio is a relationship between the mass at the high stress location [GEO altitude] and the Marine Node [low stress location]. Previous work (Edwards and Westling, 2003) cites a uniform tensile strength (UTS) of 130GPa for CNTs, and a density of 1.3g/cc, for a specific strength of 100 MYuri, and a taper ratio of 1:2. Dr. Edwards uses this number as a starting point, with the implication that if CNT tethers will not reach this specific strength, the effect will be an increase in the taper ratio and the total mass of the space elevator tether. However, the increase in taper will not be a fundamental problem or show-stopper for the construction of the space elevator.

3.2.2 Starting point

The principle for the Feasibility Condition (FC) is that a space elevator must be able to lift its own weight – fast enough to grow by bootstrapping – fast enough to replace aging material, and fast enough to have a significant margin for commercial cargo beyond these housekeeping tasks. The FC therefore sets a three dimensional design space composed of {tether material specific strength, power system specific power, system time constant}. In a similar fashion, there is no absolute requirement on the performance of the power system of the space elevator. Higher specific power allows the climbers to move faster and clear the bottom of the tether sooner, increasing the launch rate and mass throughput of the system. Edwards cites a 2 MWatt power system weighing 5 tons (0.4 kWatt/kg), able to launch a

---

[1] MYuri Definition: The units for measuring specific strength (or tenacity) are confusing - traditionally, people use either GPa/(cc/g) for the former, and N/Tex for the latter. These two units are the same in fact, and are equal to 10^6 N·m/kg [one million newton meters per kilogram], which is a force per linear density. In the space elevator context, the unit for both specific strength and tenacity has been defined as a Yuri (in honor of Yuri Artsutanov), and so a tether with a linear density of 0.001 kg/m that breaks at 2000 N will have a breaking strength of 2 Mega Yuri (2 MYuri). 1 MYuri is the same as 1 GPa per gram per cm^3 or 1 N/Tex. See Appendix E-1.

climber about once a week (Edwards and Westling, 2003). Again, the implication is that if this specific power cannot be reached, the only penalty will be a reduction in the possible payload mass throughput.

In previous discussions of space elevator design, tether strength and power systems are treated as mostly independent domains – railroad tracks and train engines, to use a familiar analogy. However, there is another assumption in the space elevator architecture that ties these two domains together. It is accepted that a space elevator is too heavy to launch directly, and so the only way to construct a viable-sized space elevator is to launch a smaller seed space elevator, and use its lifting capacity to bootstrap to a much larger space elevator. In addition, the tether material will have a certain expected lifetime in operation, and so the entire tether mass has to be replaced at a certain minimum rate, using the space elevator itself to perform the task.

These "housekeeping" lift chores create the link between the tether system and the power system, since a lower-performance tether requires more housekeeping work, and thus levies a throughput requirement on the power system, thereby denying us the option to simultaneously have both an arbitrarily weak tether and an arbitrarily weak power system. If the housekeeping chores cannot be kept, then not just the performance, but indeed the feasibility of the space elevator is cast into question. One immediate result is that if a space elevator satisfies the Feasibility Condition, then the yearly throughput is easily 100 times the maximum tether mass allowed at the lower end of the space elevator. The discouraging news is that satisfying the Feasibility Condition is rather difficult. Doing so will impose strict conditions on some of the technologies and will rule out others.

3.2.3 Feasibility Condition Definitions
To lay out the FC, we need to define some basic design parameters for the space elevator. In an example case to help understand the definitions to follow, the tether's mass is 6,000 MT, the tether climber is 20 MT including 14 MT payload with seven tether riders per week on the tether below GEO. The Feasibility Condition states that it must be possible to lift enough material for completing initial construction and for ongoing repair and maintenance, plus a useful amount of payload. The FC uses the following definitions: Standard Mass Unit (SMU): Since the space elevator is linearly scalable, the discussion below is independent of the size of the system. We therefore normalize all mass parameters by the maximum mass that is allowed to hang from the bottom of the tether [mmax] and refer to this unit as an SMU. In the example, the SMU is 29 MT.

Tether Mass Ratio (TMR): For example a 29 MT space elevator is one that can support a 29 MT load at ground level. If the tether mass is 6,000 MT, then we say the tether mass is 207 SMUs. This ratio of tether mass to lifting capacity is labeled TMR.

Tether Specific Loading (TSL): TSL is similar to the tether material specific strength, but takes into account parasitic mass (such as cross-weaves) and the margin of safety. This means that the effective tether specific strength is the definition used in the design. For example, the tether material may achieve 40 MYuri, but the TSL used in the design is only 30 MYuri. Given a specific TSL, and using the constant-stress space elevator tether formula, it is possible to calculate the taper ratio, total mass, and thus the TMR.

Payload Mass Ratio (PMR): Simplistically, we divide the mass of the climber into payload and other. This leads to the definition of payload mass ratio (PMR) as the mass of the payload divided by the climber total mass. The previous example was payload [mass moving up/down the elevator] of 14 MT and total mass of 20 MT for a PMR of 0.7.

Payload Mass Throughput (PMT): PMT of the space elevator is the amount of mass it can move per unit time. The example is seven per week or 14 x 7, or 98 metric tons per week.

Standard Throughput Unit (STU): The normalized unit for PMT is the STU, defined as one SMU per year. STUs are typically applied to payload throughput. The example is then 7 x 14 x 52 / 29 or 175 SMUs. Optimal PMT is achieved by having multiple climbers on the tether at once, each being somewhat less mass than 1 SMU. Thus for example a 29 MT space elevator will typically operate 20 MT climbers, and be able to have seven of them on the tether at once. Additionally, the PMT can also be optimized against the PMR. Climbers with a larger PMR carry more payload, but also have smaller power systems and thus move slower.

Characteristic Time Constant (CTC): The time it takes the system to lift a payload mass equal to the mass of its tether. With all of the above parameters defined, the CTC is simply the ratio of the tether mass and the payload mass throughput of the system: $CTC = TMR/PMT$. The example is then $CTC = 207/175$ or 1.18 per year. The Feasibility Condition is built around the concept of the characteristic time constant (CTC). The CTC is therefore a measure of the "specific throughput" of a space elevator system. A space elevator with a CTC of 2 years can only lift half of itself into orbit each year. The CTC will now be compared with several required time constants. We call the periods where the space elevator has to bootstrap, either during initial construction or during recovery from a break, "growth periods", to be contrasted with "normal operations".

Time-to-Double (TD): During growth periods, the space elevator relies on a certain growth rate, or time-to-double (TD). During the initial growth phase, when starting from a seed space elevator that is only 5%-10% of an operational space elevator, a TD of 1 year will result in a 4-year construction period in which the space elevator is not productive.

Fraction Weight of the Spare-in-Orbit (FS): Since we want to hold a spare tether spool in orbit to enable reasonable recovery from a tether break event, we need to count on this additional mass being launched as well. We will denote the fraction weight of the spare-in-orbit as FS. If, for example, FS = 25%, then in order to double we actually need to launch 1.25 times the mass of the tether, and if TD is still 1 year, it will take 2 doublings and therefore 2 years to fully recover from the a broken tether. There is no absolute requirement on TD and FS, but we'll argue for the moment that four years to construct and two years to recover from a break are reasonable working numbers, and we can't deviate from them by more than a factor of perhaps two.

Material Lifetime in Service (TL): During normal operations, the tether material will have some degradation rate in space as a result of cosmic radiation, micro orbital debris, thermal cycling, and perhaps simple mechanical wear and tear. These factors will result in an allowed material lifetime in service (TL). TL will be several times larger than TD, probably at least 4-5 years. We'll assume that the spare does not degrade, and that $TL > 2 \cdot TD$.

Support Growth Lift (SGL): To support growth, the space elevator must lift $(1+FS)/TD$ of its mass per year.

Aging Material Lift (AML): In a similar manner, to replace aging material, the space elevator must lift 1/TL of its mass per year. These are the housekeeping lift requirements introduced above.

Minimal Required Lift Capacity (MRL): Since during growth periods the housekeeping lift requirements are much higher than during periods of normal operations, it is enough to require that the space elevator will exactly support the housekeeping operations during growth periods, and use the additional capacity during normal operations for lifting payload. The sum (1+FS)/TD + 1/TL is therefore the minimal required lift capacity of the space elevator, in units of tether-mass-per-year.

Using these definitions, the FC can be written:

$$\frac{PMT}{TMR} = \frac{1}{CTC} > \frac{1+FS}{TD} + \frac{1}{TL}$$

3.2.4 Yearly Capacity
As the mass of the payload stays constant, but the weight varies as the distance to the Earth increases, the forces involved vary as well as the speed of movement. To have an easy definition of a space elevator and to be able to compare to the other transportation infrastructures, the measure of "yearly capacity" is expressed as kilograms of payload lifted during the year. An example is as follows:

> YC = Payload Mass x # lifts/week x 52 weeks
> In our example that would be 7x14x52x1000 = 5,096,000 kg/yr

3.2.4.1 Exceeding the Feasibility Condition
During normal operations its minimum payload throughput is a very impressive TMR•(1+FS)/TD – easily 100 mmax per year [example is 100 20 MT climbers or 2,000,000kg] when plugging in real-world numbers. The above definitions allow the engineers to trade time, power and tether strength to understand the relationships. The key is that in each area there are trade spaces available to the systems engineers who must allow global optimization versus the tendency of local optimization. It seems that the technologies are maturing in the correct direction, just not as rapidly as expected. In this section we'll try to estimate the values of PMT and TMR achievable in the foreseeable future. As such estimates go, these will only establish a very rough range, since the technologies are complex and we are trying to look rather far into the future. The goal here is to merely estimate these values to an order of magnitude, so we can determine whether the FC shows the space elevator as easily feasible, clearly infeasible, or somewhere in between.

3.2.4.2 Tether Material
Based on a gradual convergence of experimental and theoretical results, the specific strength of raw CNTs will probably not exceed 50 MYuri [Wong, S. S. 1997] [Iwanaga, 1998], as compared to previous estimates of 100 MYuri (Edwards & Westling, 2003). In particular, a failure mechanism known as the Stone-Wales causes spontaneous defects in the nanotube structure and limits the possible strength. Using 45-50 MYuri CNTs, we can expect a near-flawless spun tether to perform at 40 MYuri. With a 33% safety margin, we can load the tether at a TSL of 30 MYuri. The weight of various redundancy structures can be shown to be only a few percent of the total tether mass, so will not affect this result by much.

Finding 3-1: Space elevators can be developed with 30 MYuri tethers, as explained in the feasibility condition (Shelef, 2011).

3.2.4.3 Power Systems

The specific power of the power system is a function of the photovoltaic receiver, the electric motors, the power electronics, and any required heat-rejection systems. If one of these components has a significantly low specific power, it will be the heaviest component of the system and become the limiting factor. Since the specific heat conductivity of CNTs is so much higher than that of aluminum (better than 100x) it is clear that great strides can be made in this field relatively quickly when the need arises. This component does not seem to be a limiting factor in space elevator development.

3.2.4.4 Predictions

Based on the above, we can comfortably bracket tether specific strength at 20 – 40 MYuri, resulting in a TMR of 433 to 77. The analysis of the power system is less conclusive. Photovoltaic (PV) receivers and electric motors deliver 1 kWatt/kg even today and keep getting better. CNT electrical conductors stand to reduce the weight of motors. Improvement in efficiency will reduce the requirements on the heat rejection system. The heat rejection system itself does not have a fundamental limit preventing it from reaching similar levels, but is currently far from 1 KWatt/kg, and will require the use of either CNTs or other lightweight highly conductive materials. Looking forward 10-20 years, it is quite possible to have the entire system deliver 1 kWatt/kg.

3.2.4.5 Parameter Values

We can now take the estimates above and see how they fit into the FC. Based on the above discussion, we'll use TD = 1 years, FS = 25%, and TL = 4 years, so that the FC requires CTC < 0.66 years. As explained above, this number can be relaxed somewhat by using a smaller spare, agreeing to a longer TD, etc, so we can potentially relax the condition to TD = 1.5 years, FS = 25%, and TL = 6 years, so the FC becomes CTC < 1.0. As it turns out, realistic CNT tether performance levels require very powerful climbers, up to 12 MWatt for a 29 MT Space Elevator. To fit such a power system into the climber requires a very power-dense system, and as we will see below, this is not an easy requirement to satisfy.

Table 3-I quantifies the relationship between assumptions on tether strength and assumptions on power systems. If we start with a certain assumption on CNT strength [e.g. 25 MYuri] on the left-hand side of the table, we see the required PMT is 228-342 [depending on the CTC], and so we need to choose a line on the right-hand side [230-340] which satisfies the inequality, and thus we see we require a power system that delivers better than 2.5 kWatt/kg. Table 3-I shows the constraints imposed by the FC, and possible technology values [in gray] as detailed in the next section. Blue values are best, red are worst, PPOS must be greater than PREQ. As expected, strong tethers match weaker power systems and vice versa. The gray zones are the probable performance levels of the technologies.

TSL	A/A₀	TMR	P_REQ		P_POS	PD	
Tether specific loading	Taper ratio	Tether mass ratio	Required mass throughput		Possible mass throughput	Power density	
MYuri			STU		STU	kWatt/kg	

	TSL	A/A₀	TMR	P_REQ		P_POS	PD	
(optimistic)	50	2.6	50	50 – 75	<	100 – 115	0.5	(pessimistic)
	40	3.4	77	77 – 116		135 – 155	0.7	
CNT	30	5.0	144	144 – 216		170 – 210	1.0	Thin-film PV
	25	7.0	228	228 – 342		200 – 275	1.5	+ motors
	20	11.3	433	433 – 650		230 – 340	2.5	
(pessimistic)	17	17.30	739	739 – 1109		250 – 370	3.5	(optimistic)

Table 3-I. Relationship Power vs. Strength

3.2.4.6 Feasibility Condition Conclusions

On the bright side, we were able to show that we can make up for weaker-than predicted CNT tethers by stronger-than-predicted power systems. On the down side, we saw that the Space Elevator Feasibility Condition is actually very difficult to satisfy. On the bright side, direct solar power conversion using thin-film foils seems to be able to achieve the necessary power-mass density. On the down side, such structures are very frail. On the bright side, given the realization that we need much more power than previously thought [up to 12 MWatt per climber for a 29 MT Space Elevator], the move to free solar power relieves us of the need to construct much larger power beaming stations. The Space Elevator Feasibility Condition is a sufficient but not a necessary condition for the viability of the space elevator as a practical transport system. However, it is "strongly sufficient" in that it is able to define and capture the principal requirements on the strength of the tether and the power density of the power system. Without it, we don't really have a sufficient condition, since a space elevator can be built out of any tether material [since at worst, the tether will simply have more mass] and using any power system [since at worst, the climbers will simply move more slowly].

When compared with technology roadmaps, we see that the feasibility condition could eventually be satisfied. As it turns out, realistic CNT tether performance levels require very powerful climbers, driving the power system, and specifically the heat rejection system. Additionally, the Feasibility Condition alerts us to other aspects of the design of the space elevator. For example, consider the handling of bi-directional traffic and the disposition of climbers after they have carried their cargo. If the climbers had to come down the same tether, then this affects the throughput of the system, and thus factors into the FC. If the climbers use a second tether as a "down" elevator, then this tether increases the mass of the system since it also has to be maintained. If the climbers are cast off after each use, then we need to bring into account the cost of disposable climbers, which is significant.

The last observation ties the Feasibility Condition to a future financial study of the space elevator. We often portray the space elevator as a "free" system. The tether is an invariant, the climber is reusable, and the cost of electricity to power the laser can quickly be calculated to be negligible [especially if solar light is used for most of the trip]. However, for a full financial model, we need to factor in the cost of tether replacement, and perform financial trade-offs such as choosing between reducing throughput, using more tether material [as in a "down" tether], or disposing of the climbers. This will result in a "Space Elevator Financial Viability Condition," which will impose a tighter bound on its real feasibility. While the values of the technology parameters are still not known, the mathematical model can be constructed today.

3.3 Tether Material Requirements

As the environment has progressed over the decade since Edwards and Westling's (2003) book, there have been some exciting advances and achievements. While we do not have the material yet, there is hope. During the last five years, the space elevator community has been working with the carbon nanotube researchers and has come up with the following summaries as outlined in Tables 3-II and III.

Strength Required	Characteristic [Tether Specific Loading - TSL]	Comments
25 MYuri	Essentially the minimum that the space elevator could accept. Requires more energy to work and has a big taper ration	Almost certainly doable within ten years
30 MYuri	The number that is currently being evaluated as the "acceptable level." Has a taper ratio number that is not too large large.	Probably doable in reasonable timeline
40 MYuri	Desired level of specific loading stress	Goal for commercial material
100 GPa	Original strength used by Dr. Edwards	Reach-out goal
300 GPa	Theoretical Maximum for CNT	Lab results support

Table 3-II. Material Strength Characteristics

Requirement	Level	Comment
Specific Loading Stress Goal	40	See above chart – objective at 30
Lifetime in Environment	10 years	
Loading	7 climbers	Each having 20 MT mass with 14 MT payload
Time to GEO	1 week	
Availability of Material	2030	In 1,000km lengths
Production Length	104,000km	
Tether Design	1m wide	Curved surface and tapered from GEO [6 taper ratio for 27 MYuri]
Splice/Weave	Easy/quick	Splicing will enable many safety approaches
Electrodynamic and Electromagnetic Environment	Friendly	

Table 3-III. Basic Requirements for Tether Material

This presentation of preliminary requirements for the space elevator tether material would lead to an understanding by the developmental community [especially the CNT community] of the requirements the materials community needs to achieve for the space elevator project. Selection of the material will basically be made prior to production and will choose the best available. These could come from carbon nano-tubes [or colossal nano-tubes] or boron-nitride tubes.

3.4 Projected Tether Characteristics for a Space Elevator

Over the last few years, there have been many assumptions about the capability growth of the CNT materials. The above Tables 3-II and 3-III explain some of the projections and some of the experimentally measured CNT tether strength characteristics.

3.4.1 The Ultimate Design of a 35 MYuri strong tether

Professor Nicola Pugno recently presented a paper entitled "Towards the Artsutanov's dream of the space elevator: the ultimate design of a 35 MYuri strong tether" (Pugno, 2013). In the discussion, he lays out the failure modes and calculates the stress levels to be expected, states the flaw methodologies, and predicts the expected levels of stress in a tolerant design. His conclusions are:

- "The corresponding maximum achievable fracture specific strength is thus predicted to be ... approximately 35 MYuri."
- "The predicted maximum sliding specific strength for a single walled nanotube cable is ... approximately 37 MYuri."
- "The corresponding flaw-tolerant taper-ratio [needs] to be ... approximately 5."

When one takes Professor Pugno's design numbers into account, the 35 MYuri specific strength matches the feasibility condition and shows some optimism in the current approach and situation.

3.5 Projected Tether Strength

Over the last few years, there have been many assumptions about the capability growth of the CNT materials. Figure 3-1 and Table 3-IV explain some of the projections and some of the experimentally measured CNT tether strength characteristics.

Specific strengths in excess of 20 MYuri (the minimum required for the space elevator tether) have been measured in single CNT since 2000. Yet until recently these values had been recorded on microscopic samples only (samples with lengths of the order of 1 micron), and scaling this performance up to sizeable dimensions seemed a real struggle. In 2011, a single CNT with strength in excess of 100MYuri (Zhang et al, 2011) over a 10 cm length was reported.

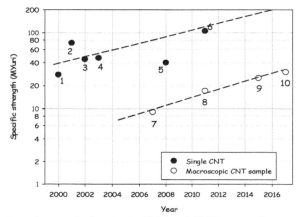

Figure 3-1. Projected strength for single CNT and CNT yarns. Commercial materials are reported for reference.

#	Year	Specific Strength (MYuri)	Size microns and nano-meters	Description
Single CNT				
1	2000	27.7	110um x 1336nm	(Yu, 2000) - Measurement of single Multi-walled Nanotube
2	2001	72.7	1um x 12nm	(Demczyk, 2002) - Individual Multi-walled Nanotubes
3	2002	44.1	∞	Belytschko - Computer Modeling of Single-Walled Nanotubes, showing failure mechanisms.
4	2003	46	∞	(Ruoff, 2003) - Summary of experimental and model results
5	2008	40	Sparse CNT Composite	(Wang, 2007) – Inferred strength of SWNTs from a 1% CNT reinforced plastic tape.
6	2011	200	10cm	(Zhang, 2011) – Experimental result on single CNT. A density of 1g/cm^3 is assumed.
CNT Yarns				
7	2007	9	few mm long	(Koziol, 2007) – CNT Yarn
8	2011	17	1mm long	(Zhang, 2011) – CNT Yarn
9	2015	25	1mm	Nominal value for Space Elevator tether, Taper Ratio=7.0 Tether Mass Ratio = 228
10	2017	30	1mm	Nominal value for Space Elevator tether, Taper Ratio=5.0 Tether Mass Ratio = 144

Table 3-IV. CNT strength

Yarns with tens of meters length have been manufactured from CNTs, but they originally had very small strength (typically smaller than 1 MYuri). In 2011 a yarn with specific strength of 17 MYuri was demonstrated. Although measurements were carried out with a gauge 1mm long, the sample could be manufactured in lengths limited only by the material supply, meaning that yarns with lengths in excess of kilometers and with the same strength can be easily envisaged. In 2013 a method to extend to long lengths strengths achieved on 1 mm long samples has been shown at Rice University (Behabtu, 2013), with yarns as long as a fraction of a km being fabricated. This sample was optimized for electrical conductivity and showed an overall strength of the order of 1 MYuri. If growth in specific strength continues at the same pace, it is possible that yarns with specific strengths in the range of 20 MYuri can be demonstrated as early as 2015. Scaling up the process to lengths in excess of 1000km might take a couple of years, meaning that a space elevator tether could be available before 2025.

Finding 3-2: If growth in specific strength continues at the same pace, it is possible that yarns with specific strengths in the range of 20 MYuri can be demonstrated as early as 2015. Scaling up the process to lengths in excess of 1000km might take a couple of years, meaning that a space elevator tether could be available before 2025.

3.6 Summary of research on CNT
CNTs have been identified as the ideal candidate because of their astonishing strength: as early as the year 2000, specific strengths > 60 MYuri were recorded for CNTs manufactured by chemical vapor deposition (CVD) with radii in the region of 50nm. Although most of the initial results were recorded for samples with lengths shorter than 1mm, in June 2011 a CNT

with specific strength in excess of 100 MYuri and length exceeding 10cm was reported (Zhang et al, 2011).

This result is promising, yet calculations have shown that this value can be achieved for short-term loading. In fact, in the long term the excess elastic energy in a strained CNT is released through the spontaneous creation of topological defects (like the Stone-Wales), the features of which depend on the CNT geometry and diameter (Zhao et al, 2002). Tethers with specific strengths of the order of 40 MYuri should exhibit long term stability (tens of years at least). Simulations (Cornwell et al, 2011) have also shown that cross linking can increase load transfer and decrease CNT vulnerability to topological defects. In particular, irradiation-induced cross linking (Filleter et al, 2013) has been achieved by exposing CNTs to ion (O'Brien et al, 2012) and electron (Peng 2008) radiation.

Still, the highest values of strength were measured on single samples with diameters smaller than 1micron and lengths considerably smaller than 1mm. Long tethers are as strong as the weakest link. The presence of a single defect eventually decreases their ultimate strength: a single defect involving a missing atom in an otherwise perfect carbon nanotube 30,000km long would have a 20% decrease in the tensile strength with respect to that of a defect-free carbon nanotube (Pugno, 2004). Yarns made of CNT a few microns long have been proved a viable solution to extend the extraordinary strength to macroscopic sizes, as stress is distributed between CNTs and a weak point in a single CNT would redistribute stress over several adjacent CNTs.

3.6.1   Carbon nanotube length

Since 1991, when CNTs were discovered, the maximum length of single CNTs has continuously increased, reaching fractions of a meter. Figure 3-2 gives the maximum CNT lengths reported in the literature in the last two decades. Since 2004 reports of CNTs longer than 1 mm have become common, with record lengths of 300mm for a single CNT (allegedly made at the MIT Institute for Soldier Nanotechnologies in 2009) and 200mm for CNT bundles (manufactured in Beijing, China, at Tsinghua University, (Wen et al, 2010)). If an equivalent of Moore's law can be established for the maximum length for CNT manufacture, the regression over the last two decades would predict an order of magnitude increase in the length over 3.6 years, or a doubling approximately every year. This seems very promising news for the space elevator tether, since it predicts km-long CNTs being available by 2022.

Yet, all so-called "ultralong" CNTs have been made using self-contained fabrication techniques, principally by chemical vapor deposition (CVD) using nano-catalysts (Wen et al, 2010). Most recently, silica nanospheres have been used as anchoring points for catalysts and CNTs to achieve high density CNT carpets (Xie et al., 2012). This methodology has been called "kite growth mechanism," since most of the CNTs are floating in the gas flow and only sink down onto the substrate when the gas flow is stopped. This method requires the sample to be grown at high temperature in a very well controlled setting (normally a tube furnace), and the tube furnace size might limit the CNT maximum length. Indeed, Figure 3-2 seems to show that CNT growth is reaching a plateau for lengths of the order of a fraction of a meter. Regressions exhibit a similar slope, which predicts an increase of the CNT length by a factor of 10 every 3.6 years. (Letters A-E and G-M in the Figure relate to references (Iijima, 1991) (Ebbesen, 1992), (Pan, 1998), (Zheng, 2004) (Hong, 2005), (Li, 1996), (Kong, 1998), (Hata, 2004), http://www.uc.edu/News/NR.aspx?ID=4811, http://www.uc.edu/News/NR.aspx?ID=5700, (Wang, 2009), (Wen, 2010), respectively. F was reported on the internet by MIT Institute for Soldier Nanotechnologies in 2009 but never formally published in the literature or on official websites.)

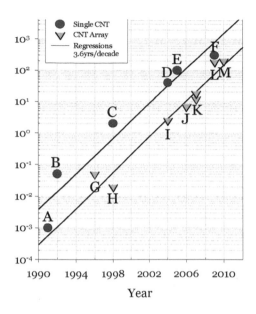

Figure 3-2. Progress in carbon nanotube (CNT) maximum length for single CNT and CNT arrays.

3.6.2 Carbon nanotube growth speed

As far as the manufacture of unwound long CNTs is concerned, Figure 3-3 shows that in recent years fabrication has become faster and faster: at the beginning of 2010 (Wen et al, 2010) growth speeds in excess of 80μm/s were achieved by using methane and water as reagent gases.

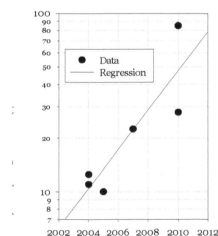

Figure 3-3. Historical data for growth rates for CNT manufactured by CVD (□m/s - micron per second). Data points have been taken from (Zheng et al, 2004; Hong et al, 2005; Wen et al. 2010; Wen et al, 2010b; Huang et al, 2004; Yao et al, 2007).

It is interesting to note that fast growth was achieved for multi-walled CNTs: indeed growth speeds of 80 - 90microns per second were achieved with double- and triple- walled CNTs. Water addition to the gas mixture injected into the furnace has been shown to be fundamental for the quick manufacture of long CNTs: when water is not present among reagent gases, the catalyst can be deactivated due to a thin layer of carbon coating; water removes this coating and revitalizes the catalyst activity (Yamada et al, 2008). It was also found that, although the use of catalysts still has an energy barrier for incorporating C atoms into the CNTs, speeds of 1m/hr can be achieved (Yuan et al., 2011)

Despite initial concerns (Hong et al, 2005) regarding the limiting factor of the furnace hot zone length, the nature of the kite growth mechanism jointly with the revitalizing effect of water should potentially allow for the growth of unlimited lengths of CNTs; in fact, only the catalyst area has to be positioned within the high temperature zone. This would allow fabricating CNTs with conventional tube furnaces with only minor engineering to be performed to collect the long CNTs: a system winding CNTs on bobbins similar to that used for long yarns (Li et al, 2004) can be envisaged.

3.6.3 Macroscopic carbon nanotube yarns

The manufacture of CNT yarns has been implemented mainly using two-step techniques, which separate CNTs growth from yarn production. These techniques include, among others, wet spinning in a solvent or in a polymer solution and, most recently, dry spinning. Long yarns of CNTs have been tested (Gao et al, 2010) for strength and have shown poor performance, but this result is more the consequence of the poor stress distribution within the CNT bundle and/or poor bonding between different CNTs than a sign of poor strength for a single CNT. Indeed, with better manufacturing techniques σ_ρ has increased from a fraction of MYuri ($\sigma \sim 0.7$ GPa and $\rho \sim 800$ kg/m^3) in 2004 (Zhang et al, 2004) to $8 - 16$ (Koziol et al, 2007; Zhang et al, 2011) MYuri ($\sigma \sim 3.3$ GPa and $\rho \sim 200$ kg/m^3) in 2011. Interestingly, it was observed that during stress tests the diameter shrank by as much as 10%, suggesting that the maximum σ could be higher than the value reported in the literature. This effect was explained by a redistribution of stress within the yarn (Ma et al, 2007). CNTs have been shown to self-assemble into mesh-like structures (Ma et al, 2009). When strain is applied to the yarn, meshes are first deformed to longer and narrower structures until some bundles are completely tightened; structures can then become overloaded and begin to fail; local stress is redistributed and at last only the strongest meshes carry the load before the final yarn rupture occurs.

Analysis showed that, in yarns, CNT extension contributes only a small percentage to the macroscopic strain (Ma et al, 2009).

A process was developed in Cambridge (U.K.) to directly spin CNT yarns drawn from an aerogel sock (Li et al, 2004). Kilometer long yarns have been manufactured at a rate of 20m/min. Yet specific strength decreased for increasing yarn lengths (Stano et al, 2008) from ~ 6 MYuri for gauge lengths in the region of 1mm to ~ 1 MYuri for gauge lengths of the order of 2cm. At the end of 2009 the quality of the CNT raw material (Zheng et al, 2009) was thought to be a limitation to further improvement: by introducing a small amount of hydrogen during the growth, well-aligned CNT arrays have been obtained, considerably improving the yarn handling/fabrication with respect to the case in an air/oxygen atmosphere. Yarns longer than 40m with $\sigma \sim 1.7$ MYuri were reported in 2010 (Liu et al, 2010). Still, CNT alignment and uniform load distribution appears to be a major issue: in 2009, theoretical studies (Pugno et al, 2009) predicted that σ_ρ has a dependence on the yarn length L (σ_L) and it is related to the CNT σ_ρ (σ_{CNT}) by:

$$\sigma_L = \sigma_{CNT} \sqrt{\frac{\left(\frac{\sigma_y}{\sigma_{CNT}}\right)^2 - 1}{\frac{l}{L} + 1} + 1} \qquad (3\text{-}1)$$

where l is a characteristic length (which corresponds to ~ 5μm for a defective CNT yarn with 10% of distributed defects), and σ_y is the yarn's σρ measured at very short lengths . A non-defective yarn with L~100,000 km is expected to have a 70% drop in strength with respect to the value of a single CNT, while a yarn with 10% distributed defects would have a 78% decrease over the same length (Zhang & Li, 2010). Interestingly, in 2012 a method to heal topological defects during CNT growth was proposed (Yuan, 2012). It was also proposed that otherwise perfect CNT with a single topological defect per meter length can be achieved.

The yarn's σρ has been shown to increase for increasing friction within the CNT bundle (Lin et al, 2010) and for post fabrication exposure to microwaves, which decreases the number of defects (Tang et al, 2010), thus increasing the strength. Still, the fundamental requirement for a strong yarn is the uniform stress distribution amongst CNTs within the yarn; this requirement yields to an increased degree of orientation of CNTs along the longitudinal direction of the yarn. This should avoid overloading CNT bundles which considerably deteriorate the overall macroscopic mechanical performance of the yarn.

3.7 Alternative Materials
CNTs are not the only material available for the space elevator tether. Several materials theoretically have the strength needed. As a tether would ideally require at least a specific strength of ~30 MYuri and commercial materials can only reach ~3 MYuri, the quest for a suitable material soon turned into an investigation of nanomaterials, which exhibit considerably larger strength than their macroscopic counterparts. Intuitively, this can be easily explained with Griffith's observation that cable strength is inversely proportional to the size of the largest crack on its surface. Nanowires can only stand cracks that are a fraction of their diameter, and thus they can exhibit strengths orders of magnitude larger than their bulk counterparts. In addition, at the nanoscale carbon and boron nitride present a form (nanotube) which does not have a bulk counterpart.

3.7.1 Nanowire and nanotubes
Figure 3-4 summarizes the data on carbon nanotubes (CNTs) (Barber et al., 2005), silicon carbide (SiC) (Wong et al, 1997), silicon nitride (Si_3N_4) (Iwanaga et al, 1998), and silica (SiO_2) (Brambilla & Payne, 2009). SiC and Si_3N_4 at their best can provide specific strengths of 16 MYuri, while the greatest value reported for silica glass is smaller, ~ 12 MYuri. The great benefit of these nanowires relies in their possibility to be manufactured in extremely long lengths with minor changes to the current fabrication technology: silica glass allows for the prompt manufacture of kilometer long wires. Si_3N_4 can also be manufactured in relatively long lengths with the current technology, but the length of defect-free Si_3N_4 single crystals has never been tested. CNTs have been identified as the ideal candidate because of their astonishing strength: specific strengths > 60 MYuri have been recorded for CNTs manufactured by chemical vapor deposition (CVD) with radii in the region of 50nm (Figure 3-4).

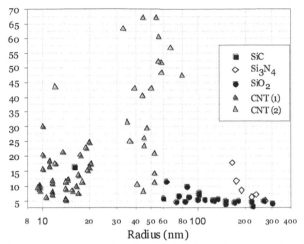

Figure 3-4. Specific strength σ_ρ as a function of size for carbon nanotubes (CNTs) and for silicon carbide (SiC), silicon nitride (Si_3N_4) and silica (SiO_2) nanowires. CNTs have been fabricated by arc-discharge (group 1, older samples) and by chemical vapor deposition (CVD) (group 2, better samples).

3.7.2 Theoretical strength

Although few materials with high specific strength have been reported in the literature, this is also due to the lack of research funding in the field of high strength materials. For this reason it is interesting to review which materials have the theoretical potential to achieve strengths in excess of 30 MYuri.

The theoretical strength of materials is related to the strength of the chemical bonds in the atoms which constitute it. Bonds can be classified according to their nature in strong and weak bonds; covalent (when there is an electron shared between two atoms) and ionic (when charges result from an electron being displaced from an atom to a different atom) bonds belong to the former group, while Van Der Waal's forces and hydrogen bonding belong to the latter group. The near totality of materials considered for high strength applications have covalent bonds.

More generally, the macroscopic specific strength of homogeneous materials can be roughly estimated from the bond strength Σ, the mass of atoms involved M and the number of bonds N per unit of volume (=A·h for area A and height h).

$$\sigma_\rho = \frac{\left(\dfrac{N \cdot \Sigma}{A}\right)}{\dfrac{M}{A \cdot h}} = \frac{N \cdot \Sigma}{\dfrac{M}{h}} = \frac{h \cdot N \cdot \Sigma}{M}$$

(3-2)

While M and N can be easily obtained from geometrical considerations and the periodic table of elements, Σ is not widely reported in the literature. Yet a good approximation for Σ can be obtained from simple mathematical considerations on the molecular potential. In molecular dynamic simulations, the interatomic potential is usually approximated by the Lennard Jones potential:

$$V_{LJ} = \varepsilon \cdot \left[\left(\frac{r_m}{r} \right)^{12} - 2 \cdot \left(\frac{r_m}{r} \right)^{6} \right]$$

(3-3)

where $\square$ is potential well depth, r_m is the equilibrium interatomic length (bond length) and r the interatomic distance. The force can be easily obtained from the potential (it is its derivative with respect to the distance):

$$f = \frac{\partial V_{LJ}}{\partial r} = 12 \frac{\varepsilon}{r_m} \cdot \left[\left(\frac{r_m}{r} \right)^{7} - \left(\frac{r_m}{r} \right)^{13} \right]$$

(3-4)

From the equilibrium position ($r=r_m$) f increases up to a maximum f_{max} for $r = (7/13)6 \cdot r_m$ and then gradually decreases to zero. Simple mathematical manipulations show that

$$f_{max} = \Sigma = \frac{504}{169} \left(\frac{7}{13} \right)^{6} \cdot \frac{\varepsilon}{r_m} \approx 2.69 \cdot \frac{\varepsilon}{r_m}$$

(3-5)

f_{max} can be considered the microscopic equivalent of the macroscopic ultimate strength. Eq. 3-5 allows for the easy derivation of molecular maximum strengths from the dissociation energy $\square$, reported in the literature.

Bond	Disassociation Energy[kJ/mol]	Length[pm]
O–O	145	148
N–N	170	145
Si-Si	226	111
C-S	272	182
Si-C	301	189
C–N	308	147
C–C	348	154
C–O	360	143
Si-O	368	161
B-N	389	
C–H	413	109
O=O	498	121
S=O	523	143
B=N	560	132
C=C	614	134
C=N	615	129
W-W	830	162
C≡C	839	120
N≡N	945	110

Table 3-V. Dissociation and length of common chemical bonds.

Table 3-V reports typical values of chemical bond dissociation energies and lengths. Covalent homogeneous materials tend to form gases, when all their bonds are saturated (like oxygen and nitrogen). Although their interatomic molecular bond strength is very high, it is impossible to form macroscopic materials because the formed diatomic molecules interact very weakly between them.

Tungsten (W) is one of the strongest homogeneous materials. Yet, because of its massive atomic mass (M = 183.84 g/mole, compared with M = 12 g/mole for carbon), its specific strength is relatively small, in comparison to carbon compounds. Carbon (C) has a relatively light weight, and its strong bond allows for the formation of extremely strong macroscopic materials (like diamond). Silicon (Si) forms a very strong bond with oxygen and carbon, providing strong materials too (silicon carbide and quartz).

Particularly interesting are the structures created by the periodic repetition of single units. The single unit is made of a group of atoms which are either connected by a single bond (like polymers) or by multiple bonds (like CNT). Ultimately, the strength of the macroscopic material obtained by the periodic repetition of these single units is given by the strength of the bonds interconnecting the units. Typical structures of polymers and CNT are shown in Figure 3-5.

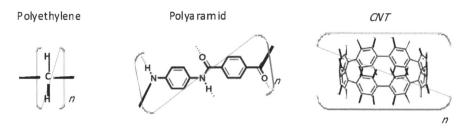

Figure 3-5. Schematic of polymers and carbon nanotube (CNT). Chemical composition of monomers constitute polyethylene (left), polyaramid (center) and carbon nanotube (right). In the center and right figures, carbon atoms have been omitted for clarity.

As a polyethylene monomeric unit has a small molecular mass (CH_2 has $M_{CH2} \sim 14$ g/mol), it also exhibits much higher strength than polyaramids, where the complex molecular structure implies a very large molecular mass (M ~ 230 g/mol). Assuming a bond dissociation energy of $\Box_{C-C} \sim 348$ kJ/mole for the C-C bond and neglecting the hydrogen bonds (which have an average strength of $\Box\Box_{NHO} \sim 20$ kJ/mol) in the polyaramid monomeric unit, the total monomer bond strength is $\Box \sim 2.69 \times 348/154 = 6.1$ (kJ/mol)/pm = 6.1 PN/mol. As a monomeric unit is about 1 nm long (h ~ 103 pm), its theoretical maximum macroscopic strength will then be of the order $\Box_p \sim (6.1 \cdot 1000)/230 \sim 26.5$ kJ/g = 26.5 MYuri. Because of the smaller monomeric molecular mass M, polyethylene has the potential to achieve even higher strengths; assuming that the C-C bond has a bond dissociation energy $\Box_{C-C} \sim 348$ kJ/mol (thus a total monomer bond strength of $\Box \sim 6.1$ PN/mol) and an average bond distance of $r_m = 154$ pm, and that polyethylene has a cell size h ~ 120 pm (carbons in sp^3 hybridization have an angle of 110°, and thus the distance along the polymeric chain is 154 pm $\cdot \sin(110/2) \sim 126$ pm) and M = 14 (= 12 for carbon + 2 · 1 for the hydrogen atoms), then the theoretical macroscopic strength for an infinitely long polyethylene chain is $\Box_p \sim (6.1 \cdot 0.12)/14 \sim 52$ MYuri.

Carbon nanotubes are meant to perform even better, as they are made only by carbon in sp^2 hybridization, the bond of which is stronger. Assuming a monomeric cell containing a single C atom with $\Box\Box_{C=C} \sim 524$ kJ/mol and $r_m = h$, then $\Box_p \sim 134 \cdot (2.69 \cdot 524/134)/12 \sim 118$ MYuri, comparable to the value obtained by molecular dynamic simulations by Yacobsen and co-workers (150 MYuri) and Belytschko and coworkers (93.5-112 MYuri). Diamond, which is also made from C atoms, but with four single bonds, has $\Box_{C\text{-}C} \sim 348$ kJ/mol, $r_m = 154$ pm and h = 90 pm (it has a zincblende crystallographic cell), giving $\Box_p \sim 46$ MYuri. This value is close to those predicted by Telling and colleagues for tension (64 MYuri).

From the above considerations it is clear that high strength materials should have small monomeric units and strong bonds interlinking monomeric units. Organic polymers (which are mainly based on carbon atoms) tend to have C-C or C=C interlinking bonds; thus they can exhibit an extremely high theoretical strength. Polyacetylene can have even better strength: $M_{CH} = 13$, $\Box_{C=C} \sim 524$ kJ/mol and h = $(\sqrt{3}/2)r_m$ (carbons in the chain have hybridization sp^2) imply an extraordinary theoretical strength of $\Box_p \sim 524/13 \sim 93$ MYuri.

Material	Predicted theoretical strength (eq. 2-5) [MYuri]	Predicted theoretical strength (literature) [MYuri]	Reference
Single Wall CNT	118	150	Yacobsen
		93.5-112	Belytschko
Polyethylene	52	42	Termonia
Polyacetylene	93		
Tungsten	6		
Silicon Carbide	23		
Silicon	12.5	10	Roundy
Silica (Quartz)	25		
Diamond	46	64	Telling
Boron Nitride	49		
Boron Nitride Nanotube	87	90	Wei
Polyborazylene	35		

Table 3-VI. Theoretical Strength of Selected Materials.

Inorganic components can provide extremely high strength too. Table 3-VI gives the theoretical strength of some selected materials. Tungsten is possibly the material with the strongest covalent bond between two identical atoms ($\Box_{W\text{-}W} = 830$ kJ/mol). Yet, because of its heavy atomic weight ($M_W \sim 184$ g/mol), it has a relatively low specific strength: assuming $r_m = 162$ pm and h = 81 pm (it has a body centered cubic (BCC) crystallographic structure), then $\Box_p \sim 830/184 \sim 6$ MYuri. Silicon has a weaker interatomic bond strength ($\Box_{Si\text{-}Si} \sim 226$ kJ/mol) but also a smaller atomic weight ($M_{Si} \sim 28$ g/mol), which results in an overall higher strength: its zincblende crystallographic structure implies $r_m = \sqrt{3} \cdot h$, giving a total $\Box_p \sim 12.5$ MYuri. This is slightly higher than the value (10 MYuri) predicted by Roundy 6 and coworkers (silicon has a density of 2.32g/cm^3). Silicon carbide (SiC) has even stronger bonds ($\Box_{Si\text{-}C} \sim 301$ kJ/mol) and smaller average weight ($M_{SiC} \sim 28+12 = 40$) with a zincblende structure of alternating C and Si atoms, which results in $\Box_p \sim 23$ MYuri. Silica, made from silicon and oxygen, has $\Box_{Si\text{-}O} \sim 368$ kJ/mol, $M_{Si\text{-}O} \sim 44$ g/mol, $r_m = 161$ pm, an average distance between adjacent silicon atoms of 312 pm and an estimated h ~ 180 pm, providing a respectable $\Box_p \sim 25$ MYuri.

Boron compounds benefit from the extremely light Boron atomic mass ($M_B = 10.8$ g/mol) to provide extremely strong compounds used for extreme applications like body armor: boron carbide (B_4C) and boron nitrite (BN). BN has strong bonds ($\sigma_{B-N} \sim 389$ kJ/mol)) and smaller weight ($M_{BN} \sim (14+10.8)/2 = 12.4$): amongst its most common crystalline structures, the sphalerite (σ-BN) and wurtzite (w-BN) structures provide a 3D structure similar to that observed in diamond resulting in $\sigma_p \sim 49$ MYuri. Indeed w-BN is harder than diamond. Interestingly, BN nanotubes (similarly to CNT) were predicted in 1994 and then experimentally discovered in 1995. Assuming $\sigma_{B-N} \sim 389$ kJ/mol and $M_{BN} \sim 12.4$, then $\sigma_p \sim 87$ MYuri can be predicted.

Amongst inorganic polymers polyborazylenes and polydimethylsiloxanes (known as PDMS in the electronic community or as silicon rubber among the general public) are the best known. Polyborazylene has $M \sim 75$ g/mol, $r_m = 130$ pm, $h \sim 400$ pm and $\sigma_{B-N} \sim 329$ kJ/mol, giving $\sigma_p \sim 35.4$ MYuri. PDMS has $M \sim 74$ g/mol, $r_m = 161$ pm, $h \sim 312$ pm and $\sigma_{Si-O} \sim 368$ kJ/mol, giving $\sigma_p \sim 26$ MYuri.

In conclusion, there are a number of materials which, in a perfectly periodical, infinitely long ensemble, can easily have strengths in excess of 20 MYuri: in addition to CNT, diamond, polyethylene, polyacetylene, boron nitride and boron carbide all have strengths exceeding 20 MYuri. From a scientific point of view CNTs are NOT the only option for a space elevator tether.

3.7.3. Scalability issues
In the real world, strength is limited by defects, which can be material impurities, the impossibility of having an infinitely long material with perfect periodicity and, above all, by a surface which interfaces the material with its surrounding environment. Particularly prone to these types of issues are 3D materials (materials which have periodicity in all three directions) like diamond, boron nitride and boron carbide. A tether can be considered as 1D material.

Thus these 3D materials would present extremely long surfaces, which are sources of defects and decrease (sometimes by orders of magnitude) the overall tether strength. Boron nitride and boron carbide are used in body armor and have been proposed for applications in rugged environments (like jet turbine nozzles), but cannot be prepared defect-free in large dimensions. Indeed, their specific strength is assumed to be in the region of 3 MYuri, even though micrometric nanowires with specific strength > 16 MYuri have been reported. Diamond has shown great strength in 1D form, with specific strength ~ 17 MYuri, but mainly in small microscopic samples.

1D materials, where periodicity occurs over one dimension only, are better candidates for the tether. In this group of materials, lateral surfaces do not induce any additional defect. Thus from the practical point of view they can represent a better option to reach specific strength > 20 MYuri. This group contains BN nanotubes and the various polymers such as polyethylene or polyacetylene.

Yet these classes of materials suffer from two other limitations: packing and stress distribution. Polymers tend to bend on themselves to form lamellae first and then spherulites, which are then interconnected by single strands of polymer. Effectively, this means increasing the molecular mass of interconnected unit cells by up to four orders of magnitude, and thus the overall specific strength can decrease to values in the region of tens of kYuri. Another problem with polymers is their tendency to branch. Single chains can branch out in tree-like structures, decreasing their overall axial strength. Finally polymers which rely on double bonds (like acetylene) can react explosively and degrade extremely fast, reducing their applications in real environments. Experimentally, macroscopic polyethylene fibers with specific strength ~ 7 MYuri have been reported (Koziol, 2007).

CNTs and BN nanotubes do not suffer from branching and are indeed extremely stable. Yet their extremely good stability renders them impossible to pack in an ordered way on macroscopic scale. Because of the perfect periodicity of their surface and the strong interatomic bonds between identical carbon atoms, nanotubes tend to have only weak interactions with other nanotubes resulting in a very loose long range packing order. Indeed, this has been the single most important issue to scale to large dimensions the properties observed at microscopic level. In a fiber made by billions of single nanotubes, axial stress at any instant is born only by a fraction of them; thus the fiber strength is only a fraction of its theoretical maximum value.

3.8 Summary of CNT Findings and Conclusions
Single CNTs with lengths of the order of few microns have shown strengths extraordinarily high (well in excess of 50 MYuri and in excess of 100 MYuri for short periods), which are suitable for the space elevator tether. The fabrication of a tether has been extremely challenging, with strengths of 17 MYuri being reported only in 2011. The technology to extend to long tethers the properties observed in short yarns is available. Once strengths in excess of 25 MYuri are demonstrated, the space elevator tether could be manufactured. If CNT yarn specific strength continues to growth at constant pace, it is predicted that a suitable strength will be available in yarn form as early as 2015.

CNTs are not the only available materials. Multiple alternatives exist, ranging from polymers (polyethylene, polyborazylene) to boron nitride nanotubes and diamonds. Yet research on these materials is not strong, and longer times might be necessary to achieve a tether with suitable specifications.

Finding 3-3: CNTs are not the only available material. Multiple alternatives exist, ranging from polymers (polyethylene, polyborazylene, etc) to boron nitride nanotubes and diamonds.

3.9 Safe CNT Manufacture
As the study is being conducted, the research & development of carbon nano-tube materials is being conducted in the laboratory and in engineering design facilities. There are concerns reference the safety of this new material and appropriate protective approaches are being instigated around the globe. This is an area of concern and must be understood as the production of CNT's approach reality.

3.10 Macro Tether Design
As will be described in the Dynamics chapter, the length of a space elevator without an Apex Anchor would be roughly 144,000 km to compensate for the mass below GEO altitude. As the tension varies along the tether, the needed cross-section will vary. The greatest stress is at the GEO location for the gravitational pull down and the centripetal toss outward. If one were to handle a 30 MYuri material, the taper ratio would be five. This taper ratio can be handled in many ways, but the two most logical would be to have a wider tether by a factor of five or a denser tether by a factor of five. When the Apex Anchor is attached to the space elevator, the natural length is roughly 100,000 km and the taper ratio stays the same. This study is going to put one more criterion on the shape of the tether as it goes from the surface of the ocean to

the Apex Anchor: consistent width to ensure that the gripping mechanism is as simple as possible. The needs for the tether design are shown in Table 3-VII.

Requirement	Level	Approach
Specific Strength of Material	38 MYuri	Sufficient for a safety factor of 40%
Operating Specific Strength	27 MYuri	Taper ratio of six
Width	1 meter	Consistency for the cross-sectional approach of the tether climber gripping mechanism
Sparseness	As needed	Near the high stress locations around GEO altitude, tether weaving is densest with the tether becoming very sparse towards the Apex Anchor and LEO altitudes – idea: depth of material constant across the width, with density across the 1 meter width variable for taper ratio
Wind Design	Sparse	With-in the wind tunnel effect of the atmosphere, the sparseness of the one meter wide tether will allow winds to flow through the tether of low densities.
Curvature	Greater than 10 cm bend	Curvature of the tether is to decrease the likelihood of small space debris cutting the tether if it was hit in its plane.

Table 3-VII. Macro Tether Design Needs

Finding 3-4: The design of the tether has a taper ratio to compensate for the greater tensions near the GEO node. With the current strength projections, the expected taper ratio will be less than eight.

Finding 3-5: The macro design of the space elevator tether is a sparsely filled, one-meter wide, curved, woven tether that is designed for winds under 100kms altitude and debris between 200 and 2,000kms altitude.

Over the last few years, the major assumption was that the width of the tether varies with altitude accounting for the winds in the atmosphere, the density of space debris and the increase in tensile stress as the tether approaches the GEO altitude. It would seem that the appropriate approach would be to have the sparseness of the one meter wide curved tether be appropriate for the demands of the altitude. As such, the climber gripper will have a constant one-meter wide tether with the density varying according to stress and other factors. The beauty of a constant one-meter wide tether is that threats can be spread out as well. The atomic oxygen can be treated with material coating in the first 500 km [length to be determined upon further study]. Small debris can be planned for with both the curved tether and the sparseness of the woven tether. The wind factor can be adapted with both the curve to directionize wind flow while the sparseness will allow winds to "blow right through" the tether.

A preliminary design has shown that a 27 MYuri tether has a rough size of 1 meter in width and 10.5 microns thick. The key is that as the taper ratio kicks in, the factor of six will ensure that a full up tether would be 1 meter wide and 62.8 microns thick at the high stress locations. With the concept of a constant one-meter wide sparse tether, the CNT yarn can be woven into a mesh that would sparsely fill the one-meter wide tether, even at the high stress location of GEO. One approach to handling this concept is to have constant strand dimensions and multiple strands across the one-meter width depending on the taper ratio. For the surface of the ocean, the one meter wide tether could have ten strands 0.2 cm wide and 525 microns thick, while at the GEO node the one meter wide tether could have 10 x 6 or 60 strands across. As the altitude increases, the strand count increases from 10 to 60 in an incremental approach. The specific weave of the tether strands and the proposed laydown of the ropes/yarns/strands will be studied in detail and proposed as the material approaches the needed production capability and manufacturing approaches. Major studies will be conducted as the design choices need to be solidified for manufacturing long, almost perfect, robust tether components.

3.11   Additional Verification/Validation Requirements in Space

It takes longer than users' expectations to utilize new materials in space or the aerospace industrial area. For example, CNT material found over 50 years ago is not popular to utilize in space. One thing needs to be evaluated carefully – the stability of strong tethers such as CNTs in the space environment. Based upon system requirements described before, the design for the tether material is to be 10 years, with a replacement planned for every 7.5 years. A good example of an in-orbit verification of material design is the JAXA announced flight opportunity, where they will launch a small facility for a material exposure experiment (Figure 3-6).

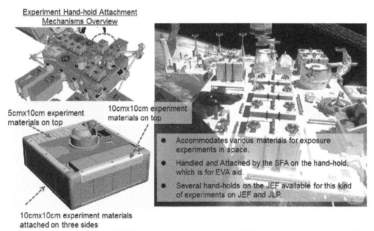

Figure 3-6. Overview of Material Exposure Experiment Using Japanese Experiment Module 'Kibo' on ISS5

The current concept by JAXA is to have private entities perform their activities on orbit using JAXA's experiment module called 'Kibo' ('Hope' in Japanese). At this point, no exposure experiment is planned by private entities but only universities or national institutes using government funds. Figure 3-7 shows a current plan for a material exposure experiment on orbit , a space elevator key technologies step. Based on this schedule, the first material exposure experiment will be scheduled in 2016.

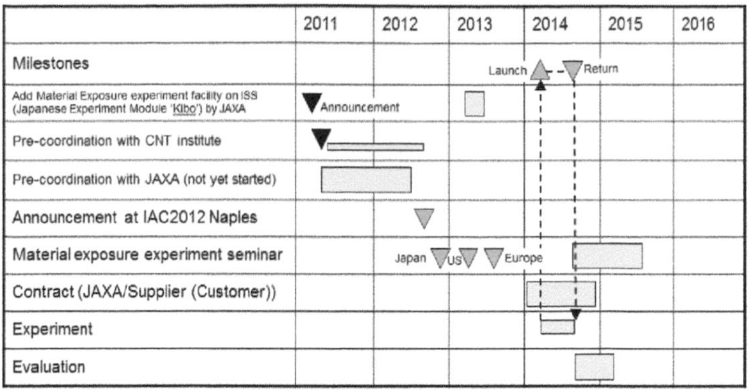

	2011	2012	2013	2014	2015	2016
Milestones				Launch ▲ – ▼ Return		
Add Material Exposure experiment facility on ISS (Japanese Experiment Module 'Kibo') by JAXA	▼ Announcement		☐			
Pre-coordination with CNT institute	▼ ▭					
Pre-coordination with JAXA (not yet started)	▭					
Announcement at IAC2012 Naples		▽				
Material exposure experiment seminar		Japan ▽ US ▽ ▽ Europe		▭		
Contract (JAXA/Supplier (Customer))				▭ ▼		
Experiment				▭		
Evaluation					▭	

Figure 3-7. Material Exposure Experiment on Orbit

Chapter 4
Spacecraft & Climbers
Deployment & GEO Spacecraft; Buildup & Operational Climbers

4.1 Background

The word *climber* is used as the operative noun to denote the space system that is ascending or descending on the space elevator tether by its own means. The variety will be great, but there are two climber types that will be described in this chapter [operational – 20 Metric Tons & buildup – much smaller for initial application of more tether materials]. In addition, the chapter will present two spacecraft [deployment satellite to bring tether material to GEO and release & GEO Node satellite as a destination for ascending cargo] required to initiate and operate the space elevator. This chapter is broken into:

> 4.2 Operational Climbers: Defined as the commercial version of a spacecraft taking customer payloads to altitudes such as GEO, LEO and Solar System trajectories. It will also return objects to disposal orbits or to the earth's surface. The ascent requires power to climb while the decent from GEO and ascent past GEO requires braking as gravity or centrifugal forces dominant].
>
> 4.3 Deployment Spacecraft: Defined as the massive space system assembled in LEO and then rocketed to GEO for initial deployment of tether. The deployment spacecraft would then deploy one end of the tether in the downward direction towards the surface of the ocean while raising the other end in the opposite direction, keeping the whole system at the allocated GEO node. At the end of the deployment phase, the spacecraft moves to become part of the Apex Anchor.
>
> 4.4 Tether Buildup Climbers: Defined as the small system that would ride up the initial "seed" tether and weave [or attach with epoxy] additional strands of the tether. Up to 207 trips could be necessary to reach operational status of the space elevator.
>
> 4.5 GEO Node Spacecraft: Defined as a massive space system for the operational space elevator located at geosynchronous altitude to enable the off-loading, loading, fuelling and handling of space elevator climbers and customer payload spacecraft.

4.2 Operational Climbers

4.2.1 Introduction

The variety of operational climbers will surprise even early believers in a space elevator. There will be tether weavers, repairers, safety inspectors along with logistical trams, commercial climbers, human rated climbers, hotels, and launch ports. An open standard will facilitate all manner of climbers to work on the space elevator. The analogy would be the railroad's width of its rails. Anyone can put a train on the rails if they adopt the standards (that is within the same country – standards may differ between countries causing problems at borders). A similar approach must be used to ensure compatibility between tethers and climbers. The complexity of the tether interface will drive the design of tether climbers and keep its maturity level between technological development and engineering applicability. Some of the baseline discussions have led to the following assumptions for this chapter and the space elevator infrastructure:

- A capability of 30 MT for the space elevator.
- Each tether climber will be structured around a 20 MT gross weight at the Marine Node location with 6 MT allocated for the vehicle and 14 MT allocated to the cargo. There could be a total of seven tether climbers on the space elevator at any one time, as

shown in Table 4-I. The current estimate is one launch per day with trip time to GEO of approximately seven days [assumes a velocity of 215km/hr or 60m/sec average].

• As the tether climber will be loaded and started at the Marine Node platform and protected through the atmosphere, the fragile solar arrays will be deployed on tether climbers at altitude prior to initiating climbing. The early morning sun will start the climb for the vehicle, which will go against gravity until night occurs. During this eclipse, the vehicle will wait on the tether and conserve heat and energy until the next morning [significantly shorter than 12 hours as it is more than 3,000km away from the surface of the Earth]. Each day's climb will have longer "daylight" with it reaching continuous solar energy rapidly except for twice a year at spring and fall equinoxes [when there will be short daily eclipses all the way to GEO and beyond].

For a 20 MT Tether Carrier – radius [km]	Contributing Forces [g & cf] Factor	20 MT Weight Equivalent	6 MT Weight Equivalent
6,378 @ surface	1.0	20 MT	6 MT
12,756	0.25	5.0	1.5
19,134	0.1	2.0	.6
26,600 @ GPS orbit	0.043	0.8	.24
27,000	.041	0.8	.24
34,000	.014	0.3	0.08
42,160 @ GEO	0.00	Zero "G"	zero
Total Equivalent Mass on Tether of seven climbers		28.9	8.66

Table 4-I. Seven Climbers Simultaneously

This portion of the chapter will be broken into four segments: historic perspective, tether climber structure, power collection-distribution, and motor-drive train.

4.2.2   Historic Perspective with Assumptions

Movement of the space elevator climber from the surface to GEO, and operations of the tether climber, require power. Stored energy is significantly too heavy to move against gravity in an economical manner; so energy must be "sent" to the elevator. The original concept was massive lasers powering all riders to GEO and beyond – requiring multiple sizable lasers operating full time all the way to 100,000kms. This requirement drove large floating platforms on the surface of the ocean with high power requirements. An extra complexity, never addressed, was the necessity not to interfere with satellites in orbit around the space elevator. This "traffic management" of beams and energy levels becomes quite serious when considering the number of satellites near the space elevator at GEO and all the LEO/MEO satellites orbiting through the beam. For the space elevator to have continuous power in large quantities, this laser complexity becomes a major factor in scheduling. [See Appendix E-2 for laser complexity description.]

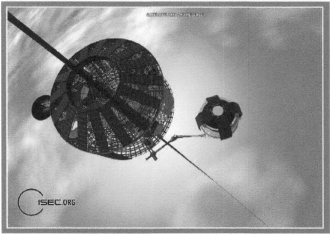
Figure 4-1. Climber as Spacecraft [chasedesignstudios.com]

The current thinking is that ubiquitous solar energy should be the source of power. This requires a large solar array capability. Most of the trip is in constant sunlight, except for periods during the early climb [first night definitely], and then short transition periods of eclipse. This chapter will talk about basic power requirements, types of viable power, and delivery alternatives. Focusing on climber designs that derive all of their power from direct sunlight conversion is now possible due to recent advances, and future projections, in photovoltaic technology. While presenting some challenges, this design eliminates the requirement for a power beaming system.

4.2.3 Tether Climber Breakout

A tether climber is no more than a spacecraft with a special propulsion unit of electrically driven wheels instead of fuel-consuming engines (Figure 4-1). The components of a space elevator climber parallel a sophisticated spacecraft because of the similarities in requirements driven by the environment. However, a significant difference is the tremendously "softer" ride on an elevator vs. a rocket with its burning chemicals restricted by its rocket structure thrusting violently. The tether climber is composed of the following major components [robotic version]:

- Structure [with cargo bays]
- Energy management [source, distribution, storage]
- Motor / Engine
- Tether interface equipment
- Drive apparatus [wheels]
- Communications payloads and antennas
- Environmental controls [heat, cold, vacuum, radiation, etc.]
- Attitude control [star sensors, GPS sensors, thrusters, spinning devices, controller, magnetic torque rods]
- Support equipment [robotic arm to load / off-load cargo, housekeeping, etc.]

The tether climber will be designed to operate above 40km altitude with some type of external protection below that altitude for winds, lightning, rain, etc. This enables the designer to specify a tether climber that operates in the void of space and can be flexible in the design space, as the accelerations and shock loads will be minimal. The tether climber will initiate its climb to mission altitude with cargo design criteria that are far less stringent than current launch vehicle design criteria. However, the first 40km will require shielding for the tether climber and its supporting components (especially fragile solar cells). Chapter 5 will discuss various approaches for tether climber protection for the first 30-50km.

Requirements: The first step in the design process is to identify the criteria. This is usually consolidated in the Systems Design Requirements Document early in the design-development process. The following is a preliminary set of requirements for space elevator tether climbers as shown in Table 4-II.

Requirement for Climber	Segment	Easy Hard
Spacious for customer's 14 MT payload	S	easy
Balanced for center of mass	S	routine
Gain and maintain 60 m/sec [minimum]	M	hard
Sufficient power for climber	E	medium
Pointing solar arrays	A	medium
Power storage and distribution	E	easy
Attitude control of climber	A	medium
Communicate with operations and customer	C	easy
Compatible with Marine Node	S	Medium
Compatible with GEO Node	S	Medium
Survivable in space environment	Ev	medium
Sufficient coefficient of friction	S	Medium
Maintain Contact with Tether	M	Medium

Segment key: S-structure, A-attitude, E-energy, C-communications,
M-motor, Ev-environmental
Table 4-II. Requirements Set for Climber

Major Climber Components[1]: The tether climber will be a spacecraft that has all the necessary components to thrive in the space environment with a mission to climb up and down the space elevator. Each of its major components will be discussed below with some estimates of mass and power required to function in the up/down operational environment above the atmosphere. The vehicle will operate mostly in the sunshine, and hibernate during eclipse. During the day, the dominant factor will be pointing the solar arrays at the sun and keeping the equipment in the proper thermal range while climbing at 60m/sec. During the short nights, the principal activity will be keeping the components within their thermal range [heating] while preparing for the next day's travel.

Carbon NanoTube (CNT) Improvements in Spacecraft: Mass and power estimates shown in this chapter are for the current design of spacecraft with traditional designs representing the last two decades of orbital and interplanetary spacecraft. For comparison, the "w/CNTs" estimate has been taken from several sources that deal with application of new materials technology based upon a projection of the lightness and strength of CNT based spacecraft elements from structures to wires to components inside batteries. The future world of

---

[1] Authors' note: How to handle radical improvements in mass of spacecraft for new structures based on CNT? Estimates are made compared with current values in summary tables.

spacecraft design will be much more sophisticated and effective with respect to mass and energy because of these breakthroughs in materials. The history of spacecraft costs shows that, as exorbitant investments were required to achieve difficult and critical missions, savings in mass [such as a 75% mass savings in structures using CNTs] and cost were exploited enthusiastically. Other elements [such items as power distribution, collection and storage] are being assessed as this study is being conducted. The authors have taken estimates from the reports and entered numbers they believe will be in effect when the space elevator is developed, post-2030. The chart (Table 4-III) below addresses traditional communications satellites that currently have a mass of approximately one to two metric tons. In addition, the table shows the proposed reduction in mass through the use of CNT materials for strength, stiffness, electrical conductivity, electrical insulation, heat transfer and heat isolation. The surprising result is that CNT's can save the spacecraft designer up to 75% of the mass in the long term though smart designs and maximum use of the characteristics of CNTs. This would mean, in the not too distant future, that a new spacecraft could weight 25% of current spacecraft and, as such, could be roughly 25% of the cost [to the first order, cost and mass are directly related]. This could easily lead to more spacecraft and more missions accomplished in space. In the sense of the space elevator, cargo loads would contain four times as many spacecraft or four times the capability to orbit when compared to today's spacecraft characteristics.

Finding 4-1: CNT materials will be incorporated into the structural design and will substantially lessen the mass of components and structures through-out future space elevator satellites, including all varieties of tether climbers.

Structure [with cargo bays]: The structure of the tether climber will be designed to respond to the requirements developed during the design phase. A potential image is shown in Figure 4-2, Climber Structure.

The layout of a structure can be in many shapes; but the above image is reasonable and shows the climber's various components. The core tunnel is arranged for the flow of the tether with the motor and wheels penetrating this long corridor. The rest of the structure is laid out so that the balance is centered to minimize stresses on the tether. The center of mass should be aligned with tether flow access. The structure can be used for many things; however, it is needed for the attachment of supporting components and protection of the spacecraft from environmental threats. The layout of the solar arrays on the body would be convenient to begin energy collection, with the majority of the cells being supported below the climber structure shown in Figure 4-3.

	Fltsatcom 6 Original Mass [kg]	Mass with CNTs	DSP 15 Original Mass [kg]	Mass with CNTs	Tether Climber 6 MT	Mass with CNTs
					Payload	
Payload	226	57	563	141	Support	555
Structure	168	42	408	102	Structure	1500
Thermal	17	4	42	11	Thermal	120
Power	340	85	825	206	Power	2340
TT&C	26	7	63	16	TT&C	180
ADCS	52	13	127	32	ADCS	360
Propulsion	35	9	85	21	Drive Motor	740
Total Mass "dry"	871	218	2115	529	Total Mass "dry"	5795
propellant	81	20	162	41	propellant	205
Total Mass "wet"	952	238	2277	569	Total Mass "wet"	6000
					Payload	14000
					Tether Climber	20000

Table 4-III. Reduction of Mass by CNT Incorporation (SMAD. pg 894)

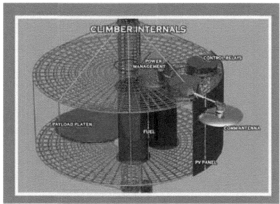

Figure 4-2. Climber Structure [chasedesignstudios.com]

Figure 4-3: Solar Climber Structure [chasedesignstudios.com]

As the structure will be made from a composite material [most probably from CNT mesh], the mass will be small but the strength and stiffness significant. The estimated mass for a climber of this size would be around 6 MT with a structure about 20 meters in diameter and 15 meters in height. The volume inside is huge, allowing large cargo shapes inside the protection of the structure.

Estimates	Current Material	with CNTs
Mass of structure:	6 MT	1.5 MT
Size of structure: cylinder with dia x height [m]	3 x 20	20x15

Energy management [source, distribution, storage]: The next major section of this chapter talks about energy movement and collection. The estimates are:

Estimates	Current Ratio	w/ CNTs in Kg
Mass of Solar Array	0.83	1,942
Mass of Battery	0.17	399

At the present time, Lithium Ion Batteries (LIBs) are used extensively in cell-phones, notebooks, and digital cameras. Traditional LIB density of energy is about 100W/kg. Future LIBs' (including CNTs) density of energy is expected to be about 470W/kg. LIBs are also used in space, such as in the Japanese SERVIS series. LIBs are expected to be applied to electric vehicles and railways as high output types. The LIB's output density is about 1000W/kg in Japan as of 2010. The government of Japan establishes 2000W/kg for Electric Vehicles and Hybrid Vehicles by 2020, and 3000W/kg for hybrid train by 2030 (TSM, 2010).

Energy Storage, LIB watts/kilogram	100	3,000

Motor / Engine & Drive Apparatus: The last section of the discussion on operational climbers is about the drive train of the climber to include the electric motor for wheels of the climber. Linear motor drives, similar to the space elevator, are suitable for the tether climber. In 2003, a linear motor car achieved a speed of 581km/h during its manned test run in Yamanashi Prefecture. Tsuchida *et al* (2009) have discussed the optimization of vertical linear motors for tether climbers. On that method, the climber elevates by the rollers' friction force. Tether climber research and development has been carried out around the world investigating drives by the friction method and optimization of friction drive mechanisms. This friction method is also considered an effective means for the initial space elevator.

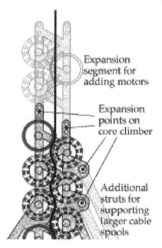

Figure 4–4. Climber Drive Apparatus [HighLift]

The mechanism is simple and easy to manufacture. It can be applied to tether climbers, fixed-point observation from the sky in a balloon system, and a stratosphere elevator. At Japan's Space Elevator Technical and Engineering Competition 2011 (JSETEC, 2011), the tether climber averaged about 17m/s (60km/hr) on a rope tether and about 9 m/s on a belt tether. This proved that friction drive by rollers can be successful. At the European Space Elevator Challenge 2011 (EUSPEC, 2011), they ranked the competitors to calculate exact energy efficiency. If you adopt a friction drive system to lift climbers, you require selection of the friction material with CNT. The material is selected taking into account the various elements, coefficient of friction, wear resistance, use in outer space, aging and so on. The coefficient of friction is the most important; but it also depends upon the pressing mechanism, contact area, etc. Tsukiyama clarified the tribological properties of CNT film by experiment. He produced a CNT film. The interface strength was 85 GPa when the length of the CNT was 100nm (Tsukiyama, 2010). In addition, Umehara (2007) obtained knowledge of CNT's coefficient of friction through testing.

Communications Payloads and Antennas: The need for the climber to be in continuous link with operations ensures the architecture of the space elevator network is closed. The climber should be in constant communications with the GEO node [which will then be in contact with operations in the base station below and headquarters on the mainland]. Most probably, when taking into account the current architecture in space today and trends towards the future, the frequency of choice will be Ka-band with a backup emergency broadcast capability in S-band. An estimated weight for S-band equipment is roughly 5.9kg made up of antenna, diplexer, receiver, and transmitter. The Ka-Band equipment would be about the same, as the frequency is higher for a smaller dish but the equipment to support it is heavier and more complex. An alternative, to save mass, would be to use laser communications from the tether climber to GEO communications node [above atmosphere only]. The mass and power savings could be significant. Initially the communications connection would be with the ground as the system is raised to 40km, and then the Ka-band system takes over pointing up to the GEO station.

Estimates	with CNTs
Mass of Communications Package	150 kg

Command and Data Handling [computer, data handling, and command breakout – CADH]: The key element in this package is the computer that accepts the commands from the operations center, interprets the information, disperses commands to the appropriate activity, accepts feedback, interrogates sensors [such as thermal or pointing], refines information from elements of spacecraft and formats the information for shipment by the communications segment.

Estimates	with CNTs
Mass of CADH	30 kg

Environmental control [heat, cold, vacuum, radiation, etc.]: Heat treatment is a major problem in space. It is possible to convert heat energy to another form of energy and circulate it or discharge it. Thermal electric conversion could be leveraged. In 2012, Suemori made thermoelectric transducer film of CNT-polymer composite material. It had a thickness of 0.3mm and was flexible. This raised the voltage by 106.9mV on temperature differences of 25 and 36 degrees and had a high figure of merit [about 0.03] (Suemori, 2012).

Estimates	with CNTs
Mass of Environmental Control Elements	120 kg

Attitude Determination and Control [star sensors, GPS sensors, thrusters, spinning devices, controller, mag torque rods, etc.]: Control of the climber will be relatively simple compared to current spacecraft, as one axis is defined by the tether path. The only variable would be the rotation around this axis. However, due to the tether curvature, the space elevator will not be exactly vertical and will have some variations off nadir pointing [probably no more than 20 degrees]. A key is that the solar arrays are designed to point at the sun. A heavy spinning mass [reaction wheel or momentum wheel] may not be required if the spacecraft climber is able to stabilize close to vertical and then use its multiple magnetic torque rods to orient the vehicle towards the sun. Multiple torque rods could be aligned on different axes to allow for multiple interactions with electromagnetic fields providing forces aligning the spacecraft face towards the sun.

Various sensors would identify the location of the sun [and perhaps stars – but that level of sophistication is probably not required], identify the hot or cold parts of the spacecraft, and understand the radiation levels being encountered. One set of sensors that will be required is GPS for both location and orientation, as a differential measurement can be taken that would then give the operator knowledge of the spacecraft's orientation and pointing. Once the spacecraft is oriented correctly, control mechanisms on the solar arrays can be exercised, and the direction to the sun can be identified, leading to pointing of the arrays. This is especially important as the efficiency of solar arrays is a function of angle – falling off rapidly when not pointed correctly [a function of the sine; so close to 90 degrees is good enough]. Pointing of the solar arrays at the sun will be discussed in the next section, but the idea is simple. Solar panels would be hung below with semi-rigid rods separating them vertically and small cables connecting them to change the up-down angle for better pointing at the sun as it goes through its daily motion – reference the tether axis [or could have some type of rotation device at each connection point on the semi-rigid rods]. Motion would range from pointing below the horizon at sunrise, to pointing up at noon to pointing over the shoulder, then pointing down at sunset on the other side; and finally rotating back in the same axis for the next sunrise.

Estimates	with CNTs
Mass of sensors and computer:	60 kg
Mass of reaction wheel [if needed]	300 kg

4.2.4 Solar Power

This space elevator architecture has a basic 20 MT tether climber (6 ton structure, motor, power collector and a 14 ton payload capability) starting on the surface of the ocean in a one-gravity field. As it rises, the mass stays the same [because the energy source is external – not carried by the rider]; but, the attractive force falls off as per the $1/r^2$ rule. The initial power requirement is estimated to be 11.8MWatts [electric]. This falls off by three fourths at a 6378km altitude or a 12,756km radius. Therefore, the critical power projection is near Earth with solar power sufficient along the path from start to finish. This approach does not require laser projection of power. At the present time four factors dominate the discussion:

- Solar arrays should be able to accomplish the mission (Shelef, 2008c). The projections of increases in solar efficiencies and decreases in weight are remarkable and should easily match future space elevator needs.
- NASA's solar array research has hardware in testing that is called "Solarosa" and provides: 400 to 500W/kg BOL [beginning of life] with 60 to 80kw/m^3 BOL. This would yield a mass requirement of 23.5 metric tons. Two notes for thought. BOL does not play as the climbers are returned and can be refurbished, and this is 2012 technology with tremendous research going on for lightweight flexible solar arrays. If the technology improves by one order of magnitude, the climber design for power falls into place. [NASA Tech Briefs, Nov 2012]
- The sun provides free energy without the complexity of generating power on the Earth or in orbit [space technology has been leveraging this "free energy" for the last 50 years]. In addition, there is no pointing of lasers or adaptive options required for atmospheric corrections.
- The perception, by engineers and scientists who actually build space systems, is that providing high-power, continuous, multiple sources [location diversity and multiple climbers simultaneously] laser power from the surface to tether climbers adds significant complexity and risks. [See Appendix E-2 for laser complexity]
- The complexity of scheduling permission to radiate upwards with full power lasers is daunting and almost impossible with current LEO-MEO-GEO missions. The sensitivity of satellite sensors looking down is great and the probability of impact is high [especially with GEO satellites near the longitudinal node of the Space Elevator] especially when high power lasers are on 24/7/365 to support continuous operations of multiple climbers. Our history inside the Laser Clearing-house (LCH) leads us to conclude that continuous upward looking high power lasers will require major policy changes both nationally [within the DoD, Intelligence and NASA/NOAA communities] and internationally.

Finding 4-2: The strongest concept for tether climbers is solar only from 40km altitude based upon projection of technology. There are three viable concepts to move the climber from the Marine Node to the appropriate starting altitude: box satellite with extension cord, spring forward, and High Stage One.

Finding 4-3: Large, light-weight, deployable, advanced solar arrays will power the tether climbers above 40km altitude.

With this background, the team has gone towards tether climbers with solar arrays that are large, lightweight, highly efficient, point-able, and based upon heritage.

Proposed Power Architecture: The future architecture for space elevator electric powered climbers will be:

- 6 MT climber [electric drive motor, structure, solar arrays, command and control computer, communications equipment, drive/break wheel apparatus, heat rejection panels, etc.]
- 14 MT capacity for cargo to GEO and beyond. Very little restriction on size or shape with small dynamic loads along the way.
- Up to seven tether riders on the tether at any one time, spaced as per velocity and load requirements.
- Tether climber delivered to 40 km altitude [chapter 5 describes three methods] for initiation of climb.
- Initial solar array power to provide energy from daybreak to first sunset [somewhere above 3,300 km altitude]
- Tether Climber to "sleep" during eclipse.
- Solar energy usage begins again at second sunrise and continues towards the space elevator apex anchor.

This space elevator architecture was illustrated in Figure 4-2 and leads to a discussion of day/night power usage. While a set of several solar panels can give the climber large amounts of power, they can only do so when illuminated. Regrettably, at the equator in LEO, illumination only occurs 12 hours a day. It is advantageous to launch the climber, from its 40km altitude starting point, at sunrise so large amounts of power are available. When night falls, the best alternative is to wait until local dawn to proceed. Normally, the climber would have traveled far enough by nightfall that power requirements would have dropped significantly and the length of the night is reduced. An engineering design must be conducted to determine how heavy the power system would be and how far the climber has climbed after 24 hours. In both summer and winter, sunrise and sunset are coincident with the ecliptic plane, whereas in spring and fall, midnight and noon are. Sunset for the climber occurs well past 18:00 hrs for two reasons: first, having traveled a certain distance, the climber is located at a higher radius so that it does not have to rotate 180° to clear the night side. Second, as a function of the sun's angle above the equator, the climber at sunset is located away from the ecliptic and, therefore, sees a smaller portion of the Earth's shadow corresponding to the Earth's radius at that solar latitude.

Table 4-IV shows some examples of climbing locations of the space elevator while in the spring/fall (worst case) scenarios. For two examples [60 and 100m/sec] the calculations have been run to show a few times and radii of activity. Day one and two are shown with sunrise and sunset which yields the full time for climbing. The dark eclipse time is calculated to show night duration, and sunset time is illustrated. Days one and two are natural progressions, starting at 06:00 hrs until dark. Day eight [for 60m/sec] and day six [for

100m/sec] are shown as they are when the space elevator climber reaches GEO altitude. Note that in this worst case scenario, even at GEO, the climber will experience only a brief period of darkness – about 35 minutes. For the rest of the year, eclipse effects are less and less during climbing, until the winter and summer solstices, when the distance to full sunlight is at only 8,290kms. This can be reached in less than two days for a 60m/sec climber and by mid-day the second day with a faster climber. Between those two extremes of seasons, the path to full daylight varies. The conclusion is that the first night period will last between four and five hours. The climber will emerge from the first night at approximately 02:00 hrs, and will normally not go into darkness again. At 06:00 hrs, when the next climber is ready to go, the tether will have between 70% and 83% of its capacity available for it.

	Speed in m/sec	60	100
Day one	Sunrise radius (km)	6378	6378
	Sunrise time	6	6
note:	eclipse angle	66.17	55.21
time in decimal hr	sunset time	21.79	22.16
	Distance Traveled (km)	3412	5817
	Radius at sunset (km)	9790	12195
Day two	Sunrise radius (km)	9790	12195
	Sunrise time	2.21	1.84
	eclipse angle	48.91	42.27
	sunset time	22.37	22.59
	Distance Traveled (km)	4355	5976
	Radius at sunset (km)	14145	18172
		day eight	day six
At GEO	Sunrise radius (km)	37904	37234
	Sunrise time	0.64	0.68
	eclipse angle	16.94	17.21
	sunset time	23.44	23.43
	Distance Traveled (km)	4925	6552
	Radius at sunset (km)	42828	43786

Table 4-IV. Time to Sunlight

4.2.5   Climber Design for Proposed Power Architecture

The main challenge in designing a solar powered climber is the large and flimsy nature of the panels (Shelef, 2008c). Typical in-space structures benefit from the lack of an atmosphere and gravity. In our case, we do not have the latter advantage and must design the structure to withstand 0–1g while being tiltable. Figure 4-2 showed the basic concept. Each panel's shape and position are completely determined by a large number of marionette-style pull-strings that suspend it against gravity. Except for the top panel, the panels are simply supported by the strings. Inflatable or foam-filled tubes can act as stiffeners without breaking the mass budget. The distance between the panels is 3-4 times their diameter, corresponding to a shading angle of 14-18 degrees. This distance can be reduced at the expense of not getting optimal sun tracking around local noon. As the system has to function in zero g as well, a trailing "caboose" car keeps minimal tension in the strings when necessary. Each panel is assembled around a tether glider (Figure 4-5) that prevents contact with the fast moving tether. The glider is connected to the panel by a number of radial tension wires that can only transmit transverse loads. The glider neither carries the panel nor is carried by it; and, it does not control the tilt angle of the panel. As the panels are so much heavier than the tether, and since the tether cannot exert sideways tension-related forces, the gliders force the tether to conform to any transverse motion the panels may exhibit rather than moving the panels to conform to the position of the tether. Each glider consists of a round cavity whose circumference is slightly larger than the width of the tether. For a one meter wide tether, the cavity is about 33 cm in diameter. To assure separation, we make sure that the tether is electro-statically charged before it gets to the first glider. This may already be the case due to solar wind and radiation; but, if it isn't, it is easy to achieve artificially. The glider ring is also then charged, so it repels the tether. A back-up gas cushion system can keep the tether from touching the glider if the primary system fails.

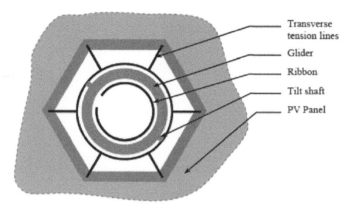

Figure 4-5. Glider Structure [Shelef 2008c]

Finding 4-4: Operations are to launch at daybreak from above the atmosphere, climb using solar during the first day, rest during the first night, and then solar during the rest of the trip [with small eclipses outage]

4.2.6   Engineering Reality Check
A possible candidate for such a power architecture is the Solar climber – a design capable of achieving sufficient and significant power levels required for climbing the tether (Shelef, 2008c). The enabler for this design is the recent development of very low weight, thin-film, photovoltaic technology able to provide as much as 5kWatt/kg. Recently a German experiment developed a self-deploying solar panel demo weighing 32kg and able to provide 50kWatt of electric power under full sunlight illumination. The array size is 20m x 20m, and operates at slightly under 10%. The power density of the complete panel [foil and booms] is 1.6kWatt/kg. The superstructure weighs as much as half the complete panel while the combined mass-area density is $0.08kg/m^2$. As this is today's technology, it is for a 10% PV array. If we were not to improve the capability in the next 20 years, the need would be for 7.4 MT and $590,000m^2$. The power generation would be 5% of the mass of the system and require an array of 770m x 770m.

The next few years will see tremendous leaps in efficiency and reduction of the mass. The next table (Table 4-V) was taken from a US Air Force document (USAF, 2012) showing the expected increases in efficiency of PV arrays for spacecraft. In the article is a statement: "The importance of these S&T efforts lies in the fact that every 1% increase in solar cell energy generation efficiency translates to a 3.5% increase in power [or decrease in mass] for the system.

Energy Generation		
Near (FY 2011-15)	Mid (FY 2016-20)	Far (FY 2021-25)
30-35 % efficient PV cells	40 % evolved PV cells	70 % efficient PV cells (e.g. quantum dots)

Table 4-V. Energy Generation Technologies [small portion of chart] (USAF, 2012)

If this is the true criterion of future solar arrays for space systems, the move from 10% efficient panels [like the one described previously as a current prototype] to 40% efficient will be phenomenal. The increase in power would be approximately 105% [30 x 3.5% increase] or 104kWatts for the same mass and area. This could also lead to an output power of approximately 50kWatts with less mass and area. If the industry approaches 70% efficiency, the impact on the PV arrays would be 210% improvement. [Approximately 60 x 3.5 with "quantum dots."] Table 4-VI shows the relationship between the current array prototype discussed and the needed size with the current array and two future cases.

	Current Array	Current Array for 20 MT tether climber	Future Array for 20 MT tether climber	Future Array for 20 MT tether climber
PV Efficiency	10 %	10 %	40 %	70 %
Output KWatt	50	11,800	11,800	11,800
Improvement	Current	Current	30% efficiency or 105% power	60% efficiency or 210% power
Mass required in kg^2	32	7400	3610	2400
Area Required m^2	400	590,000 or 770 m x 770 m	290,000 or 540 m x 540 m	191,000 or 440 m x 440 m

Table 4-VI. Projected Improvement in KWatt Capacity

The beauty of this calculation is that it matches the image that Frank Chase put together with many panels hanging below the tether climber, as shown in figure 4-3.. In the best-case situation, the arrays could be ten in a series with 44 m x 440 m panels looking at the sun in a very benign environment above 40 km altitude. The use of solar arrays for powering the tether climber seems like the obvious choice when one considers the heritage, amount of effort going into solar array development, solar cell efficiency, CNT advances and battery improvements. One interesting note is that the development of ultraviolet solar cells would increase the efficiency significantly. The convenient aspect of this development is that there is a tremendous effort around the globe to increase the efficiency and manufacturability of solar cells and their associated equipment for both terrestrial and space uses. As a result, the

---

[2] These projected numbers are probably high as the sparseness of the array will increase power and decrease mass required for the same level of output.

technologies for the space elevator climber must be projected to be accessible in the time period discussed with capabilities that other industries are projecting.

4.2.7 Motor and Drive Train:
The conversion of electrical energy into climbing power against gravity will require a lightweight motor and drive train. Similar setups exist around the world [wheels on each side of shaft pressing against them for friction to move forward] – Figure 4-6 is one of a gigantic Ferris Wheel in London called "The London Eye." The concept is very similar to the setup for the space elevator drive wheels.

Figure 4-6. Opposing Wheels in Action [Goodell Image 2012]

4.2.8 Solar Climber Conclusion
From a power engineering perspective, a solar power architecture will lower cost and simplify the system considerably. From a mechanical engineering perspective, they are challenging. A solar-based system can launch climbers weighing up to 70% of the tether lift capacity once every 24 hours, with a total trip time to GEO of 7 days. As the larger mass throughput allows us to maintain a heavier tether, this improvement enables us to construct the space elevator from weaker materials and power it with solar arrays. "On the bright side, direct solar power conversion using thin-film foils seems to be able to achieve the necessary power-mass density. On the down side, such structures are very frail – especially considering that the structure must work in both gravity and zero-g" (Shelef, 2008b). "Solar powered climbers are a very different beast than their beam-powered cousins. They are a lot more gossamer-like and "float up" mostly under their own power. From a power engineering perspective, they simplify the system considerably and definitely lower cost. From a mechanical engineering perspective, they are very challenging" (Shelef, 2008c).

4.3 Deployment Spacecraft
4.3.1 Introduction
From Dr. Edwards' basic book (Edwards and Westling, 2003), the initial deployment of the space elevator must be done from GEO to ensure stability of the tether and so that it does not sweep a complex orbital area. To reach the GEO node allocated to the space elevator infrastructure requires movement of large masses from the surface of the Earth. This section of the chapter will discuss the spacecraft required in GEO. The approach to reach LEO will probably require multiple launches to handle the required mass [and fuel] for GEO lift. There are many options for launch services with many promises of lower costs and greater capabilities by the early 2030s. As such, discussions on which launch vehicle will be used will be general and costs will be estimated. The current model for lower cost launch to LEO is the Falcon 9 launcher. The system engineering solution will be selected through a commercial competition and will enable lifting the appropriate mass to LEO. Once at LEO,

there are many choices to reach a GEO node. As the mass will probably exceed the capacity of one launch vehicle, the assembly of the total deployment spacecraft will occur in space – either at LEO or GEO. There are many engineering trades that do NOT have to be accomplished now with minimal information available.

The choice of thrusting rockets to raise the orbit from LEO to GEO is varied and does not have to be made today. However, the space industry routinely rises to challenges. The choices range from chemical fuels [such as the current upper stages] to the continuous thrust of high ISP ion engines or even advanced magnetoplasmadynamic and/or nitrogen tetroxide / monomethyl-hydrazine MMH/NTO engines such as those talked about in Dr. Edwards' book. Launch for a space elevator deployment satellite will be early in the 2030 time frame; therefore many varied types of in-orbit propulsion could be proven by then. One approach, that has begun to get traction, is the use of nuclear propulsion once away from the Earth's atmospheric drag. The concept is that if one wants to go around the solar system in a timely manner, one must have nuclear propulsion with hydrogen as the propellant. These engines have been designed for 60 years and have been proven out in a 1-g environment.

4.3.2   Requirements
This portion of the chapter lays out the needs of the initial infrastructure.   Overall requirements for the Deployment Spacecraft should be something like:

- Support initial tether deployment from GEO [estimated to have an initial length of at least 80,000 km]
- Protect and then deploy initial "seed" tether [estimate – large drum/reel with shield and motor to reel in and out]
- Provide stable location control at GEO and while in orbit.
- Ensure sufficient energy to operate at LEO, during transfer orbit and during operations at GEO, and sufficient to maintain GEO Node stability.
- Ensure sufficient communications during flight operations and continuously during GEO node activities.
- Ensure GEO node maintenance [with angular momentum – orbit altitude loss compensation] as needed.
- Ensure timely raising of orbit from LEO [could be months long with continuous thrust approach]
- Enable assembly of deployment spacecraft in LEO or after rise to GEO [trades to be conducted]
- Launch deployment satellite to LEO [approximately 86,500 kg total with multiple launches, or equivalent of four Proton Launch Vehicles]

When one looks at these requirements [and then designs space systems to support the build-up], an estimate must be accomplished to initiate discussions. The baseline number will be an 86 MT satellite in LEO.

4.3.3   Lift to LEO
As stated earlier, the rockets of the future should be incrementally improved with respect to cost and reliability; but the basic physics require a delta velocity of roughly 9.2km/sec to reach LEO, which requires a fuel ratio of at least 85% of the mass on the pad prior to launch. As such, if the launch vehicle were to lift 14 MT, six launchers would be required for the space elevator deployment satellite to reach LEO. Each launch will probably be equatorial to

increase payload delivery and begin the space elevator inclination. A possible low latitude launch site could be French Guiana or even from the equator by SEALAUNCH.

4.3.4   Movement to GEO

As expressed earlier, there are two major near term studies to be conducted as the project approaches development. The prototype development should test the chosen approach in orbit prior to operational lift and flight initiation. The two studies should be:

Major Trade Study #1:   Propulsion method to move from LEO to the GEO node. Time is not the critical issue as mass to orbit is extremely expensive. The two proposed approaches have been MMH propulsion [needs massive research and testing] and greatly improved ion engines. Deep Space One proved the reliability and thrust for operational ion engines; however, a major R&D program must be implemented to ensure "modest thrust" as a goal with meter wide ion thrusters developed. It would seem that NASA, JAXA, Indian Space Agency, and the Chinese Space Agency would need this capability to move cargo in orbit to and from the Moon and other solar system destinations. As such, emphasis must be placed on supporting government development of the needed technologies. Dr. Edwards' approach was MHD [magnetohydrodynamic energy conversion] propulsion. This has great potential for in-space propulsion and should definitely be a part of the trade space. In addition, Nitrogen tetroxide/monomethyl-hydrazine (NTO/MMH) are in common use today and can be extrapolated to future capabilities.

Major Trade Study #2:   Assembly in orbit at LEO or at GEO? If human support is required, Low Earth Orbit seems to be preferable. The same vehicles currently used to support the space station re-supply could be used. These same vehicles could place humans at an assembly location to support the activities of the space elevator. However, the assembly will probably be accomplished autonomously. Everything has been accomplished before in orbit – including autonomous fueling. The baseline for this study will be autonomous assembly in LEO, equatorial orbit, with semi-continuous communications from a GEO communications satellite.

Finding 4-5: Although massive at 86.5 metric tons, the movement from LEO to the GEO node of the deployment satellite is not technologically challenging. Improvements in mass to GEO could be gained with significant improvement in thruster performance by demanding development of massive ion engines or equivalent efficiency improvements.

4.3.5   GEO Operations / Spacecraft

Once the spacecraft has been assembled at LEO and raised to GEO (or raised to GEO and then assembled), operations begin to initiate the space elevator with a single tether [to be designed later with the objective of being light enough to get the reel to GEO and strong enough to reach to the ocean [and apex anchor] while supporting itself. Figure 4-7 shows a design that contains all the important components.

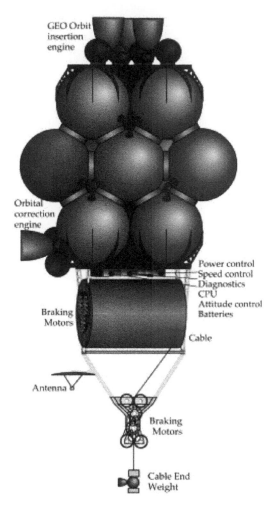

Figure 4-7. Deployment Satellite [HighLift]

The simple approach [to be refined by major studies] would be to have one reel lower the tether to the surface. The massive spacecraft would then rise above GEO while maintaining the center of orbit with the center of gravity [hence maintaining location at the allocated GEO node]. A more complex trade study could result in having multiple reels of tether material maintaining the climber mass at GEO and deploying up and down simultaneously. The components and their mass estimations are shown in the next table (Table 4-VII) and explained after the figure.

- Tether Payload: The tether must be delivered to the GEO node so that it may be reeled out in a smooth and controlled manner. The current assumption is that the whole deployment satellite will become the Apex Anchor as the tether is reeled downward with a commensurate motion upward from angular momentum and center of mass adjustment from the motion of separation. Once the tether is secured at the Marine Node, the deployment satellite would then reel out more of the tether, allowing the heavy mass to reach outward and add more tension, thus stabilizing the tether as well as adding structural features. This initial "seed" tether would have a minimum diameter but still have the required strength to weight ratio to ensure survival while minimizing weight.

- Reel & Drum: Early in the design of the first space elevator a mechanical system for deploying the tether would be tested extensively. Some keys will be that the speed should be high enough to make the deployment time reasonable [less than 1,000rpm], but slow enough to ensure that the tension is controlled and the dynamics of the deployment are not "out of spec." A spool of approximately 6m in length with a diameter of 2m would provide sufficient mechanical leverage and hold the required initial tether length of greater than 80,000km.

- Structural Elements: The image of the deployment satellite seems to show a whole series of propellant tanks with a huge reel/drum of tether material and a mechanism to release the tether downward. All of these elements must be firmly held together to enable stabilization of the structure during thruster firing and deployment operations. The assumption is that the structure will be essentially one quarter the mass required today as CNT's will be standard for structural elements needing to resist torque, strain, tension and compression. Another aspect of this deployment satellite is that the structure can be "fine tuned" during the LEO assembly process. Today's major issue is that the satellite in orbit must first survive the rock and roll of launch. The structure is designed for this max–g environment, and then the spacecraft could live for 15 years in its zero-g environment. As there is a need to assemble major components of the deployment satellite in LEO, a "smart" design and different approach for a future deployment system could be employed. The components of the satellite that are launched must survive the rock and roll of the first 500 kilometers, but then reside in zero-g. The resulting deployment satellite that must be moved to GEO will only experience small acceleration loads, even using large ion engines. This leads to a great reduction in structural infrastructure requirements. As such, the assembled spacecraft could have significantly less mass in structure for the trip from LEO to GEO and operations there. Consequently, the structure needed in a deployment satellite assembled in LEO is of a different magnitude than one needed to survive launch from the surface.

- Power Subsystem: As the deployment satellite will require power to operate a space system, the natural element for power generation is solar cells with efficiencies approaching 48% [in labs today] and extremely light for weight savings. This portion of the satellite will be developed by the current space industry as it is to their advantage to have the most efficient and lightest solar arrays available. The energy would be stored in lithium ion batteries as well as, perhaps, in spinning mass energy storage devices [laboratory experiments exist today] that can double as stability devices. The power control and distribution of energy is a well understood discipline in satellite systems design.

Component	Mass Estimate [kg]	Requirements
GEO Satellite		
Tether payload	40,000	Holds greater than 80,000 km
Reel and Drum	3,800	6 m in length and 2 m in diameter
Structural elements	2,000	CNT based – light & strong
Power subsystem	500	Solar arrays with minimum batteries
Attitude control	500	Spinning mass and mag torque rods
Thruster elements	4,000	Structural & tank elements
C&C comms	200	Ka or laser comm's
Thermal & S/C support	1,500	Radiators on opposite side
Fuel		
GEO node maintenance	900	Ion engine fuel compensating for momentum loss
GEO insertion propulsion	30,400	Assumes advanced ion engines
Attitude control propulsion	200	Cold gas for backup
Apex Anchor Satellite	2,500	Mission equipment for operations
Total Estimate	86,500	Mass to be assembled in LEO [or GEO] for mission

Table 4-VII. Mass of Deployment Satellite

- Attitude Control with Propellant: Attitude control will be essential during assembly and transportation to GEO. While the deployment satellite is in LEO (on its way to GEO), as well as early on at GEO, the attitude control will probably be achieved by spinning masses [control moment gyros (CMGs), etc] and torque rods [more effective in LEO]. Once the tether has deployed a sizable distance, the gravity gradient factor will help stabilize the deployment satellite.
- Command & Control Communications: C&C communications will be achieved through relay satellites, as there is a requirement for constant connectivity. As a result, there will be a geosynchronous communications satellite antenna required to track the LEO grouping of sub-satellites, monitor the assembly, and then track the deployment satellite as it goes from LEO to GEO. Once in GEO, the space elevator's communications architecture will kick in with connection to Headquarters from GEO and control of the link monitored continuously. As such, the command and control of operations will be persistent during LEO, continuous during GEO operations and then part of the network infrastructure upon completion.
- Thermal and S/C Support: Overall support of the spacecraft will involve many disciplines including thermal, radiation, electromagnetic, orbital location knowledge and projection, pointing and stability. During the 14 orbits per day while in LEO, the thermal stresses will be greatest and will manifest themselves inside all aspects of a spacecraft. Keeping the propellant at an appropriate temperature, allowing external components to be in full sun, scheduling heating elements, and understanding the flow of heat throughout the spacecraft will all challenge designers. However, after 50+ years in space, specifically LEO, the challenges are achievable and fun to address.
- GEO Node Maintenance: The ability to stay at the designated GEO altitude over a specific longitudinal line will be a challenge during deployment of the space elevator

tether. Many papers have shown the loss of altitude and angular momentum exchange of the total system as the tether is deployed and the momentum is transferred from the orbital aspects to the rotating spacecraft. This will require a periodic makeup burn of propellant to ensure that the GEO node is within the allocated location. The large ion engines that raised the orbit of the huge space system should be able to ensure that the node is maintained.

- Thruster Elements: The large task ahead for thrusters is to raise a very large mass from LEO to GEO in an efficient manner without time being a large factor. As such, the cluster of large [1 meter diameter] ion engines will provide continuous thrusting to raise the altitude in a spiral orbit. The specifics of the thrust, efficiency of the engine, and the time it will take to move the mass to GEO will be understood in greater detail as the mission approaches. There will also be thrusters for attitude control and, of course, maintenance of the orbit once the tether is deploying.
- GEO Insertion Fuel: The amount of hydrogen, or xenon, will be calculated once the key elements of the thrusters are described. This will be the most massive of the major elements of the deployment satellite, but well within today's technology. The ability to refuel tanks in-orbit has been proven and the storage of fuels for over 15 years has been shown.

4.3.6   Summary
Major studies to be conducted to support this activity of a deployment satellite will address the approach to accomplish:
- Launch from equator
- Assemble in orbit [while refueling]
- Raise the orbit to GEO [MMH – ION – VASIMR]
   VASIMR is Variable Specific Impulse Magnetoplasma Rocket.

However, as the authors have seen all of the functions achieved in orbit, almost routinely [except for the tether deployment], the real question is not can they be done, but which approach will be most successful.

4.4 Tether Buildup Climbers
4.4.1   Introduction
There are two ideas for the transition from a "seed" tether to a full up operational space elevator:
- Tether Weave: The original idea from Dr. Edwards' book is to increase the strength of the initial tether by climbing with small spacecraft which would "entwine" new tether material onto the seed tether to increase the strength and the redundancy of a full tether. This mission is given to the "buildup spacecraft," which are described below.
- Bootstrap Lifting: This is a major change and will be discussed in Appendix E-5 on space elevator substantiation. The concept is relatively simple – once you have a "seed" tether from GEO to the surface of the ocean, the original tether would incrementally lift stronger and stronger tethers from the surface of the ocean by using the GEO reel [leveraging the inherent tension in the tether to raise the operational one-meter wide sparse tether], one increase in size at a time. First you raise twice the "seed" tether, then four times the "seed" tether [when the double reaches GEO], and so forth. As this approach needs major research, it will be referenced in the Appendix E-5. However, there is such a huge potential for decrease in complexity that it must be studied in more detail.

4.4.2 Tether Weave Approach

The description of this approach (Edwards and Laine, 2003) will have two components, the tether deployment and the buildup spacecraft that will weave the tether. (Laine, website)

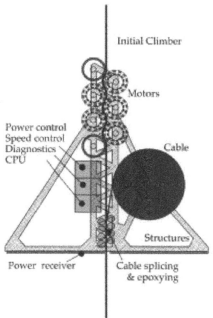

Figure 4-8. Buildup Spacecraft

- Tether Buildup Approach: The "seed" tether" buildup (which has been extended down from GEO and is attached in the Marine Node) is estimated to require 207 trips of tether buildup climbers. The simple concept is that the tether would be identical to the "seed" tether initially so that the process would first double, then triple, etc. At some point, the strength of the tether would hold larger climbers for heavier tether assembly, enabling a faster buildup. Edwards and Laine (2003) show how this is accomplished with periodic splicing as the spacecraft rises. The initial spacecraft climber would be 619kg with a tether payload of approximately 288kg of new tether.
- Buildup Spacecraft: The requirements for a buildup spacecraft begin with safe and reliable application of new tether material to the existing tether. The next requirement is that it must rise from the surface of the Earth to GEO under its own power and maintain operations 24/7 while it applies new tether material. Multiple buildup spacecraft could be on the tether at any given time, as the gravitational pull varies as it goes away from the Earth and the mass decreases as the tether is released to attach to the current space elevator tether. The image of the buildup spacecraft is shown, without its required solar panels.

As Figure 4-8 shows, the motor has many rollers to ensure sufficient friction on the seed tether and an apparatus to splice and bind new tether to the old. Edwards and Laine's design depended on laser energy from the surface of the Earth. This approach would work and could be the method of choice as we get closer to the actual implementation of the space elevator infrastructure. However, the baseline is that these small climbers would be driven by solar energy. The following paragraphs summarize the makeup of the buildup satellite.

Basic requirements include: kilowatts of mechanical power [perhaps up to megawatts], high efficiency and reliability, operates initially in the atmosphere [but mostly in vacuum], and is deposited at the top end [apex anchor] as mass after its run up the tether. Michael Laine describes the motor as follows:

> "The motor would be based on permanent magnet brushless multi-pole technology to achieve a high efficiency with low mass. Cobalt-steel alloy and Neodynium-Iron-Boron magnets would be used along with a liquid cooling system and a two or three stage transmission. During most of the ascent these motors will run at greater than 96% efficiency and above 90% for most of the remainder. A 10kW motor of this design would have a mass of 14kg, require5 kg of control electronics and could be produced in quantity for under $9k. A 100kW motor of this design would have a mass of 105kg, would require 20kg of control electronics and could be produced in quantity for under $50k." (Laine website)

A track and roller system is shown in the image. One of the large unknowns today is the friction coefficient for CNT tethers. This must be understood prior to the actual design of roller and gripping mechanisms. Thermal concerns are definitely an issue with a small spacecraft made mostly of CNT structures, a motor, and a gripping mechanism. However, as space designers have been working in all environments inherent in a space elevator's path, the design [with respect to the thermal and other environmental effects such as radiation and electromagnetic fields] can be achieved. The command and control of buildup climbers will be handled similarly to future space elevator climbers – through a GEO based communications architecture back to the headquarters operations center. This will require a small Ku or Ka band antenna pointed up towards a large gain antenna at the GEO node. As the strength of the tether increases with each addition of tether, the mass of the buildup climbers can increase enabling larger tethers to be added to the current space elevator. The estimate is that 207 trips must be taken to build up the tether to an operational level; however, more could be accomplished to widen the tether and make a larger, more capable, space elevator. Current estimates are this process would take two years to a 20 MT capable space elevator and another six months for a 30 MT tether.

In addition, there have been many discussions on the increase in capability of the buildup climber as well as what to do if one malfunctions or gets stuck on the initial tether. All the expressed solutions seem reasonable, as the climbers will not have humans aboard and can be "discarded" or sent out to the Apex Anchor depending upon the problems that occur. The infrastructure developer will decide when it is time to go operational with the first space elevator and when it is appropriate to build the second space elevator. It is important for a second elevator to be deployed as soon as possible to ensure that we never again fall back into the grasp of Mother Nature's gravity well.

4.5 GEO Node Spacecraft
The requirements for the geosynchronous altitude node of the space elevator infrastructure stretch across the full operation of missions. The key is that the GEO altitude is the optimum mission altitude for the space elevator leading to an environment designed for off-loading

climbers and customer spacecraft. The environment allows the hardware to remain as placed for future work. The future concept is that there would be a large volume of mission operations taking place. These activities would include:

- off-loading of hardware,
- repair of climbers,
- preparation for decent of climbers,
- storing of supplies and components,
- assembly of hardware into full up spacecraft,
- fueling [re-fueling] of spacecraft,
- parking lot for mission spacecraft,
- center for the space elevator communications node,
- autonomous mission control center,
- loading collected space debris for return trip to surface, and
- reloading onto tether climbers for higher altitude trips.

A large volume of space should be controlled inside a large sphere to enable all items to be worked on and located. There would be pressurized and non-pressurized areas to enable human activities in the future. Figure 4-9 shows a visualization of what a GEO Node Hangar could look like - a Frank Chase Tether Climber image "parked" inside the GEO Node satellite with its solar arrays compressed in "storage mode."

Figure 4-9. GEO Node Work Space[chasedesignstudios.com]

4.6 Verification and Validation for Space Systems

As a note to close out this chapter, there are additional verification /validation requirements for space systems that prepare for harsh environments. These are shown in Table 4-VIII as the chapter concludes with the understanding that the items discussed will be part of the design spectrum levied on the total system of systems.

	Tether Climber	Deployment Spacecraft	Buildup Spacecraft
Radiation damage of the tether and climber electronics	X	X	X
Radiation exposure to people riding the elevator	X	X	X
Meteor damage to the tether	X	X	X
Orbital debris damage to the tether	X	X	X
Atomic oxygen erosion of the tether	X	X	X
Lightning, hurricanes, hail, jet streams	X	X	X
Induced oscillation	X	X	X
Induced currents in the tether	X	X	X
Terrorists attacking the system	X	X	X
Airplanes and ships hitting the tether or end station infrastructure	X	X	X
Thermal fluctuations - heating	X	X	X
Wear and tear on the tether	X	X	X
Energy density stored in the tether	X	X	X
Others if applicable			

Table 4-VIII. V&V Climbers and Satellites

Insight provided:

Mr. Yoshinori Takezawa and the Nihon University Team provided valuable insight for this chapter.

Chapter 5
End Station Infrastructure

5.1 Background
The objectives of this chapter are to initiate discussion on the Apex Anchor, to firm up the location of the initial space elevator Earth's terminus, and to present three options for the Space Elevator Stage One. Indeed, the requirements for the Earth's terminus have not been fully established, nor have the customer desires been identified. Until those are listed, the selection of location and Stage One approach must be addressed as a trade study with best factors and limiting issues. These lists of benefits and concerns will be important when choosing the final design for the Earth terminus of the space elevator.

All three options have merit, but a key theme being pursued in this study is for the tether climbers to use solar power only. As such, solar cells must be deployed as the principal source of energy for each climber. With this in mind, solar cells would suffer tremendous damage from winds in the atmosphere. Consequently, loading a tether climber at altitude on a platform called High Stage One, at 40km, would be a natural answer. This could lead to payloads being loaded onto tether climbers on a High Stage One with only solar power as the source of energy for climbing. The other two approaches also allow the tether climber to initiate the climb with solar energy above the atmosphere. A significant question is how do we place a full up tether climber, driven by solar power only, above the atmosphere? This chapter will discuss three approaches and mention a few alternatives to those. The three approaches are:

> Option One: Marine Stage One
> MSO – Box Protection
> MSO – Spring Forward
> Option Two: High Stage One

The two ends of a space elevator have many possible engineering paths. It turns out that one of the biggest discussions is about location of the base station, or Stage One. The trades for the Earth's attachment reach across political, investment, engineering, weather, and operational issues. A simple solution could be that one or more heavy ships would act as a base for operations in the open ocean. In addition, it could move the tether out of harm's way from space debris by initiating a resonance motion. Much more is discussed in the sections on location and technologies. The counterweight, or Apex Anchor, is the mechanism that allows the tether to maintain tension and perceived rigidity. The makeup of the Apex Anchor and its components are discussed to ensure a consistent design with simple engineering solutions.

5.2 Overview of History and Past Work
It has often been assumed that the tether should extend right down to the Earth's surface, but this chapter shows the benefit of starting the climb above most of the atmosphere. The original work by Edwards and Westling (2003) leverages laser projected power as the principle source of energy. This study report will illustrate how solar power is sufficient and so much easier. The three approaches discussed below assume the tether climber reaches above the atmosphere from Earth based infrastructure and then deploys the climber when above the stresses of the atmosphere. The beauty of this solution is its simple two phase approach and the dependence on the ubiquitous source of energy traditionally leveraged by the space community.

5.3 Assumptions
This chapter makes a few assumptions to be consistent with the rest of the study document.

1) Stage One is responsible for deflecting the tether to avoid space debris.
2) Initially, the space elevator will be used for unmanned payloads, with eventual progression to human travel.
3) Tether climbers can be powered by lightweight solar panels, but it is still desirable to plan for the possible requirement to transmit beamed power, whether by laser or other means.

5.4 Apex Anchor
A tether 150,000km long is in balance without requiring a counterweight. The centripetal force of the part beyond geosynchronous orbit offsets the gravitational forces that are nearer to Earth. In addition, the angular momentum of the upper mass beyond GEO must be in synch with the angular momentum aspects of the lower mass and the orbital angular momentum. A counterweight can be used to shorten the overall length, and thus, a trade-off in overall mass.

Finding 5-1: The Apex Anchor will be at roughly 100,000km altitude and will provide significant tension in the ribbon to adapt to the various forces on the tether dynamics, including tidal forces and tether climber motion.

Potential Apex Anchor Forces
To ensure that all forces are accounted for and allowed [Earth's gravity, centripetal force, lunar gravity, solar gravity, tether climber forces, and others such as electromagnetic interactions; to be discussed in chapter seven and eight.] the Apex Anchor will have more mass than required. This extra mass at a greater distance (vs. the characteristics at the time of the Earth connection with the initial space elevator tether) will ensure an appropriate tension in the tether to create extra rigidity and stiffness along the path of the tether climbers. In the next chapter the size and magnitude of the tether and Apex Anchor are described. The conclusion is that the nominal space elevator being discussed in this cosmic study has:

Tether Mass: 6,300,000kg
Apex Anchor Mass: 1,900,000kg

Apex Anchor Sources
Mass for the counterweight is available from many sources to include near-by asteroids, tether climbers, dead GEO satellites, and additional mass from Earth as required. The initial masses will probably come from the vehicles used to place the initial tether fibers into orbit and from the small tether climbers used in the tether's construction. Using this material as a counterweight lowers the total mass that has to be lifted into orbit. The choice of capturing an asteroid was an early idea and might become real with a robust space infrastructure as the space elevator becomes routine; however, near-term solutions must dominate. The only source of "extra" mass beyond LEO that can be accessed relatively easily is the set of "dead" satellites at GEO. All satellites that are not operational will be drifting around the Earth near the GEO orbital belt, either below or above the "Clarke orbit" with small velocities. These masses can be captured and moved into the appropriate GEO orbital spot to tie onto the space elevator and be released out to the end mass location. These mass elements would supplement the initial spacecraft which created the space elevator and then were sent to the end of the tether. The basic systems engineering requirements are that the Apex Anchor mass

be easily transported on the tether and not be explosive. Mass is good in the space elevator context. In addition, the Apex Anchor will have the ability to be refuelled, thus providing thrust in various directions, as directed by the Tether Operations Center, to dampen harmonic motion and enable movement of the space elevator.

Finding 5-2: The Apex Anchor will do far more than "just be a mass at the end of the space elevator."

Additional verification/validation requirements for Apex Anchor
As a note to close out this portion of the chapter, there are additional verification/validation requirements for space systems that prepare the systems for the harsh environment. The Apex Anchor should be tested for the following basic requirements prior to deployment.

	Apex Anchor
Radiation damage	X
Meteor damage	X
Orbital debris	X
Thermal fluctuations	X
Wear and tear on the tether	X
Energy density stored in the tether	X
Others if applicable	

Table 5-I. Apex Anchor V&V

5.5 Marine Stage One

Stage One is a term that defines the complex of facilities located at the Earth's terminus of the space elevator. It includes the physical equipment to anchor the tether to the Earth and the facilities to conduct operations. The following sections first address the potential locations for space elevators and then describe two significant options. The first is the traditional concept of an ocean platform Stage One and the second is the Stage One at altitude – High Stage One. The Marine Stage One has two approaches to fulfil the requirement that the climber be initiated above the atmosphere; Box Satellite and Spring Forward. The second Stage One option takes the complexity of traveling through the atmosphere "off" the space elevator tether and places it on an Earth-based structure up to 40km high, above the stratosphere. The stresses induced by the lower and upper atmospheres are dealt with by structures based firmly on the Earth's surface. These two options are being presented because the complexity of the Earth's terminus is still being investigated. New technologies are surfacing and the full set of space elevator requirements has not been finalized. As such, the two options are presented:

> Option One: Marine Stage One
>   1a - MSO – Box Protection
>   1b - MSO – Spring Forward
> Option Two: High Stage One

Search for Location
There is tremendous trade space open for the design of the lower portion of a space elevator. While the deployment phase will have the tether respond as a spacecraft with free ends and a center of mass, the mature space elevator will require a system attached to the Earth. The mature space elevator will have many options that will enhance its survivability and

economics. There are many questions and issues that must be addressed to enable a final design to be developed for the Stage One infrastructure. Four key questions are addressed in this chapter:

Q1 – Can the Stage One be off zero latitude?
Q2 – Should the Stage One be located on land or at sea?
Q3 – Where should Stage One be located around the equator?
Q4 – Should the Stage One be at altitude?

The Stage One location will be selected with many factors included in the trade space. Some of the anticipated desires of the customers and users are:

- Safety
- Easy logistics (the operations phase must be designed early)
- Political stability
- Legal Factors [see chapter 12]
- Interoperability (standards are set in the transportation infrastructure allowing conforming manufacturers to build tether climbers for the basic design)

To expand the thinking relative to Stage One, the following table shows a preliminary set of desired performance requirements.

Basic	Detailed
Safe Operations	No catastrophic severance of space elevator
	No loss of climbers off tether
	Tether survival against multiple small debris hits per kilometer per year
	No explosions on tether
	Safe laser power support
	No orbit/fly/float/drive within the space elevator corridor
	Debris/meteorites tracked and predicted
	Robust ability to move tether from major space debris
	Ability to move tether from major spacecraft
	Inspector/repair tether climber infrastructure
	Low occurrences of lightning
	Low occurrences of high winds/hurricanes
Lower Latitude	Low percentage of cloud cover
	High payload mass capable space elevator
	Ocean basing
	Flexible location of Stage One
	Large area open for infrastructure
Easy Logistics	Existing transportation infrastructure available
	Comfortable living facilities for operators
	Open area for logistics support
Political Stability	International waters
	Country stability
	21st century political approach

Basic	Detailed
Interoperability	Tether design acceptable to all tether climbers (standards based)
	Easy interface with transportation infrastructure
	Central location of Stage One infrastructure
	Local support for logistics
	Easy support for science investigation (vertical emplacement)

Table 5-II. Performance Requirements (Swan et al, 2007)

Some questions must be addressed to ensure approaching all these issues. The next few paragraphs address the basic four questions outlined previously.

Q1 – Can Stage One be off zero latitude?

Over the short history of the engineering design for a space elevator, the assumption has most often been that the terrestrial end must be at zero latitude. This has been coupled with the idea that the nadir point of the geosynchronous location is essential for stability. Further analysis leads one to believe that the initial "grounding" of the long tether at the end of the deployment phase must be at that nadir location; however, once the space elevator is initiated, the basic location can move off the equator. The preliminary answer from early analysis seems to be a movable Stage One off nadir, with the appropriate compensation for the total space elevator beyond the GEO location (Gassend, 2004). This capability could provide flexibility to the location of the Stage One station and could allow dynamic coupling to negate natural modes of motion. However, the question requires a large simulation that incorporates each element of the space elevator, all the masses attached to the tether [hotels/nodes/logistic centers], and of course all the moving tether climbers. An assumption has always been to just run the tether down to the equator. As studies have come to the conclusion that there is potential flexibility to the location of the Stage One, the question must surface and be answered as to why move off the zero latitude location. Here are three good reasons:

- Better location for Stage One: Flexibility in choosing the Stage One location would enable the design team to pick islands, areas of ocean without currents, or politically wise locations.
- Move tether out of radiation belts: The passage through the radiation belts will be one of the major hazards to both humans and robotic equipment. As such, reduction of the time inside these belts would assist in the safety and operations of the system.
- Move tether for defensive purposes: Placing the tether upon soil owned by certain countries would enable more security. Placing the tether in the middle of an open ocean area would enable protection to be well defined and broadcast to the public.

The map below (Figure 5-1) represents the loss of payload capability as the Stage One moves from the equator. At the equator, there is 100% carrying capability, while at its limit of 48 degrees north or south, the carrying capability goes to zero and the tether can only support itself.

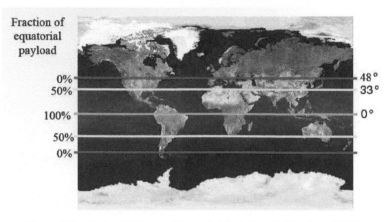

Figure 5-1. Payload Mass vs. Latitude North/South (Gardner 2003)

Answer Q1:   Yes, Stage One could be located off the equator, but best for carrying capacity if there.

Q2 – Should Stage One be located on land or at sea?

The analysis of this question results in trades crossing both management and engineering disciplines. Both of these areas are addressed with trades identified; however, the final design consideration will be influenced by the stakeholders and financers.   The space elevator systems architect must ensure that all factors are considered to include items that do not influence engineering designs, because these could dominate.   A likely determinant for location will be input by the financial investors and their perceived return on investment. Early science fiction about the space elevator had Stage One based at the top of a tall mountain, which would enable the team to start the trip at a higher altitude, further from Earth's center of gravity. Stage One could easily be tied to the ground so that the base would not move. There are several mountain tops close to the equator that could be a base location. The advantages are leveraged from the attribute of high altitude starting location vs. the difficulties of working at the altitude in the cold, with major weather periods, and immature transportation infrastructure.

An idea similar to the land-based Stage One is a floating Stage One infrastructure at sea. The strengths are based around the heritage of the sea with its own laws and history of political insulation.   In addition, a background exists for sea based infrastructure with logistics strengths for long distance transportation, simplicity, and proven technologies.   There are expanses of the ocean that are open and usable with minimal impact to current human endeavours. Gardner (2003) presented a solid answer to the question of "where at sea".   He showed that there was a location 2000km west of Ecuador that had favourable characteristics: one lightning strike per year per square kilometer (Figure 5-2), very low probability of hurricanes and cyclones, and almost no wave issues. In addition, there are locations in this region that have very high percentage of cloud-free days for efficient laser power or communications transmission (as shown in Figure 5-3).

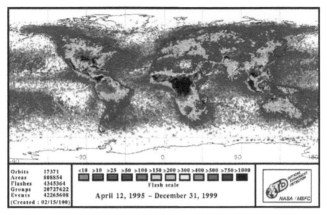

Figure 5-2. Lightning Rate Image (Edwards and Westling, 2003, p.106)

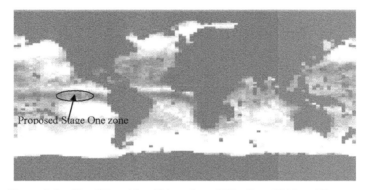

Figure 5-3. Cloud Densities (Edwards and Westling, 2003, p.64)

Table 5-III shows the trade matrix comparing land and sea based alternatives. This analysis looks at the management side of the issue as well as the engineering side. The breakouts cover sovereignty issues, personnel issues, engineering issues and, especially, risk trades. Table 5-III leads one to the conclusion that operating in a hostile environment, like a mountain top, has major disadvantages, whereas operating in a quiescent ocean area lends itself to leveraging the heritage of sea based transportation and logistics.

	Land Based	Sea based
Management		
Sovereign Country vs. Law of Sea	Laws of nations Sovereign rights Ownership influence Minimal international control Access control to project Political upheaval Potential for Nationalization	International law of the sea Adapted oil platforms Large open areas Traditional logistics simplicity (ships and tugs)
Personal Issues	Passports Local laws Local customs Languages	Freedom of access Easy work permits Work rules dominant Project focus infrastructure
Engineering		
Top of Mountain vs. Sea Surface	Access issues Road/rail to top Support infrastructure Weather problems	Open area (400km radius) Easy movement Ship based proven Engineering history (ships) Quiescent weather patterns (2000km west of Ecuador)
Risk	No local personnel	Open areas for damage control
Stage One	Every mountain different	Stage One ties easily to huge ship
Duplication	Varying transport infrastructure	Easy transportation

Table 5-II. Stage One Locations – Sea vs. Land

Most past discussions have assumed a single tether stretched from a Stage One to a space elevator centered at GEO for an Earth based bridge to the stars. Indeed, the deployment and early phases of a space elevator will have a single tether attached to the Earth at the equator. Stage One will have many requirements leading to a development program and eventually a base station. Two major items have surfaced during the analysis; flexibility in location and massive Stage One infrastructure support at the terminal end. Each of these will stimulate much discussion prior to project initiation. Location flexibility is derived from the recognition that survivability of a space elevator is paramount and must be ensured through design, development and operational procedures. The ability to move Stage One leads one toward a sea based option with the natural location flexibility of large ships or floating platforms. The size of a Stage One station seems to be growing as the project progresses. The idea of continuous operations with launches on a seven carriers per week schedule implies that the Stage One infrastructure supports:

- Space elevator cable attachment
- Movement of space elevator base
- Mass necessary to hold space elevator in place
- An operations center
- Room for cargo and carriers ready for flight
- Room for just returned cargo and carriers
- Room for repair of cargo or carriers
- Personnel housing

- Personnel support infrastructure
- Communications infrastructure

The principal requirements for a Stage One infrastructure seem to be driving factors in the design process. As one addresses the trades for this issue, an aircraft carrier solution becomes compelling. Movement flexibility is required to produce the above infrastructure characteristics, and the room available on an aircraft carrier would be sufficient for infrastructure support and personnel. If it were a nuclear powered aircraft carrier, one major concern would be solved – readily available power.

For the earth terminus of the space elevator, various factors contribute to the analysis. The need is for a free movement capability around the Stage One infrastructure; to interface with terrestrial transportation; and political freedom afforded to international endeavours. These three factors could lead the decision toward a Stage One architecture that is sea based. [Chapter 12 agrees with this conclusion] Many studies have been conducted looking for the proper placement along the equator.

Answer Q2 – Stage One should be sea-based

Q3 – Where should Stage One be located around the equator?

Over the last ten years, there have been many suggestions with the focus on meeting the requirements. This has led to many options including near Perth, Australia, near Brunei (Edwards and Ragan, 2006), in the Indian Ocean, as well as in the Atlantic and Pacific (Knapman and Lofstrom, 2011). These are shown in Figure 5-4.

The equatorial area of the Pacific Ocean west of the Galapagos Islands at longitude 100°W has particularly calm weather and is the favoured site. Ascension Island in the Atlantic at longitude 14° W and latitude 8° S is possible. Another possibility is the Salomon Islands, part of the British Indian Ocean Territory; this uninhabited atoll is at 5°S and 72°E. A surface station could be based on the largest island, Boddam, which is about 2km long. The second surface station would be at sea. Sites on land include French Guiana at 4°N and 53°W and Brunei at 5°N and 115°E. All five sites are marked by stars in Figure 5-4 and Figure 5-5.

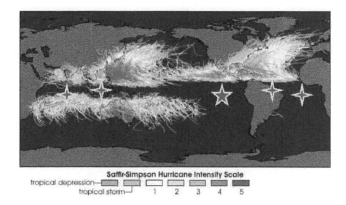

Figure 5-4. Recorded tracks of tropical storms over the last 150 years

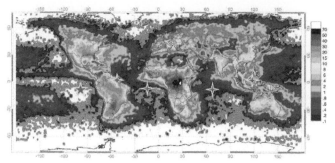

Figure 5-5. Annual rate of lightning flashes observed by NASA satellites:
Apr 1995-Feb 2003

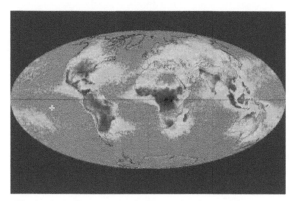

Figure 5-6. Recommended Location in Pacific

Cyclonic storms, i.e., hurricanes, tornadoes or typhoons, are rare at the equator. As Figure 5-4 shows, they have not been observed at all in the last 150 years in the zone south west of the Galapagos. Electrical storms do occur at the equator and are very frequent in central Africa and elsewhere on land. However, Figure 5-5 shows that the rate of occurrence in the region west of the Galapagos Islands is extremely low, and it is less than one strike a year in the middle of the Indian Ocean. Stage One will require lightning conductors to carry electric currents to the surface so that they do not affect the main space-elevator tether.

Finding 5-3: There are many good locations for the terrestrial stage, but the most obvious ones are near the equator in the middle of the ocean. The preferred option is 1000km west of Galapagos.

Basic	Detailed	Low Lat.	Sea–Land
Safe Operations	No severance of total space elevator	+	S
	No loss of tether climbers off tether	+	
	No explosions on tether		
	Laser power support safe		L
	Laser power support not melt tether		
	No orbit/fly/float/drive within the space elevator corridor	+	S
	Debris/meteorites tracked and predicted		
	Robust ability to move tether from major space debris	+	S
	Ability to move tether from major spacecraft	+	S
	Inspector/repair tether climber infrastructure	+	
	Low occurrences of lightning		S
	Low occurrences of high winds/hurricanes		S
Lower Latitude	Low percentage of cloud cover	+	S
	High mass capable space elevator		
	Ocean basing	+	S
	Flexible location for Stage One	+	S
	Large area open for Stage One infrastructure	+	S
Easy Logistics	Existing transportation infrastructure	+	S
	Comfortable living facilities for operators	+	S
	Open area for logistics support	+	S
Political Stability	International waters	+	S
	Country stability	+	L
	21st century political approach	+	S
Interoperability	Tether design accessible to all tether climbers (standards based)		
	Easy interface with transportation infrastructure	+	S
	Central location of Stage One infrastructure	+	S
	Local support for logistics	+	S
	Easy support for science investigation	+	

Table 5- III. Requirements Fulfilment Matrix
[S=sea advantage, L=land advantage; + = low Latitude advantages]

5.6 Marine Stage One Components

Marine Stage One will be discussed as to the components of the infrastructure, and the ability to start at altitude will be laid out. This is the complex in the central Pacific at a location close to a sweet spot in quiescent weather such as 8 degrees south latitude and 120 degrees west longitude. This segment of the infrastructure is made up of:

- Floating Operations Platform
- Telemetry, Tracking, and Command (TT&C) Facility
- Satellite Processing Center
  - o Satellite Payload Center
  - o Satellite Operations Center

Floating Operations Platform (FOP)

This is the platform in the eastern Pacific. It will be a floating platform of the size of an aircraft carrier or large oil tanker. It will be large enough to accommodate the tether terminus, the TT&C facility, the laser operations platform, and the power generation facilities [diesel or nuclear]. It will have living quarters, kitchen, laundry, recreational, and medical facilities for the supporting and visiting staff.

Figure 5-7. Drill ship examples

Drill-ships (Figure 5-7) are self-propelled, carrying a complete ship's crew while underway, as well as a crew of drilling personnel [operations personnel in our case]. Drill-ships are moored either by the standard anchoring system or by *dynamic positioning* of the vessel. Dynamic positioning is the use of a computer-operated inboard thruster system which keeps the vessel on location without the use of anchors. The vessel also supports helicopter landings and loading/unloading from ocean going vessels. It will be able to move meters to thousands of meters for operations needs including weather, or tether movement.

Telemetry, Tracking, and Command (TT&C) Facility

This will be the facility with an antenna to track and receive data from the satellite or tether climber. It will likely be on the FOP but may be on its own platform nearby. It will likely be unmanned and operated remotely by the satellite owner's operations function. Periodic maintenance will be performed by local maintenance personnel.

Satellite Processing Center (SPC)

As the satellites are loaded to the FOP from the ocean going cargo vessel, the step by step process will be leveraged to mate the satellite with the space elevator climber. Common processes should be developed so that many types of spacecraft (S/C) can be transported from ocean level to space with identical actions – thus simplifying the historic complexity of preparing S/C. This center will be in constant contact with both individual satellites and their payload operations centers.

Aircraft Facilities

Apart from the infrastructure needed to support and operate Stage One, facilities could include a floating airport capable of handling regional jets that link to the nearest international airport, which is at Quito in Ecuador in the case of the site west of Galapagos. A runway about 1200 meters long is needed for this class of aircraft. It may be better to operate a helicopter shuttle from the Galapagos. For example, the Super Puma helicopters used in the North Sea have a range of 700km. An aircraft carrier could supply a landing surface easily.

Answer Q3: The space elevator Marine Node should be located west of the Galapagos [of course, > 200km}

Finding 5-4: Stage One will either be on the surface of the ocean or at a reasonable altitude [30-50km] escaping the Earth's atmosphere. This trade is being undertaken and clearer choices will be available in the near future.

Finding 5-5: Marine Stage One has tremendous operational advantages. Its primary advantage is that ocean-going operations are routine with international delivery of materials and cargo becoming less expensive and more reliable every year. This is based upon thousands of years of ocean transportation of goods and over 120 years of ocean drilling platforms.

Getting to 40km

Q4 – Should the Stage One be at altitude?

Need: The ability to only use solar energy for the tether climber to lift itself to the GEO location is dependent on starting the climb with fragile solar cells above the atmospheric effects. To ensure that the design of the space elevator infrastructure is as simple as possible and leveraging a technology that has been proven both in space and terrestrially, the tether climber must start above the atmosphere. By deleting the requirement for lasers to supply the energy to the climbers, the design has become more reasonable and it leverages the tremendous efforts being place in the lightweight solar cell industry as well as leveraging the carbon nanotube developments in energy creation and movement as well as storage. As a result of this desire to use only solar cells to provide power to the tether climbers, the first 40km must be traversed while the climber and its solar arrays are protected from the environment. There are three approaches to basing at the sea level at the present time that will be addressed with variations being studied by many people. The three approaches are called: Marine Stage One – Box Satellite, Marine Stage One – Spring Forward, and the High Stage One approach. Each will be discussed and the concepts presented.

Marine Stage One – Box Satellite: the approach here is the movement of the tether carrier and its power source, solar arrays which would all be placed inside a protective box and raised to an appropriate altitude so that it could start at daylight and climb towards GEO. The current concept for tether climbers is that the system will only climb while in sunlight and hibernate during eclipse. Some discussion points are as follows:

- Starting Point: Ocean surface
- Clear Atmosphere: Assumed to be 40km [tbd after further study]
- Box Concept: The box would be made from a very light material that would totally encompass the tether climber and its solar cells so that all the effects of the atmosphere would be kept from the climber system. The idea is that the major wind forces, the lightning, etc., would be denied access to the vulnerable climber and its solar cells. The size, shape and material will be determined after much study into the future needs of tether climbers.
- Power: During the ascent from ocean surface to the appropriate height [40km], the climber and its customer payload would have power supplied by a lightweight carbon nanotube power cable. An alternative could be localized laser power; however, this is not the preferred approach.
- Speed: The requirement is that the climber be free of the Box Satellite prior to the dawn of the next day when power could be applied to the solar cells of the climber.
- Post Release: Once the tether climber is released from the box satellite, the box and all its support equipment will be returned to the surface for re-use. The total mass of this Box Satellite must be calculated as part of the total load of the space elevator and could impact the number of climbers on the tether at any one time.
- Propulsion: Currently, the thinking is that the same motor and engine drive could be used to propel the Box Satellite and its payload [tether climber and solar cells] to the 40km altitude. Alternatives could include rockets, balloons to a certain altitude and then another means of propulsion. Also, counter weights could be leveraged from a higher location on the tether of the space elevator.
- Return: Currently, the thinking is that the Box Satellite is reusable, but this could be argued if the benefits out-weigh the negatives with "throw-away" satellite boxes.

Marine Stage One – Spring Forward: This approach for the initiation of tether climbers is one that takes advantage of the characteristics of the tether and leverages the routine of transportation infrastructures. The idea is simple:

- Reel in the tether
- Attach tether climber [with protective covering]
- Allow tether to pull the tether climber beyond 40km in altitude

The concept comes from the basics of a very long springy material that has stretch characteristics of approximately 0.1% or 1m in each kilometer. This is an estimate and will have to be assessed after the material is developed for the space elevator. When the space elevator is 100,000km long, the natural stretch of the material is approximately 100,000m or 100km. Leveraging this material's stretching capability, the space elevator can easily handle the first 40km of altitude movement up and down. After the space elevator is established in its operational position, the machinery can be established to rapidly reel in the tether and then reel out the tether with climber. The objectives of this approach, called "Spring Forward" are:

- Avoid the atmospheric effects on the tether carrier by sending it up inside a protection box.
- Simple Operations
- Have power during activities
- Launch Tether Climbers once per day
- Enable the solar arrays to be deployed at altitude

Approach for Spring Forward:

The primary purpose of this approach to launching space elevator climbers is to enable the first 40km to be negated with shields for the environment. The shields would then be returned to the surface as the tether climber is kick-started for GEO and beyond with solar arrays deployed. This enables the designers to negate the effects of the atmosphere and allow the solar arrays to be fragile, large and efficient. This would enable the space elevator climbers to operate ONLY on solar power after the 40km altitude release from the shields. This ability to design the solar arrays for "no winds" enables a simple design for the tether climbers enabling a raise from 40km to 100,000km. The approach to enable this concept is relatively simple:

Step 1: Reel In – Develop a large mechanical device that reels in the tether to the base station in roughly 8 hours. The previous carrier was released for climb at daybreak at altitude [6 am roughly], so the tether is free to be reeled in during the daylight hours while the previous climbers are traveling upward.

Step 2: Attachment – After the tether has been reeled in, the next space elevator tether climber will be aligned at the base station with the tether. The climber will be loaded with cargo and then attached to the tether in the position for it to climb. Below the climber will be a cylindrical shield large enough to hold the solar arrays of the tether climber. This shield will be aligned with the tether and attached to the tether climber. In addition, a light-weight electrical cable with fibre optics communications capability will be attached to the climber to provide power for the first 40km until sunlight the next morning.

Step 3: Release and Climb – This step occurs when the tether climber has been prepared for lift and climb with its power cable attached, its solar arrays attached and the operations center approval. As the ribbon is reacting to the stretch, the tether climber will rise up to the altitude that is above the major effects of the atmosphere while being protected by the shield. During this rise, the winds, and other effects, will be negated with the shield and operational procedures.

Step 4: Preparation for Climb – Once the tether has pulled the tether climber up above the atmospheric effects, the climber must be prepared for its long ascent to GEO and beyond. The first step is to pull the climber out of the shield while deploying the solar arrays. The current concept is that it would be stacked and then pulled vertically out of the cylinder until the solar arrays are hanging down from the climber pointed towards the direction of the rising sun. Meanwhile, the power cable is providing the necessary energy for heat and preparation for climb. In addition, the co-axial cable will have communications with the climber and the mission cargo to ensure they are ready for the seven day climb.

Step 5: Check-out – This is a critical step in that the climber will be released for ascent when approved from operations center. As the sun rises, the solar arrays will provide the energy to the batteries and the climber engine. When everything is checked as appropriate, the tether climber will be released for climb.

Step 6: Climb – this is the actual mission of the space elevator infrastructure. The key is that the initiation of ascent occurs outside of the atmospheric effects enabling the design team to use only solar arrays for power sources.

Shield Design: The key here is that the package [tether climber and solar arrays] must be protected during the spring back to 40km from the surface of the ocean on the stage one platform. The simple concept is to have a cylindrical shaped shield be wide enough to handle the package in its compact form at zero altitude and long enough to include both the tether climber and the stacked solar arrays. The initial concept is that the shield would be a permanent cylinder attached to the space elevator tether at its 40km altitude location. It is then pulled down [stretching the tether] to the stage one ocean platform where it would be opened and loaded. The shield would have to include protection from all the aspects of the atmosphere to include massive winds, lightning, upper atmospheric static charges, and other effects as they are understood. The climber, once it reaches the appropriate altitude, would then climb vertically out of the shield and extend the solar arrays before leaving the fixed position of the shield.

Power Cable: An extremely light-weight carbon nanotube power cable has great potential in so many areas, to include electrical conductors. With an outer layer of CNTs [they are also great insulators] and an inner conductor for power, the CNT "extension cord" would provide continuous power from the initial stages of assembly at stage one, through the climb above the atmosphere and then for the first 40km or so while deploying the solar arrays. Once the solar arrays supply power after daybreak, the power extension cord can be disconnected and return with the shield back to the Marine Stage One.

Additional verification/validation requirements for Marine Node: As a note to close out this part of the chapter, there are additional verification/validation requirements for space systems that prepare the systems for the harsh environment.

	Marine Node
Lightning, hurricanes, hail, jet streams	X
Induced Oscillation	X
Induced currents in the tether	X
Terrorists attacking the system	X
Airplanes and ships hitting the tether or end station infrastructure	X
Others if applicable	

Table 5-V. Marine Node V&V

5.7 High Stage One
This second option in location of the space elevator Earth terminus takes the complexity of traveling through the atmosphere off the space elevator tether and places it on an Earth-based structure 30-50km high. To find the optimal altitude, much further work is needed on the solar panel design for the tether climbers. The stresses induced by the lower and upper atmospheres are dealt with by infrastructure based firmly on the Earth's surface. The space elevator is able to deal with the effects of Earth's turbulent atmosphere without adding

substantially to the weight that has to be supported from geosynchronous orbit. High Stage One achieves this by keeping the tether in and above the mesosphere. It helps to choose a site near the equator where there are no recorded tropical storms, such as the area of the Pacific to the south west of the Galapagos Islands or the Atlantic near Ascension Island. If the space elevator went down to the surface it would have to cope with wind pressure in the stratosphere. Using guy wires for stabilization or increasing the tension in the tether will cause strong variable forces that would have to be supported from the top. In addition, there are electrodynamic and electromagnetic threats as well as particle physics issues.

The concept is simple: place the working end of the space elevator on a firm platform at altitude. This facility would be capable of supporting 3000 tons at 40km altitude with NO forces on the space-elevator tether. As such, stresses on the tether become only space oriented forces, not atmospheric forces. The Lofstrom Loop (Lofstrom 1985) was defined in 1985 as a launch location at altitude alternative and is explained in the following sections. It ensures stability of the platform at altitude and provides routine access from the ocean surface to 40km altitude using electric cars similar to a funicular used on mountains today. This transfer of hazards and forces from the lower portion of the space elevator infrastructure to the terrestrial based Lofstrom Loop simplifies the problem and reduces the mass requirement of the space elevator tether by a factor of 10. Once the platform has been established at 40km altitude and the logistics "train" has geared up, the space elevator infrastructure becomes safer and simpler.

Benefit	Description	Magnitude: High, Medium, Low
Dealing with winds	The tether could experience total wind forces over 3 MN along its length. High Stage One transfers these forces to the Earth's surface, saving 60,000 tons in tether mass.	H
Guy wires	The weight and forces to deal with winds supported from the surface, not from geosynchronous orbit.	M
Deicing	Heaters to remove ice are supported from the surface, not from geosynchronous orbit.	M
Lightning	Lightning conductors on High Stage One do not add to the tether mass.	M
Space debris avoidance	In the mesosphere, it is possible to swing the tether without significant resistance from wind or friction.	H
	There is no need to move guy wires.	H
Satellite design	Satellites can be lighter, as they do not need to cope with the lower atmosphere.	M
Solar panels	Lightweight solar panels avoid wind stress if kept above 40km altitude.	M
Available technology	Magnetic levitation is a proven technology, NIB permanent magnets are in general use in electrical machinery, and the main tension-bearing material is Kevlar, which is widely available.	H

Table 5-IVI. Reasons to Move Stage One up in Altitude

Figure 5-8. Transfer Platform

The proposed solution to this atmospheric impact on the lower 40km of the space elevator is to adapt the Lofstrom Loop, also known as the Launch Loop (Lofstrom, 1985) or the Space Cable (Knapman, 2009), as Stage One of the space elevator.

High Stage One will stand on *surface stations* floating 112km apart. It will support a *transfer platform* 40km above the Earth's surface. High Stage One will lift payloads, and eventually passengers, to the transfer platform for onward travel up the space-elevator tether to geosynchronous orbit or beyond (Figure 5-9).

For the sake of redundancy, six pairs of tubes are used so that one pair can be quiesced and taken down for maintenance while the other five pairs continue to support the platform. Different numbers are possible, depending on the desired degree of reliability and the weight to be supported.

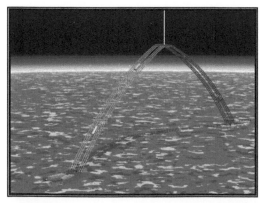

Figure 5-9. High Stage One with surface stations and transfer platform

The Lofstrom Loop is capable of propelling a vehicle into orbit electromagnetically, but the technology can be adapted to act as a high-altitude support structure. It is held aloft by fast-moving continuous belts traveling inside evacuated tubes. These are called *rotors*, the terminology used in linear electric motors (Lofstrom, 1985). In an alternative design, separate projectiles called *bolts* are used (Knapman, 2005), but rotors are preferred because they minimize losses due to any residual air in the tubes. To minimize friction and energy consumption, they use magnetic levitation with permanent magnets stabilized with electromagnets. The levitation force causes the rotors to change the direction of their momentum vectors, which provides sufficient force to support the weight of the tubes and transfer platform. The rotors continue in an indefinite loop via the transfer platform from one surface station to the other and back again.

Levitation Forces

The rotors traveling inside the evacuated tubes are able to support the weight of the transfer platform, as well as the tubes' weight, by changing the direction of their momentum vectors. However, they maintain their kinetic energy. The rotors only lose kinetic energy due to residual friction and due to gravity. They make up the effect of gravity when they descend. The surface stations give them a boost to make up for friction losses. Permanent magnets deflect them without affecting their speed, thus creating a force orthogonal to the direction of travel but without taking any of the rotors' kinetic energy. Because of the inherent instability of levitation by permanent magnets, electronically controlled electromagnets in the tubes are used to maintain a clearance of about 1 mm between the rotors and the tubes. Careful design of the permanent-magnet arrays and the electronics allows the currents in the electromagnets to be kept very small. As illustrated in Figure 5-10, the levitation force at the top of the curve supports the weight of the platform and the greater part of the tubes. Lower down, the levitation force is not vertical, and it only supports part of the weight. Tension in the tubes supports the other component of weight. Because tension in a curve causes a net orthogonal force towards the centre of curvature, the tension transmits the tube weight to the top.

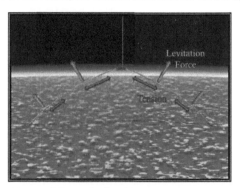

Figure 5-10. Shape of Curve indicating Tension and Orthogonal Forces

If the mass density of a rotor is m kg/meter and it changes direction by an angle φ over a distance l, then the change in momentum is $mlv\sin\varphi$, where v is the speed. This happens in the time the rotor travels the distance l, which is l/v seconds. Hence, the rate of change of momentum is $mv^2\sin\varphi$, and this is the resultant levitation force. If φ is 9°, m is 3kg/meter, and v is 1.8km/sec, the force is 1.52×10^6 N (Newtons) per tube from each side of the platform. Thus ten tubes would support 3000 metric tons weight. However, using permanent magnets, the available force is about 1600 N per meter per tube in addition to the 160 N needed to support the tubes themselves. Thus a 250m length with 10 tubes can support 400 tons. By contrast, suitably designed electromagnets can support 10,000 N per meter per tube. A length of 300m is sufficient to support a 3,000 ton platform. This structure is feasible using Kevlar as the main load-bearing material and Neodymium Iron Boron (NIB) in the magnets. Because these materials are available today, High Stage One can be built now and so provide valuable experience of reaching space using a fixed infrastructure. Hence it can be stage one chronologically as well as the lowest stage physically. To maintain stability in the presence of gusting cross winds, a technique called active curvature control transmits the forces to a set of guy wires near each surface station. The support structures at the surface station are designed to accommodate the consequent movement of about 260m in any horizontal direction.

Advantages and Disadvantages
High Stage One uses known technology and materials that are already available. The systems level TRL is low as it has not been done, but the advantages are so great it should be initiated as a research project. It can therefore be built without having to wait for new materials. Initially, it can support astronomical telescopes and other scientific instruments 40km high at a fraction of the cost of launching them into orbit. They will be easy to access for service and upgrade. Later, tourists will be able to visit the platform, and this will build experience and generate income that can be reinvested in the higher parts of the space elevator. The main disadvantage is an increase in conceptual complexity of the space-elevator project, but an early prototype [1km high] would lower the perceived risks significantly.

Variations on High Stage One
Research has been published on versions of the Lofstrom Loop as high as 140km or as low as 300 meters. The preferred altitude of 40km is low enough to avoid significant risk of damage due to space debris but high enough that there is no risk of wind damage to lightweight solar panels that may power the tether climbers (Shelef, 2008). 40km is just above a peak in wind pressure at about 38km. The surface stations can be sited on land. Alternatively, one station could be on an island or near a coast while the other station is at sea, provided there is sufficient depth. Having at least one surface station at sea allows for it to be moved, which makes erection of High Stage One easier. It is possible to have the surface stations closer together or further apart, but the 112km separation is a reasonable compromise between ease of stabilization and cost. Another design is to have four surface stations with the tubes forming a cross. A three-cornered arrangement is also possible, and both these arrangements help with stability. However, solutions are available to the problem of stability with two surface stations, and they avoid the significant cost of extra stations. The cross arrangement may be useful when moving the space-elevator tether to avoid space debris.

Cost Estimates
Cost estimates for various sizes and configurations have been published (Knapman, 2010). Even though the design is a little different, the similarities are such that we may use the same methods to calculate costs for the configurations considered in this study, including the prototypes proposed. The prototypes cover a range of sizes from 10m to 20km high (Table 5-VII). Each one incorporates a single pair of tubes.

Altitude:	10m	60m	1km	20km
Summary	Indoors	Outdoors	Moving ramp	At sea
Cost items				
Tubes	6200	37,000	592,000	16,200,000
Kevlar	100	26,000	36,000	12,300,000
Supports	2000	10,000	20,000	10,000,000
Bolts	55,700	332,000	5,452,000	20,300,000
Surface Stations	33,000	223,000	3,730,000	146,000,000
R&D	48,500	252,000	2,949,000	61,700,000
Total	$145,500	$880,000	$12.8 million	$268 million

Table 5-VII. Estimated costs of prototypes (US$)

The final configurations reach as high as 100km, with a recommendation of 40km as the optimal height. Each configuration incorporates six pairs of tubes for reasons of redundancy and strength.

Altitude:	15km	20km	30km	40km	50km	80km	100km
Cost items							
Tubes	52	82	168	258	352	789	1202
Kevlar	40	76	177	337	550	1646	2873
Supports	20	20	20	20	20	20	20
Bolts	95	130	188	254	310	477	2450
Surface Stations	80	161	247	356	491	911	1268
Vehicles	200	200	200	200	200	200	200
Platform	100	100	100	100	100	100	100
R&D	117	154	233	305	405	829	1623
Total	694	923	1399	1830	2428	4972	9736

Table 5-VIII. Estimated costs of final configurations (US$ millions)

Facilities

The facilities consist mainly of the surface stations, the transfer platform, and the mechanism to move the tether to avoid space debris. The location must be away from human habitation in view of the experimental nature of the project, dealing with novel technology. At the required scale, a very large amount of energy is stored in the moving parts, and stringent safety precautions must be taken. The distance between the two surface stations is approximately three times the altitude of the transfer station at the top. For 40km altitude, the distance is 112km.

Surface Stations

There is a station on the surface at each end of High Stage One, either at sea or on the ground. During start-up, the surface stations accelerate the rotors. Thereafter, in continuous operation, each station turns round the rotors from the incoming tubes and sends them back through the return tubes. It can build up a reserve of speed, and hence energy, by allowing the tension in the tubes to increase so that it is non-zero at the surface. This also simplifies the task of maintaining stability. In continuous operation, the incoming rotors arrive on the ramp that turns them to the horizontal. Then they proceed to the ambit that turns them around, after which they go back up the ramp. These are illustrated in Figure 5-11, in which the ramp is below sea level, and a submarine pipe brings the rotors back near the surface for the ambit and accelerator. It is possible to have the ambit submerged more deeply, thus shortening the pipe, but that would make servicing more difficult.

Figure 5-11. View of Ramp, Ambit and Accelerator Pair

On land, some of the ramp is in a tunnel, some of it supported by a gantry and some of it supported by short *support tubes* [as distinct from *main tubes*]. This represents a compromise between depth of tunneling and height of support tubes. The ambit and accelerator pair are at surface level or in shallow trenches. The details will depend on site conditions. As illustrated, there is a large ambit to avoid deceleration and acceleration. This allows powerful magnets to be used in the ambit. These may be permanent or superconducting magnets. An ambit using permanent magnets is large but reliable. Powerful electromagnets are available, but they consume substantial power. Superconducting magnets cooled with liquid helium are preferred, because of their field strength. The force on a magnet of flux density B_1 with effective surface area A in a field B_2 is given by:

$$F = \frac{B_1 B_2 A}{8\pi \times 10^{-7}}$$

Commercially available superconducting magnets can apply a 10 T (Tesla) field. Using this equation, we obtain a force F in the ambit of about 60 kN if A=100 cm^2, assuming an induced field in the iron rotor of 2 T. This result is confirmed by a simulation using *Finite Element Method Magnetics, Version 4.2*. The ambit radius is mv^2/F for a rotor mass m kg/metre and velocity v. If v is 1740 m/sec and m is 3 kg/metre, the radius is about 152 meters. If Neodymium Iron Boron (NIB) permanent magnets were used instead of superconducting magnets, the field strength would be about 1.2 T. Taking the induced field as 0.9 T, the force comes to approximately 4.3 kN, and the radius of the ambit would be 2km.

Extent of the Ramp: The overall vertical extent of the ramp required is given by $2R\sin^2\theta/2$ for radius of curvature R and angle of inclination θ to the horizontal. To achieve the best radius, superconducting magnets are needed in the ramp, cooled with liquid helium. Now θ is 55°, and R is as for the ambit, giving a vertical extent of 70 meters, which is the required depth of the submarine pipe. Its length is roughly $2R\theta$ (θ in radians), which is about 290 meters. Using NIB instead of super-conductors, the vertical extent is 910 meters, and the length is 4km. The angle of inclination of the main tubes can be varied by changing the buoyancy of the floats.

Transfer Platform: All payloads will be transferred to the space elevator tether at the 40km platform. The Stage One vehicle ascends the tubes in the manner of an electric train car. At the platform, they will be transferred to the tether climbers for the space elevator. The methods of supplying power are quite different. The climber ascending the tether will be powered by ultra lightweight solar panels. To avoid wind damage, the lightweight solar panels can be stored at the transfer platform with the tether climbers. Therefore, it is proposed to have two different classes of vehicle: one for the vehicle traveling between the surface and the platform, and one for the climber going up and down the tether. After experience is gained with unmanned operations, passengers will ascend to the platform where they may use an observation lounge and hotel facilities. Cargo transfer can be automated. There will be storage and handling facilities for several tether climbers, including the possibility of removing or replacing their solar panels and transferring them to the ground for maintenance and repair.

Optimum Altitude: The table shows options and benefits for having the transfer platform at various altitudes up to 100km above sea level. Within this range, the cost is roughly proportional to altitude.

Table VIII makes clear that many of the benefits of High Stage One are achieved at 20km, but there are greater benefits at 40km. 40km is above the peak in wind pressure seen at 38km altitude in Figure 5-14.

Altitude of transfer platform: Hazard avoided	15km	20km	30km	40km	50km	80km	100km
No damage to solar panels on tether climber				X	X	X	X
Negligible wind pressure				X	X	X	X
Ability to swing tether for space debris avoidance without wind or air drag				X	X	X	X
No ice	X	X	X	X	X	X	X
Little wind pressure		X	X	X	X	X	X
Laser power source can be away from tether and still avoid dispersion			X	X	X	X	X
Above most electric storms				X	X	X	X
Above all electric storms							X
Below space debris	X	X	X	X	X	X	
Climbing time (minutes)	10	14	18	24	30	48	60
Cost estimates (US $ millions)	694	923	1400	1810	2428	4972	9736

Table 5-IX, Optimizing the Altitude of High Stage One

Initial Erection of High Stage One

Initially, a pair of tubes is laid out flat on the surface of the ocean between the two surface stations. Slowly, the surface stations accelerate the rotor to full speed, which will take several days. The next step is to begin to raise the angle of the ramps. One surface station is at a fixed location, but the other is movable. The movable station is in two widely separated parts, the ramp and the ambit. The ambit is at the furthest point away from the fixed station, but the movable ramp starts close to the fixed station and slowly moves towards the movable ambit as the ramps raise their angle, causing the tubes and rotors to elevate between the two ramps. The movable ambit moves slowly towards the movable ramp to allow for the shortening of the surface distance as the tubes rise. Assuming the use of NIB magnets, the shape and size of the ramp remain constant during erection. If superconducting magnets are used, there is an additional step to convert the ramp to use them. They must be installed along the length of tube that serves as the ramp once it has joined with the ambit. The superconductors can then be adjusted to exploit their power by shortening the ramp. Once the first pair of tubes has been installed, the second pair is raised along it using crawlers. Next, the surface stations accelerate the rotor in the second pair until it can support itself. Further pairs of tubes are erected in the same way. It is possible to take the first pair down if desired in order to salvage the superconducting magnets that are no longer required. Finally, the transfer platform is taken up in sections and assembled at the top. An alternative method using a helium-filled tube has been described (Knapman, 2005) for use when both surface stations are on land.

Capturing the Tether
Once High Stage One has been erected, it is necessary to capture the initial threads of the space-elevator tether. These will be lowered from geosynchronous orbit. It is possible to think of ingenious methods of capturing the threads at altitude using a lasso or some form of hovering rocket. However, there seems to be no justification for spending significant time or money on such a one-off endeavour. The simple approach is to lower the threads to the ocean, where a team can gather them up using a small boat or launch. The crew can carry the threads to the surface station, where they will attach them to a Stage One vehicle and raise them to the transfer platform. When the threads are secure, further construction of the tether can proceed from the transfer platform by means of the small tether climbers.

Technology Summary
Flexible ferrous rotors travel at about 2km/sec inside evacuated tubes. They support a transfer platform at an altitude of 40km [selected from a possible range between 15km and 140km]. The structure is supported using magnetic levitation with the rotors, which causes a force that changes the direction of the rotors' momentum vectors. Their kinetic energy is depleted marginally due to residual friction. They lose energy due to gravity as they ascend, but this is made up during the descent. Cargo and passengers transfer to the main space-elevator tether at the platform. This platform can support a weight of several thousand tons.

Climate at Altitude
The environmental effects on a space elevator reach across the spectrum and are explained in detail in the Systems Approach to the Environment chapter. The question being addressed in this chapter is will an elevated starting point for the climber benefit the systems approach to the total space elevator design. This quick summary below will explain the impact of the environment effects with respect to this question; Should we start at altitude?

Electromagnetic Effects: It turns out that the electromagnetic effects will reach across the total stretch of the space elevator. During the lower regions [0 to 100km], the effects are focused upon the electric storms in the atmosphere and above. These will be discussed in detail in Chapter 7, Environment. Choosing a site with few electrical storms means that high-altitude electrical phenomena are also likely to be infrequent. Siting the transfer platform at 40km altitude will still expose the main space-elevator tether to elves, sprites and gigantic jets, but carbon nanotubes will conduct the current to the transfer station, where it will be connected to the Stage One lightning conductor. Siting the Stage One along the equator helps lower the risk as most electrical phenomena in the atmosphere and below 100km focus on the temperate zones of the Earth. The natural quiescence of the Pacific west of Ecuador should lower the risks and is shown in Figure 5-12.

Figure 5-12. Global cloud cover from the International
Satellite Cloud Climatology Project

High Altitude Winds: Winds are a challenge to the space elevator. In temperate latitudes, jet stream winds can exceed 100 meters/sec between altitudes of 9 and 15km (Barry and Chorley, 1998). Figure 5-13 shows global average wind speeds against altitude. The high speeds above the stratopause are of little consequence because of the extremely low density. Figure 5-14 takes the atmospheric density ρ into account to reach an estimate of global average wind pressure ρv^2, where v is wind speed. Maxima may be four times as great as averages; that effect can be seen by multiplying the pressure scale by 16.

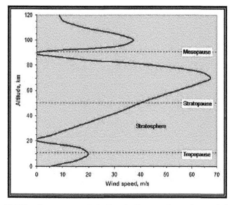

Figure 5-13. Average global wind speed against altitude [2]

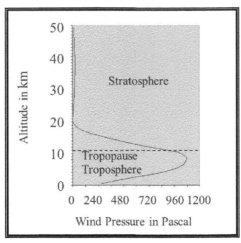

Figure 5-14. Estimated maximum wind pressure against altitude, based on average global wind speeds

Near the equator, there are only seasonal jet streams over Africa near latitudes of 15° N or S, and they do not occur over the equatorial oceans. Figure 5-15 shows that equatorial wind speeds are generally more moderate than the global average (Jiang et al., 2004), although more detail is needed on the extremes. Considerable design effort has gone into dealing with strong winds in High Stage One, based on the use of guy wires supported by the rotor via magnetic levitation. This is a great advantage over the alternative of trying to support these forces directly from the tether.

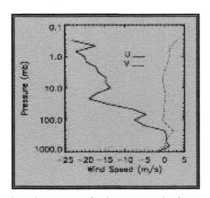

Figure 5-15. Wind speed against atmospheric pressure in the equatorial Western Pacific December-March 1991-92

Wind Pressure on the Tether: Previous calculations (Knapman, 2005) have shown that the maximum wind pressure that may be encountered in the stratosphere is about 1000 N/m^2. Edwards and Westling (2003, see their chapter 10.4) propose making the tether 20cm wide (instead of a meter) in the atmosphere. Assuming it is curved it would present a 0.1m^2 per meter cross section to the wind. If the tether is anchored at the Earth's surface, the net lateral force experienced by the tether would be 590 kN.

There would be large and unpredictable movements of the tether in gusting winds. The question is how far to allow the tether to move with the wind. Edwards and Westling suggest a maximum deflection from the vertical of 10°, which is maintained by a tension $T=F_W/\sin10°$. Since $1/\sin10°=5.8$, this requires a tension of 5.8 times the wind force. This amounts to a maximum tether movement of 2km in any direction, making it difficult to control movements to avoid space debris at the same time as variable winds are blowing in the atmosphere. This means that the tether would need to be strong enough to bear a 3.4 MN force, whereas it only needs to bear a 70 kN wind force if we use High Stage One (Table 5-X) with the platform at 40km. 410 kN is enough to sustain a 20-ton tether climber with payload, plus a 9-ton allowance for higher climbers plus the 70 kN wind force, with 50 kN to spare for moving the tether. The total mass estimate for a tether strong enough to hold 410 kN is 7,000 metric ton.

Wind forces at higher altitudes
Table 5-X shows estimated wind forces potentially encountered by the whole length of the tether above the platform for various platform altitudes. Figure 5-16 shows the cumulative effect of estimated maximum winds above the platform, taken as three times the averages. The higher the platform, the lower is the cumulative wind pressure. The table summarizes the main numbers, including the impact on the mass of the tether to cope with the consequent extra weight.

When the platform is 20km high, the tether experiences an estimated maximum cumulative wind force of 25 kN, requiring a tether tension of 145 kN [equivalent to having to support a weight of approximately 14 MT] compared with 3.4 MN [300 MT equivalent] when the tether ends at sea level. At 50km, the required tension is only 30 kN [3 MT equivalent].

Platform Altitude (km)	Estimated maximum wind force on tether (kN)	Tension in tether due to wind (kN)	Total tether tension at platform (kN)	Estimated total tether mass (MT)
0	590	3400	3830	66,000
10	210	1210	1555	27,000
15	50	290	630	10,900
20	25	145	485	8,300
30	22	125	465	7,900
40	12	70	410	7,000
50	5	30	370	6,300
80	0.015	0.09	340	5,800
100	0.00022	0.001	340	5,800

Table 5-X. Effect of wind forces on tether

Deicing Technology: Icing is a hazard up to an altitude of about 12km, and so the total weight of the deicing laminate at 0.35kg/m2 is about 840kg. To this must be added sufficient cabling to carry the power to the upper elevations. Although the maximum power consumption could be as high as 1.4 MW, it is reasonable to assume that any section of the tether would only need deicing 10% of the time at worst, bringing the peak power consumption down to 140 kW, or 11.5 kW per km. Thus the top km needs 11km of cabling to supply it, the next km down needs 10km of cabling, and so on, giving a total effective length of 66km of cabling capable of carrying 11.5 kW. For a total of 66km, the weight of the cabling is 8,000kg. The effect of this load on the space elevator tether is much smaller than that of the wind. The deicing would add a further 3,000 metric tons to the overall tether mass. Instead, High Stage One supports the extra weight.

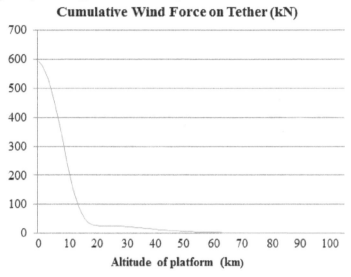

Cumulative Wind Force on Tether (kN)

Altitude of platform (km)

Figure 5-16. Estimated maximum wind force encountered by the tether above the platform for various platform altitudes

Winds and Stabilization of High Stage One

Cross winds and other disturbances will tend to cause instability. There is a natural stability in the vertical direction due to the effect of gravity offset by the curvature of the tubes and rotors. This stability is enhanced by adding moderate tension to the tubes to allow the necessary variations in the rotors' speeds without the structure sagging. Laterally, however, the structure is inherently unstable, and corrective measures are needed. The technique known as active curvature control (Knapman, 2009) uses electronic methods to correct for changes in curvature and adjust them so that they match the curvature required to counteract lateral forces. It is designed to maintain stability at higher altitudes by transmitting movements down to the Earth's surface. The maximum deflection due to wind is calculated based on previous work showing that a tube is subject to a maximum wind force of 50 N/meter (Knapman, 2005). Winds are significant at elevations up to about 15km. This translates to a maximum deflection at 3km elevation of about 260m in any direction. Guy wires are required up to this height. The alternative solution is to attach guy wires at periodic intervals all the way up the tubes. These guy wires would be anchored at the surface and would inhibit lateral movement. Small-scale movements between guy wires are suppressed by the natural stiffness of the rotors and tubes. The drawback is that the guy wires add considerably to the overall weight that the rotors must support through magnetic levitation, and this load scales non-linearly with altitude. Using active curvature control removes the need for most of the guy wires, but they are still required up to a height of 3km in order to draw the tubes back from their maximum deflection so that they line up with the surface stations. Triples of guy wires are placed at regular intervals along a tube, as in Figure 5-17. Each tube is anchored at the surface station and is under tension, so that each triple of guy wires complements the tube in a stable four-cornered arrangement (Knapman, 2011).

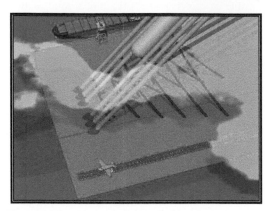

Figure 5-17. View of triples of wires along the tubes

Winds on Solar Panels of Tether Climber

The move to above the significant atmospheric winds is a key strategy for the tether climber design. As such, the calculations for the wind pressure are shown in the next table. The maximum force estimate applies to a solar array of 44x440 meters, the size discussed in Chapter 4. It clearly shows that there are forces at even 40km altitude, with the forces greatly reduced shortly after departure. These would be part of the requirements set driving the design of the tether climber. Wind effects on vehicles are also dealt with (Knapman, 2012).

Altitude (km)	Max wind pressure (Pa)	Max force on a panel (kN)
40	29	560
50	13	250
60	5.9	115
70	1.6	31
80	0.128	2.5
85	0.015	0.3

Table 5-XI Wind Pressures on Solar Panels

Moving the Space Elevator for Space Debris

The altitude of the transfer platform is chosen so that the risk of being hit either by space debris or a natural meteor is negligible. On the other hand, the space-elevator tether will be exposed to these hazards. It is designed to withstand collision with objects up to 10 cm. Larger objects can be tracked, and the tether must be moved to avoid them. One method of doing this is to pay out an additional length of tether and initiate a transverse wave from the platform. According to a recent study, up to 100 meters of tether may be required, which would permit lateral movement up to that distance in any direction (Swan et al., 2011). It is sufficient to thrust the tether at the desired velocity using winches, so long as it is timed to set up a resonant traveling wave. It is not necessary for the winches themselves to pull the tether the whole distance. The winches or a similar mechanism are to be placed on the transfer platform. It may be desirable to go for a cross arrangement of High Stage One with four surface stations instead of two.

To avoid space debris, at least three methods of moving the tether have been proposed:

1. Set up lateral oscillations which propagate up the tether from Stage One. This is suitable if there is no climber on the tether within the zone up to and near the danger zone.
2. Drag the tether with its anchor several kilometers in the required direction. This is suitable for moving the tether with a climber.
3. Swing a mass at the base of the tether. This is the preferred method for moving the tether with a climber.

The dynamics of the tether are those of a string under tension, a subject that is treated in textbooks on engineering mathematics. The equation of motion is

$$\frac{\partial^2 y}{\partial t^2} = \frac{T}{\mu}\frac{\partial^2 x}{\partial y^2} \qquad (1)$$

Here x is the lateral displacement, y is the vertical distance (both in meters), t is time, T is the tension in Newtons, and μ is the mass density in kg/meter. Taking $c^2 = T/\mu$, the general solution is known as d'Alembert's solution and has the form

$$x = F(y + ct) + G(y - ct) \qquad (2)$$

Here $F(\ )$ and $G(\ )$ are general functions. It tells us that movements of a quite general nature at the bottom are propagated upwards with a speed of c meters/sec. Downward propagation from higher up is possible in principle but is probably less useful. The tether is tapered so that the mass density is proportional to the maximum tension. Consequently, the speed c is roughly constant, with variations due to the fact that the tether tension is often below the maximum. The presence of a payload causes a wave traveling upwards to be partly reflected back down again.

A tension of 250 kN (enough to support 25 tons weight) with a mass density of 10^{-2}kg/meter [assuming a strength of 30 MYuri] leads to a propagation speed of approximately 5km/sec. Therefore, it is possible for a movement at Stage One to travel to 2000km altitude in about 7 minutes, enabling a rapid response to a space-debris alert. 2000km is significant because the majority of space debris is below that altitude.

A sinusoidal oscillation applied at the tether base will be propagated up the tether. If the frequency is once per 100 seconds, the wavelength will be 500km. Careful timing would be needed to ensure that the maximum displacement coincided with the arrival of the expected debris, with a margin for error of about 10 seconds. Such an oscillation could be started by applying an impulsive force to a weight at the tether base so as to start it swinging.

Dragging the Tether

The dynamics are different if there is a payload at an intermediate point on the tether. The tension below the tether climber must be reduced by its weight, and so the tension below a 20-MT payload can be no more than 50 kN, leading to a propagation speed of 2.2km/sec. Thus it takes about 6 minutes to propagate a movement of the base up to a tether climber at 1000km. Actually moving the payload is slower than moving a segment of the tether because the climber is much more massive. Effectively, it acts like a reflector, causing some of the movement to be propagated down again.

A reasonable method of moving the tether together with a climber as payload is to drag the base horizontally. Figure 5-18 shows five stages of movement, starting at rest (a) and then moving the base by a distance s. As soon as the movement starts, it is propagated up the tether, leading to the triangular traveling wave illustrated in (b) and (c), which has a height h. If the base travels at speed v, then $h=sc/v$. When, as in (c), the wave reaches the payload, the tether forms an angle $\psi \approx s/h \approx v/c$ radians to the vertical. This results in a lateral force $F_p = T\tan\psi \approx Tv/c$ on the payload.

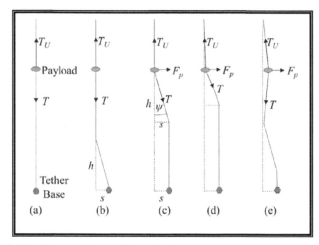

Figure 5-18. Five positions of the tether in response to movement of the base

As the payload moves, it starts to experience an impeding force from the tether above, which is at tension T_U. If the payload speed is v_p and the propagation speed above the tether is c_U, the impeding force is $T_U v_p / c_U$. Hence,

$$F_p = T\frac{v}{c} - T_U \frac{v_p}{c_U} \qquad (3)$$

The implication is that we cannot move the payload too fast, because the tether above exerts an impeding force proportional to the speed v_p. The dynamics are that the payload receives an impulsive force from the wave traveling upwards from below. Part of the wave is reflected back down again. Figure 5-18(d) shows the reflection partly overlapping the original wave. The reflected wave travels down (e), with the tether and payload displaced to the right. The base reflects this smaller wave back up again to impart another impulse to the payload.

118

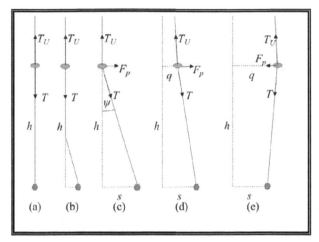

Figure 5-19. Tether positions when base movement is timed with propagation speed

A good solution is to move the base of the tether at such a speed that the traveling wave reaches the payload just as the base reaches distance s. This amounts to choosing h equal to the altitude of the payload. Then the payload experiences a positive force from below until its displacement equals s, and equation (3) becomes:

$$F_p = T\frac{s-q}{h} - T_U\frac{v_p}{c_U} \qquad (4)$$

If the payload has mass m_p, and taking $p=q-s$, we may write equation (4) as follows:

$$m_p\frac{d^2p}{dt^2} + \frac{T_U}{c_U}\frac{dp}{dt} + \frac{T}{h}p = 0 \qquad (5)$$

This is the standard equation for damped simple harmonic motion. For values of h up to approximately 2100km, it has the solution

$$p = -se^{-At}\cos Et \text{ with } A = \frac{T_U}{2m_pc_U} \text{ and } E = \sqrt{\frac{T}{m_ph} - A^2}$$

For example, if the payload's height h is 1000 km, then moving the tether base sideways by a distance s of 10 km will cause the tether to form an angle of $\psi \approx d/h \approx 10/1000 \approx 0.01$ radians (about 0.6°).

Assuming (as above) a tension of 50 kN in the tether at the base, the tension T in the tether at 1000 km (just below the payload) is 165 kN, including the 115 kN weight of the tether below the climber. The tether climber's weight adds 200 kN to the tension above, bringing T_U to 365 kN. Then $A \approx 1.8 \times 10^{-3}$ and $E \approx 2.2 \times 10^{-3}$. Hence the tether climber reaches a displacement of 10 km (i.e., $p=0$) when $Et=\pi/2$, which is when $t=710$ seconds, about 12 minutes. The propagation time is about 6 minutes (the propagation speed increasing from 2.2km/sec at the base to 3.6km/sec just below the payload), giving a total time of 18 minutes.

The base is moved in time with the propagation (Figure 5-19), and so its movement does not add to the total time. The tether climber will continue to move a little beyond this point, but the motion is heavily damped and will soon settle down.

A similar calculation for a tether climber at a height of 2000 km, where the tension T is of 300 kN at the tether climber and T_U=500 kN above, yields $A \approx 2.5 \times 10^{-3}$ and $E \approx 1.1 \times 10^{-3}$. The time to move the tether climber 10km is about 24 minutes. This must be added to the propagation time of 10 minutes (the propagation speed reaching 4.2km/sec just below the tether climber), totaling 34 minutes.

At 10,000km the dynamics are rather different. The weight of the tether climber is reduced to 3 tons, and so a tension of 200 kN in the tether at the base is possible, bringing the tension just below the tether climber to 1.5 MN and 1.53 MN above it. Now the motion is over damped, meaning that the exponent is real and the solution is:

$$ p = -se^{(E'-A)t} \text{ with } A = \frac{T_U}{2m_p c_U} \text{ as before but } E' = \sqrt{A^2 - \frac{T}{m_p h}} $$

Now, $A \approx 7.52 \times 10^{-3}$, $E' \approx 7.0 \times 10^{-3}$, and $E'-A \approx -5.2 \times 10^{-3}$. About 4600 seconds (75 minutes) are needed to move the payload 10km, assuming the base has moved s=11km (using $\ln(1/11) \approx -2.4$). Because of the greater tension, the propagation speed is approximately 5km/sec, and the propagation time is about 30 minutes, bringing the total to 1¾ hours.

To move a payload that is much higher than 10,000km in a timely manner using this method may require movement to be initiated from above as well as from below.

Movement Mechanism at the Base
By working above most of the atmosphere, we can move the base of the tether while keeping High Stage One Stationary. A movement of 10km along High Stage One involves a drop in height of approximately 500m in the tubes, from 40km to 39.5km. The maximum required angle ψ [see Figure 5-19] is 0.01 radians, which may cause the tether base to rise by up to 100 meters. Hence, a wire 700m long can support such movements. To permit movement in any direction, four of these wires are required, any two of which can be used together to obtain a precise direction angle. The strength of the wires will be similar to that of the lowest part of the tether, and they can be made of the same material. With that assumption, their combined weight is only about 30kg.

To support the wires, two sets of tubes are needed, arranged in a cross. This has the drawback that four surface stations are needed instead of two. The wires are attached to crawlers that can travel along the tubes for the required distance. A mechanical arrangement at the centre will be needed to enable it to pass over the tubes.

Swinging the Tether
It is possible to move the tether and payloads by swinging a mass at the base to set up traveling waves. This has the advantage that it can be done from High Stage One using one

set of tubes forming a single slender arch rather than the arrangement of tubes in a cross. The calculations for this more complicated case can build on the work done on dragging the tether.

The method is to swing a mass at the tether base by giving it a large impetus in the required direction. For example, a force of 250 kN exerted over a distance of 100 meters is enough to swing a 5-ton mass as far as 20km in about 9 minutes. The tubes in High Stage One are designed to cope with larger lateral forces than this in the course of dealing with cross winds.

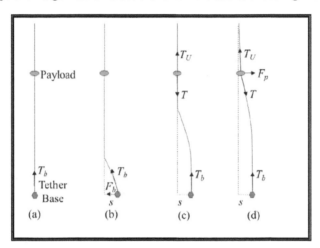

Figure 5-19. Tether positions when swinging the base

Swinging the base causes waves that are propagated up the tether, as shown in Figure 5-19. As in Figure 5-18, these waves will eventually be partially reflected by the payload, but the net effect is for the payload to be displaced by a varying force F_p which depends on the tension T in the tether and the angle of the tether to the vertical, as in Figure 5-19. The base is swung twice as far in Figure 5-19 as it is dragged in Figure 5-19 and this leads to faster movement of the payload.

Conclusion on High Stage One

Answer Q4 –The tether base is best placed above almost all of the atmosphere. Further research is needed to determine the optimal altitude.

Finding 5-6: The High Stage One has tremendous operational advantages. However, as technological maturity is less than optimum, there must be a risk reduction program with significant early prototype testing.

The advantage of starting to climb with solar arrays only at altitude are remarkable; however, the starting point of the Marine Stage One or the High Stage One both have advantages. This study tends to support High Stage One as a baseline, with the Marine Stage One as a valid alternative. The full program should continue as the risk of design for the Stage One has viable alternatives and can proceed when authorized.

Technology Readiness and Risk Assessment
There are a number of questions and issues that can only be resolved by building working prototypes. The purpose of prototyping is first to verify the theoretical predictions in the design and then to assess reliability and safety. The following steps are proposed, although experience with the earlier steps will doubtless lead to some modification of the later steps.

1. Produce more detailed design documents, especially in the area of magnetic levitation.
2. Build a working bench-top model to verify the magnetic levitation design. The model produced by Paul Birch some years ago used somewhat different technology from that proposed for the space elevator High Stage One.
3. Build a version large enough to test the vacuum technology – about 10 meters high inside an isolated warehouse or similar large indoor space. This version will be the first test of the scaling calculations.
4. Build an outdoor version to test the stability in wind, including guy wires and active curvature control – about 60m high in a remote field or moor. This is also a chance to examine weather proofing and other issues of robust outdoor operation.
5. A version 1km high should be useful for astronomy. This needs to be built on high ground to gain the maximum benefit. Situated in a suitable part of Hawaii, the Andes or the Canary Islands, it would become the highest terrestrial astronomical instrument in the world. It should be built in stages of increasing size, beginning at 60m and being raised step by step to the target height. The design is illustrated in Figure 5-20. A pair of tubes is laid out between two ambits, and a small part is raised using two ramps. One ramp and ambit are fixed; the others are on wheels. To increase the tubes' height, the movable ramp is moved step by step towards the movable ambit, which has to advance some distance towards the ramps to allow for the shortening distance over the ground as the tubes rise, as illustrated in Figure 5-21 and Figure 5-22. The ramps are about 5m high, and they sustain forces up to 26 MT vertically and 9 MT horizontally.
6. Next, a marine platform must be tested. Although there are advantages to operating at sea, there are increased logistical challenges and costs compared with a site on land. Therefore this step is not proposed earlier. A large version is proposed that will eventually reach up to 20km. However, it is first laid out horizontally with the ambits far apart. The components are tested in this configuration above the full speeds needed for elevation. As previously described (Knapman, 2011), the two ramps begin close together and are very slowly separated.

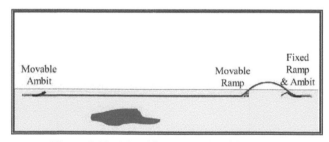

Figure 5-20. Movable ramp and ambit on land

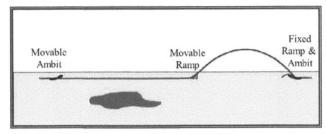

Figure 5-21. Intermediate position of movable ramp and ambit on land

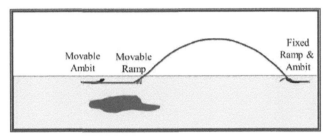

Figure 5-22. Late position of movable ramp and ambit on land

The four phases of development shown in Figure 5-23 culminate in the 20km high prototype. That leads directly to the production version, which consists of six pairs of tubes and all the infrastructure. Each phase includes building up, which covers design, detailed scheduling, arranging finance and recruiting staff. The cautious schedule assumes a moderate increase of funds annually and allows time to review one phase before starting the next. In the aggressive schedule, the build-up activities overlap with the work of the preceding phase, and some prototyping activities are accelerated by increasing the budget in the early years.

Table 5-XII shows the finance needed for the cautious schedule from 2014 to 2030. The numbers are in millions of US dollars. Table 5-XIII gives the finance needed for the more aggressive schedule, which requires higher funding in the early years but can be completed in 11 years.

'14	'15	'16	'17	'18	'19	'20	'21	'22	'23	'24	'25	'26	'27	'28	'29	'30
0.1	0.3	0.2	0.5	0.8	1	2	5	6	10	120	80	60	210	700	500	400

Table 5-XII. Funding required each year for cautious schedule 2014-2030

'14	'15	'16	'17	'18	'19	'20	'21	'22	'23	'24
0.1	0.5	1	2	10	15	120	180	560	700	500

Table 5-XIII. Funding required each year for aggressive schedule 2014-24

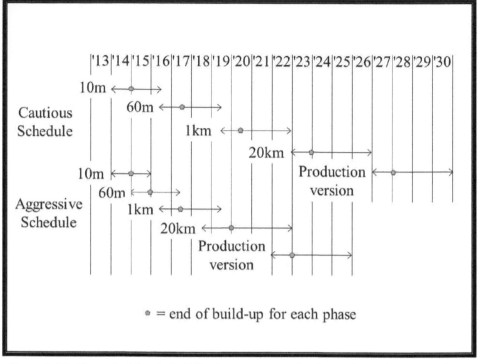

Figure 5-23. Two schedules for building four prototypes, leading to the production version with platform at 40km altitude

Verification/validation requirements on High Stage One
As a note to close out this part of the chapter, there are additional verification/ validation requirements for space systems that prepare the systems for the harsh environment (Table 5-XIV).

	High Stage One
Lightning, hurricanes, hail, jet streams	X
Induced Oscillation	X
Induced currents in the tether	X
Terrorists attacking the system	X
Airplanes and ships hitting the tether or end station infrastructure	X
Others if applicable	

Table 5-XIV. High Stage One V&V

5.8 Summary of Findings and Conclusions

There are many benefits to building a prototype High Stage One while we are waiting for a strong enough material for the space-elevator tether. It will provide valuable experience in operating infrastructure for space access and will generate a revenue stream, initially from scientific investments and later from tourism. High Stage One will solve the problems of winds and storms that would otherwise present significant challenges to the space elevator, because High Stage One can carry the additional weight and forces involved without loading the tether itself. Moving the tether at the Earth's surface to avoid space debris would be difficult if there were strong winds blowing in the stratosphere at the same time. High Stage One will be able to do this at the transfer platform, which is above 99.7% of the atmosphere.

The recommendation is to use High Stage One. The principal benefit is an overall mass saving by a factor of 9.5, taking wind and deicing into account.

- A factor of 9 can be saved in tether mass by offloading the wind forces on to Stage One: the mass can be 7000 rather than 64,000 MT.
- Heaters to remove ice are offloaded on to High Stage One and do not need to be loaded on to the tether. This gives a further mass saving of 1500 MT.
- The weight of the tether below 40km is not needed. Allowing for wind and deicing, this relieves the tether of another 640 kg of weight, and thus of another 110 MT in overall tether mass.
- The cumulative effect of High Stage One is to bring the tether mass down from 66,000 to 7000 MT, a factor of 9.5.
- Moving the tether at sea level involves moving a ship, which is a slow process. At high altitude, the tether can be moved quickly, minimizing the delay in avoiding space debris.
- At high altitude, it is possible to swing the tether without significant air resistance or wind force.
- Fragile solar panels on tether climbers are at little risk of damage if they commence their climb at 40km altitude.
- The base technology is available now. High Stage One can be built with Kevlar using magnetic levitation, which is a mature technology.

Finding 5-7: The strongest concept for space elevator climber is solar only from 40km altitude based on projection of technology. As such, there are three viable concepts that will move the climber from the Marine Node to the appropriate starting altitude: extension cord, spring forward, and High Stage One.

Chapter 6
Dynamics

6.1 Background

The future of a space elevator transportation infrastructure is based upon fifty years of spaceflight and, specifically, space tether flight successes. The basic gravity gradient stability leads to a dynamically stable space elevator, while understanding historic space forces gives confidence that the structure can be adapted for effective use despite tidal forces from the Sun and the Moon, as well as aerodynamic forces near the surface of the Earth.

This chapter begins with the history of space tether deployment. The fundamental aspects of space tethers will be addressed, including stable conditions, natural dynamics, operation, and deployment. Currently, the records of the longest thin and tape tether deployments in space are 31.7km and 132.6m, respectively. In addition, the TiPS tether (4km) (TIPS, 1996) survived in-orbit for over ten years.

While historical space tether success is a useful starting point for assessing the dynamics of a space elevator, there are a few major differences with this structure and typical space tethers, which affect the dynamics greatly and must be noted.

There is a massive relative difference in tether length (three to four orders of magnitude) between the space elevator and a typical space tether. As a result, the mass of the climbers are very small compared to the mass of the tether, which is usually not the case. Also, unlike typical space tethers, when climbers scale an operational space elevator, the tether itself is not deployed or retrieved. The most obvious difference concerns the deployed state, and is that space tethers normally link two satellites, while a space elevator's tether links one satellite directly to the surface of the Earth, leading to a pivot point there. Finally, typical space tethers reside exclusively in a vacuum of space and thus need not contend with large scale aerodynamic effects.

The body of this chapter focuses on the dynamics of an operational space elevator, including a description of its nominal state, its general behavior, and its response to various loading conditions. The more complex dynamics associated with the deployment of the structure are presented as well. The dynamics associated with a severance in the tether are addressed in both a passive and active sense. The worst case analysis is indispensable for such future systems and will be discussed with a focus on risk reduction. The end of the chapter includes findings and conclusions from the various authors. The list of sections is shown below to illustrate the contributors and the flow of the chapter.

6.1 Introduction [Stephen Cohen, Hironori A. Fujii, Arun Misra]
6.2 Historic Lessons Learned from Space Tethers and Solutions [Hironori A. Fujii, Arun Misra]
6.3 Dynamics of Space Tethers [Takeo Watanabe and Arun Misra]
6.4 Description of Nominal Space Elevator Structure [Stephen Cohen]
6.5 Basic Dynamics of Operational Tether [Stephen Cohen and Kenji Uchiyama]
6.6 Induced Dynamics [Stephen Cohen, Hironori A. Fujii, and Kenji Uchiyama]
6.7 Deployment Dynamics [Arun Misra]
6.8 Space Elevator Severance [Paul Williams and Peter Swan]
6.9 Conclusions [Stephen Cohen]

6.2 Historic Lessons Learned from Space Tethers and Solutions

6.2.1 Introduction

This section chronicles past space tether missions and highlights lessons learned from them that can be applied to a space elevator initiative. There have been many space experiments with tethers, starting with early Gemini manned space systems and continuing today. An expansion on the history of space tethers can be found in Appendix E-3.

The lessons learned through space tether activities do not translate directly to all facets of space elevator dynamics. The area of particular relevance concerns the deployment of the initial space elevator tether, as this represents, in principal, a scaled up version of a traditional space tether deployment. Risk reduction will be discussed throughout the chapter.

6.2.2   History of Space Tether Projects

- First Space Tether - Project Gemini 11 & 12 [1966]:
  Successful deployment and stable rotation. Stable swing and local vertical were obtained.
- Successful Deployment of 20km - Delta II second stage [SEDS 1993]:
  A 25 kilogram daughter satellite was deployed down from a Delta booster upper stage on a 20km long nonconductive tether, and then cut loose at the right moment to send it into the atmosphere on a predetermined trajectory.
- Demonstration of Long-term (10 years) Tether Operations [TIPS 1996]:
  TiPS tether (4km) was deployed successfully and survived over 10 years in orbit.
- Retrieval of a Tether in Space [TSS-1 1992]:
  A 550 kg spacecraft, on a 20km long conductive tether, was deployed from a Space Shuttle for tens of meters and was then retrieved after failure of full deployment.
- Generation of High Power [TSS-1R 1996]:
  Full 20km length was deployed of electro-dynamic tether which generated 3,500 volts at ampere-level current. The tether's insulation was damaged, and an arc flashed between the tether and the shuttle's deployment boom, breaking the tether. Two secondary benefits: (1) current levels were twice what had been expected; (2) the released satellite popped up to an orbit 140km above the shuttle, demonstrating the use of tethers for orbital insertion.
- Student Deployed 30km Tether [YES2 2007]:
  Unreel a tether 31.7km long to drop a 6 kg re-entry capsule, *Fotino*.

6.2.3   History of Deployment of Space Tethers

The history of space tether systems is a history of deployment of tethers. Figure 6-1 shows the chronological trend of tether deployment. In the initial period, during the days of Gemini 11 and Gemini 12, tethers were only several tens of meters long. They grew longer as systems developed, reaching several hundreds of meters in the joint U.S.-Japan Tethered Payload Experiment (TPE) and Cooperative High-Altitude Rocket Gun Experiment (CHARGE) series. Tether deployments reached 20km in the Small Expendable Deployer System (SEDS) and Tethered Satellite System (TSS) series that the U.S. launched in the 1990s. In 2007, Europe's second Young Engineers Satellite (YES2) experiment drastically improved on the deployment record for a thin tether, making the longest artificial structure in space, which measured 32km in length.

The tape tether, which has longer survivability than the thin tether, was adopted by the U.S. Navy for the Advanced Tether Experimental (ATEx) satellite. In that case, the deployment of the tape tether failed to extend the tape tether in the reel type deployment. However, in 2010, an Electrodynamic Tape Tether (R-Tex) successfully deployed a 160 m tape tether using the

Inverse-Origami method in an international project between Japan, Europe, USA, and Australia.

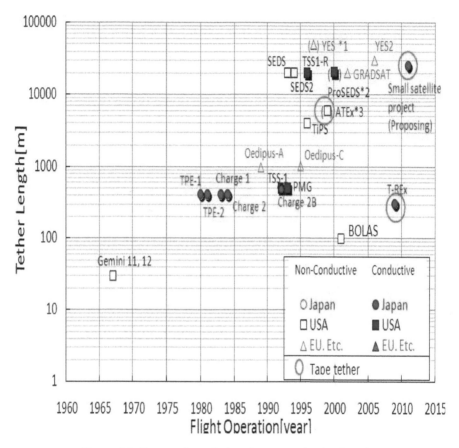

Figure 6-1. Space tether missions by year and tether length

6.2.4 Lessons Learned from Space Tethers for Space Elevator Design

• Lesson Learned (LL) #1: Theory and simulations have developed to effectively parallel actual activities (SEDS, TPE, etc.) for a space elevator based upon space tether simulation tools.

• LL #2: Tape type/multi-fibered tethers provide sufficient life (TiPS, T-Rex, etc) for a space elevator.

• LL #3: Systems analysis of the total system is necessary.

• LL #4: Space environment including zero-g, vacuum, small-g by spin, must be simulated or tested prior to operations.

• LL #5: Control of tether motion with "Braking mechanism", "Tension measurement/control" and "length measurement/ control" systems are important (SEDS, TSS, YES, T-Rex) and are effective for different modes of movement.

- LL #6: The gravity gradient force must exceed uncertain frictions/drag (Gemini, YES2, SEDS) and can be calculated and simulated.
- LL #7: Real-time state observation and state estimation are necessary in combination with a computer simulation (SEDS).
- LL #8: While dynamics can be simulated, the actual dynamics will ensue surprises. Unknown features may possibly exist in dynamics.
- LL #9: Preparation for potential sever will decrease impact of event. Severance speculation, detection through maintenance, and repair are also necessary.
- LL #10: Much better knowledge of orbital debris is required. Complete debris data is the starting point for successfully avoiding severance.
- LL #11: Distributed system with discrete sensors/actuators and full state feedback control is impossible. Active control may be possible.
- LL #12: Integration of total space experience from space tethers to full up space stations will be necessary for the successful design of a space elevator.

6.2.5   Historical Flight Summaries

In the following text, we explain how a few major tether missions worked. The experiences gained in these missions have validated the mission software, paralleled the simulation software results, and reinforced the idea that space tethers work in the space environment and that a space elevator can as well. Much of the data in this section is taken from the Tethers in Space Handbook (Cosmo and Lorenzini, 1977).

TSS

During TSS-1, which was launched July 31, 1992 on STS-46, the Italian satellite was deployed 268 m directly above the Orbiter where it remained for most of the mission. This provided over 20 hours of stable deployment in the near vicinity of the Orbiter - the region of deployed operations that were of greatest concern prior to the mission. The TSS-1 results conclusively show that the basic concept of long gravity-gradient stabilized tethers is sound and settled several short deployment dynamics issues, reduced safety concerns, and clearly demonstrated the feasibility of deploying the satellite to long distances; this allowed the TSS-1R mission to be focused on science objectives. The TSS-1R mission was launched February 22, 1996 on STS-75. During this mission, the satellite was to have been deployed 20.7km above the Space Shuttle on a conducting tether where it was to remain for more than 20 hours of science experiments, followed by a second stop for an additional seven to nine hours of experiments at a deployed distance of 2.5km. In fact, it was deployed to 19+ kms and then failed with a sever of the tether due to manufacturing [or maintenance] flaw in the material.

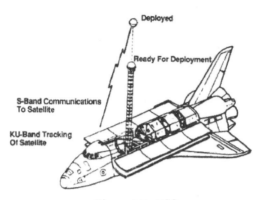

Figure 6-2. TSS

SEDS

The SEDS project started as a Small Business Innovative Research contract awarded to Joe Carroll by NASA MSFC. SEDS hardware proved to be able to successfully deploy a 20km tether in space. After the third stage separation the end-mass was deployed from the second stage. SEDS-1 demonstrated the capability of de-orbiting a 25 kg payload from LEO. SEDS-2, on the other end, demonstrated the use of a closed loop control law to deploy a tethered payload along the local vertical.

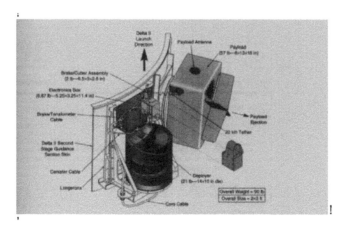

Figure 6-3. SEDS Deployer

TIPS

The Tether Physics and Survivability (TiPS) Experiment was conceived as a quick response, simple experiment to study the long term dynamics and survivability of tethered space systems. The experiment was a free flying satellite consisting of two end bodies connected by a 4km non-conducting tether.

Figure 6-4. TiPS

YES2

The second Young Engineers' Satellite, YES2, was the longest man-made structure launched. It was a piggyback payload on the Foton-M3 microgravity platform with the objective of a controlled deployment of a 32km tether.

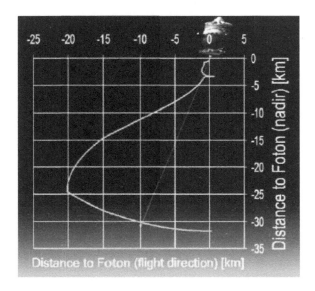

Figure 6-5. YES2

6.3 Dynamics of Space Tethers

The basis for all analyses of space tethers concerns the gravity gradient phenomenon. The dynamics of a space elevator are also governed by the Earth's gravity gradient; it is responsible for the dynamic stability of the system.

If two satellites, linked by tether, form a dumbbell-shaped system, gravity inclination passively stabilizes the position of the system. Here, a dumbbell-shaped tether system on a circular orbit is imagined, as illustrated in Fig. 6-6. In this situation, the forces applied to the upper and lower satellites are centrifugal force and gravity. In this simple analysis, the mass of the tether can be disregarded, and it is assumed that the upper and lower satellites have the same mass. If the orbit radius centered by the system's mass is set at r_0 and the tether is $2L$ long, the orbit radius of the upper satellite is $r_1=r_0+L$, while that of the lower satellite is $r_2=r_0-L$. The whole system is on a circular orbit at a mass-centered orbit velocity, which is as follows:

$$V_0=r_0\omega_0 \tag{6.1}$$

Here, ω_0 is the orbit angular velocity. In this situation, as the following formulas show, centrifugal force exceeds gravity in the upper satellite and gravity exceeds centrifugal force in the lower satellite.

$$m(r_0 + L)\omega_1^2 > \frac{GMm}{(r_0+L)^2} \tag{6.2}$$

$$m(r_0 - L)\omega_1^2 < \frac{GMm}{(r_0-L)^2} \tag{6.3}$$

For this reason, the upper satellite tries to ascend to a higher altitude and the lower satellite tries to descend to a lower altitude. It is the difference of these two forces that causes tension to manifest in the tether. When the position of the system has an angle from the vertical direction to the fringe of the pitch, these forces, which do not pass through the system's center of mass, constitute a torque, which always acts opposite to the angle of deviation from the nominal state. This restoring phenomenon is gravity gradient torque, and the position of a tether system is passively stabilized by it. The tether tension acting on a sub satellite with a mass of m, deployed from a large spacecraft, is

$$T=3Lm\omega_0^2 \tag{6.4}$$

It varies quadratically along the tether, reaching a maximum of $3L(m + \frac{1}{2}m_t)\omega_0^2$ at the spacecraft end, where m_t is the tether mass. The movement around the pitch is librational motion in the orbital plane, and its circular frequency is $\sqrt{3}\omega_0$ [Cosmo 1997]. The out-of-plane roll frequency is $2\omega_0$. These basic results have been validated by multiple space tether flights.

Because a space elevator can be thought of as a very long tether system (with the aforementioned distinctions), its orientation, throughout deployment and operation, will also be stabilized by gravity gradient torque. While the deployment phase will require additional stabilizing efforts by way of active control, the space elevator, once deployed and operational, will be passively stabilized by this effect.

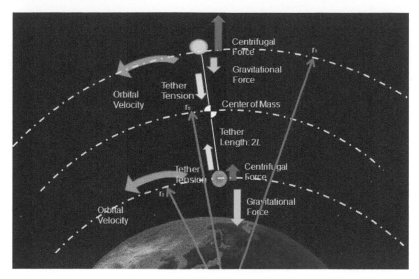

Figure 6-6. Gravity gradient forces

6.4 Description of Nominal Space Elevator Structure

6.4.1 Introduction

Before analyzing the dynamics of a space elevator, its nominal state, free of any excitations, must be described. In particular, the mass distribution of the tether so as to ensure constant stress throughout it and equilibrium of the structure must be derived. The cross-sectional area profile of the tether will be derived. Such a derivation was done by Jerome Pearson (Pearson, 1975), but this area profile did not take the nominal strain of the tether into account. The profile will thus be modified accordingly. With the tether shape established, the mass of both the tether and the apex anchor may be determined as a function of tether length and material parameters. Additional mass components are assessed as well.

Although this section deals only with nominal deformation, a full dynamic model is introduced. This model, shown in Figure 6-7, is referenced throughout much of the remainder of the chapter.

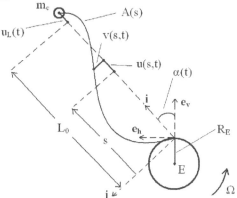

Figure 6-7. A schematic diagram of the space elevator

The space elevator model consists of a tether and apex anchor, and exists within the equatorial plane. The angular velocity of the system Ω is equal to the rotation rate of the Earth. Its period is approximated to be 24 hours (although, strictly speaking, the sidereal period is slightly less than that). The rotating unit vectors e_v and e_h point in the local vertical and horizontal directions, respectively. Unit vector i is along the reference line, which extends from the base to the apex anchor. The unit vectors i and j are obtained by rotating e_v and e_h through an angle α. This rotation of the reference line is defined as the libration angle of the tether. s is the distance of a tether element before deformation from the base of the elevator (the ability for this base to move will only be addressed later). Longitudinal and transverse displacements of a tether element are denoted by u and v, respectively. The tether has nominal (unstressed) length L_0 (this is its length before deployment). The apex anchor mass is denoted by m_c because from the perspective of dynamics, it can be thought of as a counterweight. The tether cross-sectional area profile A varies as a function of s.

The analysis in this section involves a simplified version of Figure 6-7, as the nominally deformed configuration of the space elevator is defined by $\alpha = v(s) = 0$ and $u(s) = u_0(s)$. The analyses and figures for this section have been discussed in great detail by Cohen and Misra (Cohen, 2007).

6.4.2 Cross-sectional Area Profile

Pearson (Pearson, 1975) showed that an ideal tether design would have constant stress across its length, and derived an appropriate area of cross-section tapering function. However, he did not take the longitudinal extension caused by the tension in the static tether into account while deriving this function. A more accurate expression for the cross-sectional area profile is now sought. The tension in the static tether will cause it to extend longitudinally from its unstressed state by $u_0(s)$. The nominal strain in the tether is given by

$$\varepsilon_0 = du_0/ds = \sigma_0/E \qquad (6.5)$$

where σ_0 is the nominal stress in the tether (constant throughout) and E is the modulus of elasticity of the tether material. Using zero deformation at the base as a boundary condition, the deformation of the static tether from its nominal, unstressed state is given by $u_0(s) = \varepsilon_0 s$. Thus, if the nominally stretched tether is to have length L, its original length must be given by $L_0 = L/(1 + \varepsilon_0)$. It is noted that even for a small nominal strain, the difference between the tether length before and after deployment would be thousands of kilometres, since the nominal strain will be of the order of 10^{-2}, and the length of the tether of the order of 10^5km.

Consider an element of tether dm at a distance r from the centre of the Earth. The forces acting on the element are shown in Figure 6-8.

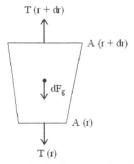

Figure 6-8. Free body diagram of a tether element

T is the tension in the tether and dF_g is the gravitational force acting on the element. From Newton's second law,

$$dma_r = \sum F_r = T(r+dr) - T(r) - dF_g \tag{6.6}$$

Substituting values for tension, gravitational force and acceleration,

$$dm(-\Omega^2 r) = \sigma_0 A(r+dr) - \sigma_0 A(r) - dm(\mu/r^2) \tag{6.7}$$

dm is the product of the bulk density γ and the infinitesimal volume Ads, while μ is the gravitational constant of the Earth. The spatial coordinate r and the tether coordinate s are related by

$$r = R_E + s + u_0(s) = R_E + s(1+\varepsilon_0) \tag{6.8}$$

where R_E is the radius of the Earth. Making the above substitutions and then simplifying, Eq. (7) becomes

$$\gamma A(s)ds\left\{\mu/\left[R_E + s(1+\varepsilon_0)\right]^2 - \Omega^2\left[R_E + s(1+\varepsilon_0)\right]\right\} = \sigma_0 dA \tag{6.9}$$

It is now useful to introduce the characteristic height of the tether, which is defined by $\bar{h} = \sigma_0/\gamma g_0$. Here, g_0 is the surface gravity of the Earth, and is equal to μ/R_E^2. The characteristic height is a measure of the strength to density ratio of the tether material (its 'tenacity'), scaled with respect to the surface gravity of the Earth to have a unit of length.

Substituting $\Omega^2 = \mu/R_G^3$, where R_G is the geosynchronous orbit radius, $\mu = g_0 R_E^2$, and $\sigma_0 = \bar{h}\gamma g_0$ into Eq. (9) and then simplifying and integrating, one arrives at

$$A(s) = c\exp\left(-\frac{R_E^2}{\bar{h}(1+\varepsilon_0)}\left\{\frac{1}{R_E + s(1+\varepsilon_0)} + \frac{\left[R_E + s(1+\varepsilon_0)\right]^2}{2R_G^3}\right\}\right) \tag{6.10}$$

where c is a constant of integration. The boundary condition for the above equation is that the net force acting on its free end must be equal to the tension ($\sigma_0 A(s)|_{s=L_0}$) in it at that point. In order to satisfy this condition, the apex anchor with mass m_c must be attached there. So, while the apex anchor will serve multiple purposes including deployment and some degree of active control, it also allows for equilibrium in the nominal state.

The forces acting on the apex anchor can be made equal to the tension at the tip by forcing

$$m_c\left[\Omega^2\left(R_E+L\right)-\mu/\left(R_E+L\right)^2\right]=\sigma_0\left.A(s)\right|_{s=L_0} \tag{6.11}$$

Through differentiation of Eq. (6.10), it may be shown that the maximum value of area of cross-section occurs at the location $s=\left(R_G-R_E\right)/\left(1+\varepsilon_0\right)$, which corresponds to the radial position, $r=R_G$. The area at this location may be set to the useful design parameter A_m, which is the maximum area of cross-section of the tether, and is a free design parameter – the mass of the tether is proportional to it. Then, after some manipulation, the cross-sectional area profile may be expressed as

$$A(s)=A_m\exp\left[F(s)\right] \tag{6.12}$$

where

$$F(s)=\frac{R_E^2}{\bar{h}R_G\left(1+\varepsilon_0\right)}\left(\frac{3}{2}-\frac{R_G}{R_E+s\left(1+\varepsilon_0\right)}-\frac{\left[R_E+s\left(1+\varepsilon_0\right)\right]^2}{2R_G^2}\right) \tag{6.13}$$

or equivalently,

$$A(r)=A_m\exp\left[\frac{R_E^2}{\bar{h}R_G\left(1+\varepsilon_0\right)}\left(\frac{3}{2}-\frac{R_G}{r}-\frac{r^2}{2R_G^2}\right)\right] \tag{6.14}$$

An almost identical solution as that given in Eq. (14) was obtained by Pearson (Pearson, 1975). The only difference is that the $\left(1+\varepsilon_0\right)$ term did not appear in his solution. This is because the nominal strain was not considered in his taper function derivation. As the nominal strain is not negligible, this modification to the profile of the area of cross-section is essential. Ultimately, this modification accounts for the fact that it is the nominally stretched tether that must be in equilibrium; the manufactured tether will actually be shorter by a factor of $\left(1+\varepsilon_0\right)$.

The resulting taper ratio of the tether, which is defined here as the quotient of A_m and the area of cross-section at the Earth's surface A_0, is given by

$$A_m/A_0=\exp\left[\frac{R_E}{\bar{h}\left(1+\varepsilon_0\right)}\left(1-\frac{R_E}{R_G}\right)^2\left(1+\frac{R_E}{2R_G}\right)\right] \tag{6.15}$$

For a material with $\bar{h}=2{,}762$km and $E=1{,}000$ GPa, the taper ratio is exactly 6. Note that this characteristic height corresponds to a nominal stress of 35.2 GPa and a bulk density of 1,300 kg/m^3. This nominal stress is arrived at by assuming a tether material with a tenacity (allowable ultimate strength in GPa divided by density in g/cc) of 38 MYuri and a nominal margin of safety of 40%. Note that the 38 MYuri value corresponds to the maximum *allowable* stress; this figure will have been arrived at through vigorous testing, and will have been down-graded appropriately.

The taper function of a material having these values is plotted in Figure 6-9. The max area of the manufactured tether is located at a length of $(R_G-R_E)/(1+\varepsilon_0)$ from the Earth side end. Once deployed, this tether element stretches to the geosynchronous altitude, becoming the *only* tether element that is in a natural Earth orbit.

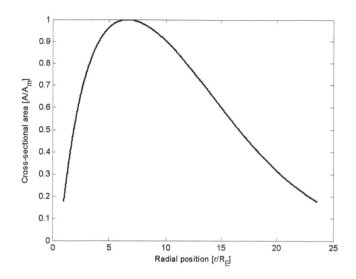

Figure 6-9. Cross-sectional area profile of the tether for $\bar{h} = 2{,}762$km

In reality, the tether will likely be in the area of 100,000km, which is about $15.7R_E$ in length. Thus, the domain of the profile in the above plot beyond 16.7 will not exist; the apex anchor at the tip will replace all of this additional tether material serving to balance the structure. It may be concluded that the minimum cross-sectional area will be situated at the Earth end of the tether.

Finally, the nominal tension in the tether may be expressed as

$$T_0(s) = \sigma_0 A(s) = \sigma_0 A_m \exp\left[F(s)\right] \qquad (6.16)$$

It is clear from this expression that the nominal tension in the tether at all locations is proportional to three tether features: the nominal stress, the maximum cross-sectional area, and the taper function. The tension profile is in fact identical to the area profile. The tension is therefore non-zero everywhere, including both endpoints, and is a minimum at the base. Still, the tension at the Earth connection point is substantial, and the marine node will experience a nominal upwards pull.

6.4.3 Mass of Components

Now that the area profile of the tether has been specified, the mass of the space elevator components may be evaluated. By manipulating Eq. (6.11), the mass of the apex anchor may be expressed as

$$m_c = \gamma A_m \bar{h} \frac{\exp\left[F(s)\big|_{s=L_0}\right]}{(R_E/R_G)^2 \left(\left[R_E + L_0\left(1+\varepsilon_0\right)\right]/R_G - \left\{R_G/\left[R_E + L_0\left(1+\varepsilon_0\right)\right]\right\}^2\right)} \qquad (6.17)$$

Clearly, the required apex anchor is proportional to the maximum area of cross-section of the tether, and is also dependent on other material and design parameters.

The mass of the tether is given by

$$m_t = \gamma A_m \int_0^{L_0} \exp[F(s)]\,ds \qquad (6.18)$$

Using the same material parameters as were previously assumed (E = 1,000 GPa, σ_0 = 35.2 GPa and γ = 1,300 kg/m^3, which results in a taper ratio of 6), the mass of the tether (ribbon), apex anchor (counterweight), and their sum (total), all divided by the max cross-sectional area of the tether, may be plotted as a function of chosen nominal tether length L_0 (Figure 6-).

A tether with L_0 = 100,000km and A_m = 10 mm^2 (say, 1 m width by 10 μm thickness) would have a mass of about 1000 tons. The corresponding apex anchor mass would be about 300 tons. We see that the tether mass behaves quasi-linearly, while the apex anchor mass behaves much like a rational function. A short tether in the range of 50,000km would result in a lighter tether of about 500 tons, but a far heavier apex anchor of 2,000 tons.

This result has a serious design implication: once the length of the tether is chosen, the mass ratio between the tether and apex anchor becomes a fixed value. The tether is expected to be thickened over time. It is essential that when such a procedure is carried out, the mass of the apex anchor be increased by the same proportion. If the necessary tether to apex anchor mass ratio is not maintained, the structure will not maintain nominal equilibrium: it will find a slightly modified equilibrium configuration – one where the stress profile is no longer constant.

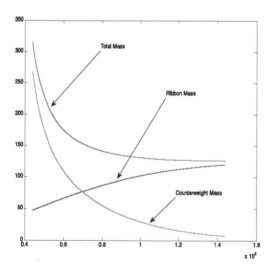

Figure 6-10. Tether, apex anchor and total mass per unit area (A_m) of tether vs. nominal tether length; taper ratio = 6

The other two mass components that must be addressed are those of the marine node and climbers.

The mass of the marine node is difficult to predict, but will surely be at least two orders of magnitude greater than that of the tether. Dynamic simulations have shown that a floating marine node with a mass of this order will behave like a fixed point. As a result, its particular mass is of little consequence to the dynamics provided that it is on the order of tens of thousands of tons or greater.

The masses of climbers are limited by the thickness of the tether, although the reason for this is not trivial. When a climber is loaded onto the tether near the base, the equilibrium of the structure is affected (the only climber position that does not affect equilibrium is that of GEO). The climber's presence creates a discontinuity in the tension profile, resulting in a slight loss of altitude of the apex anchor. The principal effect is that the portion of tether below the climber loses tension. For the stability of the structure, it is essential that tension be maintained at all tether locations. As already noted, the minimum nominal tension manifests at the base end; for a max area of 10 mm^2, nominal stress of 35.2 GPa, and taper ratio of 6, this tension value is about 58.7 kN. If a 6,000 kg climber is mounted near the base of the tether, this tension which existed below it in the nominal state disappears entirely. This is what limits the payload capability of the space elevator.

It should be noted that a climber situated above GEO causes the portion of tether below it to stretch additionally from its nominal state, leading to an increase in tension. However, a minor adjustment of the position of the apex anchor can negate this effect. It is thus the initial loading scenario that represents the mass limiting condition. Once a climber has displaced several thousand kilometres up the tether, its presence reduces the tension below it to a much smaller degree. At this time, a new climber may be mounted onto the tether and begin its ascension. For the purposes of dynamic analyses, it is sufficient to note that the mass of a climber will be about three orders of magnitude less than that of the tether. Given the assumed tether parameters, a 1,000 ton tether will safely support multiple 1 ton climbers, provided that they are sufficiently spaced apart.

From a design point of view, it is desirable to assign preliminary realistic values for the masses of the various components. First, the desired climber throughput is selected – this points to a certain climber mass. Once the mass being lifted is known, the tether can simply be scaled (cross sectional area) to a suitable value. In this study, this area is tuned so as to ensure that the tension below the lowest climber is always at least 30% of its nominal amount. The space elevator parameters are then given as follows, when prescribing a nominal tether stress of 35.2 GPa, tether bulk density of 1,300 kg/m^3 and modulus of elasticity of 1,000 GPa (taper ratio of six):

Design Climber Mass (including payload):	20,000 kg
Equivalent Climber Mass at base of 7 spaced climbers:	29,000 kg
Corresponding Max Area of Tether:	62.8mm^2
Corresponding Tether Mass:	6,300,000 kg
Corresponding Apex Anchor Mass:	1,900,000 kg

Finally, it is worth noting that these design parameters are not affected if a GEO station of *any* mass is added to the space elevator. For this reason, it appears natural that ascending climbers be "discarded" at the GEO altitude. A large mass at GEO *will* however affect the dynamics of the structure as it causes an increase in rotational inertia about the marine node.

6.5 Basic Dynamics of Operational Tether
6.5.1 Introduction
This section investigates the basic dynamics of the space elevator, including modal analyses, numerical results for non-zero initial conditions, and comments on stability and damping.

Before any elastic modes are discussed, a rigid tether model is presented and analyzed. The primary tether response to excitation is an inverted pendulum vibration. For this reason, the rigid body mode must be very well understood. The natural frequency of this mode will be fully analyzed.

Then, a more complete dynamic model, which includes tether elasticity, will be described and analyzed. This will be presented in two ways. First, ordinary differential equations will be obtained using the assumed modes method. These equations may be simplified, and a modal analysis including mode shapes and frequencies will be presented. Second, the elastic tether model will be evaluated using partial differential equations. Numerical simulation results will be shown for various initial conditions.

Finally, an overall dynamical view will be summarized, featuring comments on stability and damping.

6.5.2   Rigid Body Mode
A simplified dynamic model is presented in Figure 6-11. Further details about this model have been described by Cohen and Misra (Cohen, 2009).

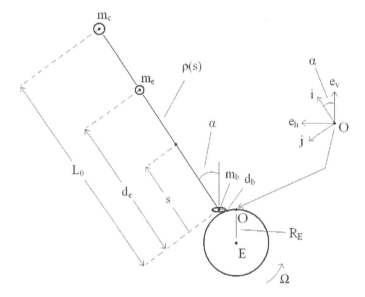

Figure 6-11. Non-elastic tether dynamics model of the space elevator

Unlike the model presented in Figure 6-7, this one uses a rigid tether. By neglecting the infinite degrees of freedom inherent to an elastic body, the dynamic system reduces to a three-degree-of-freedom system, including the libration angle α, the climber position d_e, and the marine node displacement d_b. The masses of the marine node (base) and the climber (elevator) are denoted m_b and m_e, respectively.

The three equations governing the motion of the three d.o.f. system are derived using the Lagrange approach. In order to use this approach, position and velocity vectors are determined, energy expressions are derived, and Lagrange's equations are constructed. The three ordinary differential equations that result are presented below:

$$D_e'' + h_L D_b'' \sin\alpha - (1+\alpha')^2 D_e - h_L D_b \sin\alpha - (2h_L D_b' + R_L)\cos\alpha$$

$$+\lambda \frac{(D_e + R_L \cos\alpha + h_L D_b \sin\alpha)}{\left\{ \left[(h_L/R_L)D_b \sin\alpha + \cos\alpha + (1/R_L)D_e\right]^2 + \left[(h_L/R_L)D_b \cos\alpha - \sin\alpha\right]^2 \right\}^{\frac{3}{2}}}$$

$$= Q_{de}/m_e L_0 \Omega^2 \quad (6.19)$$

$$D_b'' + \frac{M_e}{h_L} D_e'' \sin\alpha + \frac{1}{h_L}\left(M_p \hat{I}_2 + M_e D_e + M_c\right)\alpha'' \cos\alpha + \frac{2(1+\alpha')}{h_L} M_e D_e' \cos\alpha$$

$$-\frac{(1+\alpha')^2}{h_L}\left(M_p \hat{I}_2 + M_e D_e + M_c\right)\sin\alpha - D_b + \lambda M_b \frac{D_b}{\left[(h_L/R_L)^2 D_b^2 + 1\right]^{\frac{3}{2}}}$$

$$+\lambda M_e \frac{\left(D_b + (1/h_L)D_e \sin\alpha\right)}{\left\{ \left[(h_L/R_L)D_b \sin\alpha + \cos\alpha + (1/R_L)D_e\right]^2 + \left[(h_L/R_L)D_b \cos\alpha - \sin\alpha\right]^2 \right\}^{\frac{3}{2}}}$$

$$+\lambda M_p \int_0^1 \frac{\exp[F(\xi)]\left(D_b + (1/h_L)\xi \sin\alpha\right)}{\left\{ \left[(h_L/R_L)D_b \sin\alpha + \cos\alpha + (1/R_L)\xi\right]^2 + \left[(h_L/R_L)D_b \cos\alpha - \sin\alpha\right]^2 \right\}^{\frac{3}{2}}} d\xi$$

$$+\lambda M_c \frac{\left(D_b + (1/h_L)\sin\alpha\right)}{\left\{ \left[(h_L/R_L)D_b \sin\alpha + \cos\alpha + (1/R_L)\right]^2 + \left[(h_L/R_L)D_b \cos\alpha - \sin\alpha\right]^2 \right\}^{\frac{3}{2}}}$$

$$+K_b D_b + C_b D_b' = Q_{db}/m_{tot} \Omega^2 h \quad (6.20)$$

and

$$\left(M_e D_e^2 + M_c + M_p \hat{I}_3\right)\alpha'' + h_L\left(M_p \hat{I}_2 + M_e D_e + M_c\right)D_b'' \cos\alpha + 2M_e(1+\alpha')D_e D_e'$$

$$+\left(M_p \hat{I}_2 + M_e D_e + M_c\right)\left(-h_L D_b \cos\alpha + 2h_L D_b' \sin\alpha + R_L \sin\alpha\right)$$

$$+\lambda M_e \frac{D_e\left(h_L D_b \cos\alpha - R_L \sin\alpha\right)}{\left\{ \left[(h_L/R_L)D_b \sin\alpha + \cos\alpha + (1/R_L)D_e\right]^2 + \left[(h_L/R_L)D_b \cos\alpha - \sin\alpha\right]^2 \right\}^{\frac{3}{2}}}$$

$$+\lambda M_p \int_0^1 \frac{\exp[F(\xi)]\xi\left(h_L D_b \cos\alpha - R_L \sin\alpha\right)}{\left\{ \left[(h_L/R_L)D_b \sin\alpha + \cos\alpha + (1/R_L)\xi\right]^2 + \left[(h_L/R_L)D_b \cos\alpha - \sin\alpha\right]^2 \right\}^{\frac{3}{2}}} d\xi$$

$$+\lambda M_c \frac{\left(h_L D_b \cos\alpha - R_L \sin\alpha\right)}{\left\{ \left[(h_L/R_L)D_b \sin\alpha + \cos\alpha + (1/R_L)\right]^2 + \left[(h_L/R_L)D_b \cos\alpha - \sin\alpha\right]^2 \right\}^{\frac{3}{2}}}$$

$$= Q_\alpha/m_{tot} \Omega^2 L_0^2 \quad (6.21)$$

141

The three above equations, which govern the three d.o.f. system, contain some new parameters – K_b and C_b are non-dimensional spring and damper constants associated with the floating platform (the marine node). The Q terms denote the generalized forces that are associated with the generalized coordinates (d.o.f.). Also, for convenience of analysis, these equations have been non-dimensionalized. Non-dimensional masses are defined (by division with the total mass of the system) as

$$M_e = m_e / m_{tot}, \quad M_b = m_b / m_{tot}, \quad M_c = m_c / m_{tot} \quad \text{and} \quad M_p = \gamma A_m L_0 / m_{tot}$$

(6.22)

The distances are also non-dimensionalized, and are defined by

$$D_e = d_e / L_0, \quad D_b = d_b / h \quad \text{and} \quad \xi = s / L_0 \tag{6.23}$$

Here, h is an appropriate scaling factor for the small displacements of the base, to be chosen when doing numerical computations. Other useful distance ratios are given by

$$R_L = R_E / L_0 \quad \text{and} \quad h_L = h / L_0 \tag{6.24}$$

Non-dimensional time τ is defined by

$$\tau = \Omega t \tag{6.25}$$

The prime symbols in the equations of motion denotes differentiation with respect to τ. The constant λ appearing in the equations of motion scales the Earth's gravitational constant as follows:

$$\lambda = \mu / \left(\Omega^2 R_E^3 \right) \equiv \left(R_G / R_E \right)^3 \tag{6.26}$$

Finally, non-dimensional integrals appearing in the equations of motion are

$$\hat{I}_i = \int_0^1 \exp \left[F(\xi) \right] \xi^{i-1} d\xi, \, i = 1, 2, 3 \tag{6.27}$$

where

$$F(\xi) = \frac{R_E^2}{h R_G} \left[\frac{3}{2} - \frac{R_G}{(\xi L_0 + R_E)} - \frac{(\xi L_0 + R_E)^2}{2 R_G^2} \right] \tag{6.28}$$

The equations of motion contain mainly inertial (including Coriolis and centrifugal components) and gravitational terms.

While Eqs. 6.19 and 6.20 will be referred to later in the chapter, only Eq. 6.21 is relevant to the goal of analyzing the rigid body mode of the space elevator. This equation may be simplified greatly in a number of ways. First, it is assumed that no climber is present, and that the marine node does not move. Then, as the libration angle will be less than a few degrees, even in a worst case excitation scenario, the equation can be linearized by letting $\cos \alpha = 1$ and $\sin \alpha = \alpha$. In this case, the equation reduces to that of a simple pendulum:

$$\alpha'' + \omega^2 \alpha = 0 \tag{6.29}$$

where ω is a constant (non-dimensional natural frequency of oscillation) and is given by

$$\omega^2 = \frac{R_L \left(M_p \hat{I}_2 + M_c \right) - \lambda R_L^4 \left\{ M_p \int_0^1 \frac{\exp \left[F(\xi) \right] \xi}{(\xi + R_L)^3} d\xi + \frac{M_c}{(1 + R_L)^3} \right\}}{M_c + M_p \hat{I}_3} \tag{6.30}$$

In the simplest terms, when tether elasticity is neglected, the space elevator's dynamic behaviour is just like that of a regular pendulum, which experiences simple harmonic motion in response to any deflection from equilibrium. The difference between the two is that the pivot point of the space elevator is located at the bottom rather than the top. It is clear then that the equilibrium configuration defined by a vertical tether is a stable one. It is important to note, however, that any oscillations about this position would be largely undamped.

The non-dimensional natural frequency of oscillation, ω, depends mainly upon the length of the tether and its taper ratio. Without question, the period of oscillation of this pendulum mode will be on the order of days (the long period may be attributed to the tremendous amount of inertia of the structure).

In Figure 6-12, the non-dimensional natural frequency for a tether measuring 100,000km is plotted for a wide range of taper ratios (the nominal margin of safety and design stress are kept constant). It may be noted that the frequency reduces with an increase in taper ratio. The non-dimensional period of libration is given by $2\pi/\omega$. Since ω is non-dimensionalized with respect to the spin rate of the Earth, the dimensional period of oscillation of α in days is given by $1/\omega$. For anticipated numerical values of the space elevator ($L_0 \approx 100,000$km and $3 < A_m/A_0 < 10$), this period will be about five days. Note that a longer tether corresponds to a longer period for the pendulum mode.

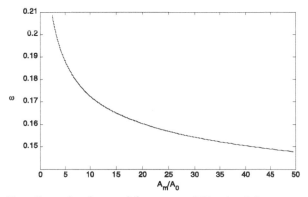

Figure 6-12. Non-dimensional natural frequency of libration (ω) vs. taper ratio; $L_0 = 100,000$km

6.5.3 Transverse and Longitudinal Modal Analysis via Assumed Modes Method
A modal analysis of the elastic tether model will now be carried out so that the frequencies and shapes of the elastic modes may be found. Thus, this section refers again to Figure 6-7. Additional details on what follows have been documented by Cohen and Misra (2007).

Both longitudinal and transverse displacements of the tether, u and v, are expanded in series form as products of a set of generalized coordinates and spatial basis functions (assumed modes method). The longitudinal extension is expressed as

$$u(s,t) = \varepsilon_0 s + \sum_{i=1}^{N} a_i(t)\psi_i(s)$$

(6.31)

N generalized coordinates, $a_i(t)$, and appropriate admissible basis functions, $\psi_i(s)$, are used to describe the extension of the tether from its nominal amount $u_0(s) = \varepsilon_0 s$. The transverse displacement is represented as

$$v(s,t) = \sum_{i=1}^{M} b_i(t)\phi_i(s) \tag{6.32}$$

M generalized coordinates, $b_i(t)$, are used to describe this displacement. Again, $\phi_i(s)$ are admissible basis functions. The libration angle α, which defines the pendulum mode, is not included in the transverse displacement function, $v(s,t)$, because it is non-elastic. However, it is critical that α be accounted for in the modal analysis: it is considered to be the zeroth mode of transverse oscillation.

Generalized coordinates α, a_i, $i = 1, 2,...N$ and b_i, $i = 1, 2,...M$, fully define this $N+M+1$ degree-of-freedom system. As was done in section 6.5.2, the ordinary differential equations governing the elastic tether dynamic model may be obtained using a Lagrangian approach. These lengthy equations will not be included in this text. Instead, the simplified equations, which result from decoupling longitudinal and transverse terms, are now given. Note that the displacements of the tether will be very small compared to the length of the tether, and as such, decoupling the longitudinal and transverse displacements has a negligible effect on the modal analysis.

If the terms associated with the gravitational force are expanded binomially and third and higher order terms are ignored, the equations describing the **longitudinal** extension of the tether may be expressed as

$$\mathbf{M}^A \mathbf{A}'' + \mathbf{K}^A \mathbf{A} = 0 \tag{6.33}$$

where the elements of matrices $\mathbf{M}^A$ and $\mathbf{K}^A$ are given by

$$M_{ik}^A = M_p \int_0^1 \exp[F(\xi)]\psi_i\psi_k d\xi + M_c\psi_{i1}\psi_{k1} \tag{6.34}$$

and

$$K_{ik}^A = \Omega^2 \int_0^1 \exp[F(\xi)]\left(\frac{d\psi_i}{d\xi}\right)\left(\frac{d\psi_k}{d\xi}\right)d\xi - M_p\int_0^1 \exp[F(\xi)]\psi_i\psi_k d\xi - M_c\psi_{i1}\psi_{k1}$$
$$-2\left(\frac{\beta}{\Lambda}\right)^3\left\{M_p\int_0^1 \frac{\exp[F(\xi)]\psi_i\psi_k}{\left[(1/\Lambda)+\xi(1+\varepsilon_0)\right]^3}d\xi + M_c\frac{\psi_{i1}\psi_{k1}}{\left[(1/\Lambda)+1+\varepsilon_0\right]^3}\right\} \tag{6.35}$$

where both indexes i and k vary from 1 to N. The equations describing the **transverse** displacement of the tether may be expressed as

$$\mathbf{M}^B \mathbf{B}'' + \mathbf{K}^B \mathbf{B} = 0 \tag{6.36}$$

where

$$\mathbf{B} = \left[\alpha, B_1, B_2, ... B_k\right]^T \tag{6.37}$$

and the elements of matrices $\mathbf{M}^B$ and $\mathbf{K}^B$ are given by

$$M_{11}^B = (1+\varepsilon_0)^2\left(M_p\int_0^1 \exp[F(\xi)]\xi^2 d\xi + M_c\right) \tag{6.38}$$

$$K_{11}^B = (1+\varepsilon_0)\left[\frac{1}{\Lambda}\left\{M_p\int_0^1 \exp\left[F(\xi)\right]\xi d\xi + M_c\right\}\right.$$

$$\left.-\frac{\beta^3}{\Lambda^4}\left\{M_p\int_0^1 \frac{\exp\left[F(\xi)\right]\xi}{\left[(1/\Lambda)+\xi(1+\varepsilon_0)\right]^3}d\xi + M_c\frac{1}{\left[(1/\Lambda)+1+\varepsilon_0\right]^3}\right\}\right] \tag{6.39}$$

$$M_{i1}^B = M_{1k}^B = M_p(1+\varepsilon_0)\int_0^1 \exp\left[F(\xi)\right]\xi\phi_i d\xi \tag{6.40}$$

$$K_{i1}^B = K_{1k}^B = M_p\left\{\frac{1}{\Lambda}\int_0^1 \exp\left[F(\xi)\right]\phi_i d\xi - \frac{\beta^3}{\Lambda^4}\int_0^1 \frac{\exp\left[F(\xi)\right]\phi_i}{\left[(1/\Lambda)+\xi(1+\varepsilon_0)\right]^3}d\xi\right\} \tag{6.41}$$

$$M_{ik}^B = M_p\int_0^1 \exp\left[F(\xi)\right]\phi_i\phi_k d\xi \tag{6.42}$$

and

$$K_{ik}^B = \pi^2\left(\varepsilon_0 - \varepsilon_0^2\right)ik\overline{\Omega}^2\int_0^1 \exp\left[F(\xi)\right]\frac{d\phi_i}{d\xi}\frac{d\phi_k}{d\xi}d\xi$$

$$+M_p\left\{\left(\frac{\beta}{\Lambda}\right)^3\int_0^1 \frac{\exp\left[F(\xi)\right]\phi_i\phi_k}{\left[(1/\Lambda)+\xi(1+\varepsilon_0)\right]^3}d\xi - \int_0^1 \exp\left[F(\xi)\right]\phi_i\phi_k d\xi\right\} \tag{6.43}$$

where indeces i and k vary from 2 to $M+1$. For convenience, the displacements in the equations above have been non-dimensionalized, and are defined by

$$U = u/L_0 = \varepsilon_0\xi + \sum_{i=1}^N A_i(\tau)\psi_i(\xi) \tag{6.44}$$

and

$$V = v/L_0 = \sum_{i=1}^M B_i(\tau)\phi_i(\xi) \tag{6.45}$$

where

$$A_i = a_i/L_0, \quad B_i = b_i/L_0 \text{ and } \xi = s/L_0 \tag{6.46}$$

Two useful non-dimensional parameters used above are defined as

$$\Lambda = L_0/R_E \text{ and } \beta = R_G/R_E \tag{6.47}$$

The characteristic frequency ratio relating the axial frequencies to the Earth's spin rate is defined by

$$\overline{\Omega} = \sqrt{EA_m/(m_{tot}L_0)}/\Omega \tag{6.48}$$

Also,

$$U_1 = U\big|_{\xi=1} \text{ and } \psi_{k1} = \psi_k\big|_{\xi=1} \tag{6.49}$$

Finally, here, $F(\xi)$ is adjusted from that presented in Eq. 6. to account for the nominal strain in the tether:

$$F(\xi) = \frac{R_E^2}{\bar{h}R_G\left(1+\varepsilon_0\right)}\left\{\frac{3}{2} - \frac{R_G}{\left[R_E+\xi\left(1+\varepsilon_0\right)L_0\right]} - \frac{\left[R_E+\xi\left(1+\varepsilon_0\right)L_0\right]^2}{2R_G^2}\right\} \qquad (6.50)$$

The basis functions for each the longitudinal and transverse elastic displacements may now be prescribed, and the corresponding mode shapes and frequencies will be solved for.

The **longitudinal** basis functions shall be given by

$$\psi_i(\xi) = \sin\left[\left(i-1/2\right)\pi\xi\right] \qquad (6.51)$$

Clearly, the above sinusoidal basis functions satisfy the boundary condition at the base, while also allowing the counterweight to move. The generalized eigenvalue problem defined by Eq. (6.) may now be solved using Matlab (the numerical values assumed thus far are assumed again, such as a 100,000km long tether and a taper ratio of 6).

The first 20 non-dimensional natural frequencies are given in Table 6-I. The frequencies are again non-dimensionalized with respect to the spin rate of the Earth, Ω. So, the first longitudinal frequency of 4.39 corresponds to a period of about 5.5 hours (24/4.39). A quasi-linear increase in frequency is observed throughout all of the examined modes.

Rather than presenting the twenty corresponding eigenvectors, the modal matrix obtained from a five-mode modal analysis is presented in Table 6-II. Since the diagonal terms are by far the largest, it may be concluded that the sinusoidal basis functions given by $\sin\left[\left(i-1/2\right)\pi\xi\right]$ correspond reasonably well to the actual mode shapes of the longitudinal motion. It is useful to note that the modal frequencies and mode shapes of the longitudinal motion are independent of the particular value of A_m.

Mode #	Freq.	Mode #	Freq.	Mode #	Freq.	Mode #	Freq.	Mode #	Freq.
1	4.39	5	47.82	9	96.50	13	145.27	17	194.30
2	12.48	6	59.94	10	108.62	14	157.37	18	206.43
3	23.75	7	72.14	11	120.87	15	169.72	19	219.19
4	35.69	8	84.27	12	132.98	16	181.83	20	231.55

Table 6-I. Non-dimensional frequencies ($N = 20$) of longitudinal modes

0.998	0.332	-0.326	0.209	-0.143
0.017	0.930	0.372	-0.232	0.168
0.062	-0.090	0.850	0.322	-0.180
0.008	0.128	-0.108	0.886	0.264
0.020	-0.014	0.144	-0.120	0.922

Table 6-II: Modal matrix of longitudinal modes for $N = 5$

The transverse basis functions are chosen as $\phi_i(\xi) = \sin(i\pi\xi)$, which vanish at the two ends of the tether. Again, the generalized eigenvalue problem defined by Eq. (6.) are solved using Matlab. Table 6-III contains the non-dimensional natural frequencies for the first 20 modes of the transverse displacement of the tether. The first frequency (zeroth mode) is that of the libration. It has a value of 0.16. This corresponds to a period of about six days. While this is somewhat higher than the period obtained in the rigid body analysis, it should be noted that the tether here is actually longer: in the rigid body analysis, the 100,000km tether did not stretch, whereas in this elastic analysis, the actual deployed tether stretches from 100,000km (manufactured length) to about 103,500km. The first elastic mode of transverse vibration has a period of about ten hours. As did the longitudinal modes, the frequencies of the transverse modes (with the exception of the rigid body mode) increase in a quasi-linear fashion.

The modal matrix for the $M = 4$ case (four elastic modes, one rigid body mode) is presented in Table 6-IV. The diagonal terms of the modal matrix consisting of normalized eigenvectors are again the largest. This means that the pendulum mode and sinusoidal basis functions given by $\sin(i\pi\xi)$ are, approximately, the actual mode shapes for the transverse motion of the tether. It is apparent from the modal matrix that the pendulum mode has some influence over the elastic transverse modes, but the reverse may not be said (the first column of the matrix is nearly 1,0,0,0,0).

Mode #	Freq.	Mode #	Freq.	Mode #	Freq.	Mode #	Freq.	Mode #	Freq.
0	0.16	4	8.92	8	17.74	12	26.57	16	35.41
1	2.37	5	11.13	9	19.95	13	28.78	17	37.62
2	4.53	6	13.33	10	22.15	14	30.99	18	39.84
3	6.72	7	15.53	11	24.36	15	33.19	19	42.05

Table 6-III: Non-dimensional frequencies ($M = 19$) of transverse modes

1.000	-0.490	0.327	-0.234	0.179
0.019	0.872	-0.287	0.214	-0.115
0.009	-0.001	0.900	-0.138	0.139
0.005	0.013	-0.015	0.938	-0.085
0.004	0.007	0.023	-0.021	0.963

Table 6-IV: Modal matrix of transverse modes for $M = 4$

The longitudinal to transverse frequency ratio of the first elastic mode is about 2. This ratio increases for all subsequent modes. As was the case for the longitudinal motion, the modal frequencies and mode shapes of the transverse motion are independent of A_m.

6.5.4 Elastic Tether Assessment via Partial Differential Equations and ANC Method

In this section, the tether dynamics are assessed first by using partial differential equations (for further details, refer to Ohkawa et al. (2010) as well as "Dynamic behavior of space elevator system with flexible tether", to appear in Acta Astronautica), and later using the absolute nodal coordinate formulation [ANC] method.

The dynamics model used first is the same as that shown in Figure 6-7, with two notable exceptions: longitudinal deflection is omitted initially, and transverse deflections are denoted as $y(x,t)$, with x corresponding to longitudinal position, as is conventionally done for string problems.

Assuming that lateral deflection of the flexible tether is sufficiently small so that $\partial y/\partial x$ and $s \approx x$, the linearized equation of motion for the tether system can be obtained as follows:

$$T\frac{\partial^2 y}{\partial x^2} + \frac{\partial T}{\partial x}\frac{\partial y}{\partial x} + \rho A\left(\Omega^2 - \frac{\mu_E}{x^3}\right)y + \frac{F_{ey}}{\ell} = \rho A\frac{\partial^2 y}{\partial t^2} \qquad (6.52)$$

Here, T refers to tension, ρA refers to the mass of a unit tether element and F_{ey} is the external force along the y-axis that is caused by climber motion

One end of the flexible tether is fixed to the surface of the Earth while the other end with the apex anchor is free. The following conditions express the boundary conditions of the tether, at the root and free end, respectively:

$$y(x = 0) = \text{constant} \qquad (6.53)$$

$$\partial^2 y / \partial x^2 (x = x_t) = \text{(the bending moment at the free end)} = 0 \qquad (6.54)$$

The partial differential equations of motion of the tether are transformed into a difference equation in order to analyze numerically. An implicit method, the Crank-Nicolson scheme, is employed in the present numerical simulation. Numerical simulations using tether lengths varying from 40,000 to 140,000km in steps of 10,000km with an apex anchor and a tether length of 144,630km with no apex anchor were run. Disturbances such as climber motion, solar pressure, and the J2 term [Earth's gravitational variability] were not accounted for this analysis. The only disturbances were non-zero initial conditions.

Figures 6-13 to 6-16 show simulation results for a short (40,000km) tether and a long (144,630km) tether as examples of the numerical simulation results. Figures 6-13 and 6-14 show the dynamic behavior of the shorter (40,000km) tether when the initial condition was applied. The first mode of the flexible tether is observed under this condition (see Figure 6-13). Figure 6-14 shows the time variation of the displacement of the free end of the tether. The time period, which is 47.7 h, agrees with the analytical solution for a string when some assumptions are made. Higher vibration modes are not excited due to the apex anchor. Figures 6-5 and 6-16 show the dynamic behavior of the longer (144,630km) tether. Here, the period of oscillation is about 8 days. These results reaffirm the notion that a longer tether corresponds to a longer period of oscillation of the rigid body mode. The absence of an apex anchor causes some higher modes of transverse oscillation to be excited.

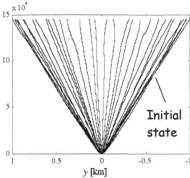

Figure 6-13. Dynamic behavior of flexible tether with apex anchor

!

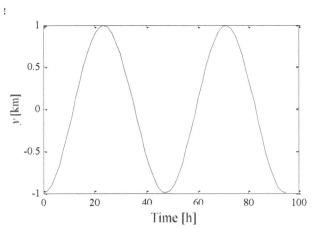

Figure 6-14. Time response of flexible tether with apex anchor at free end.

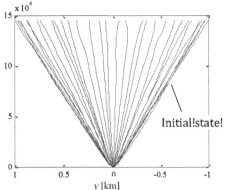

Figure 6-15. Dynamic behavior of very long tether with no apex anchor.

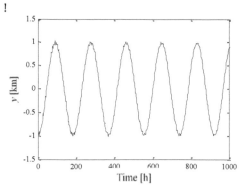

Figure 6-16. Time response of free end of very long tether with no apex anchor at free end.

It is also of interest to study the higher order modal motion of the space elevator. Figures 6-17 and 6-18 show the dynamic behavior of the flexible tether with the apex anchor (short tether) and without the apex anchor, respectively. The initial shape of the tether is a half sinusoidal wave. It is seen that the second mode of the tether is excited when the initial condition is applied when an apex anchor is in place. It is also observed that the displacement of the free end of the tether is larger than that when no apex anchor is in place.

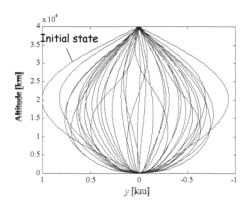

Figure 6-17. Dynamic behavior of flexible tether with apex anchor
(initial shape is a half sinusoidal wave).

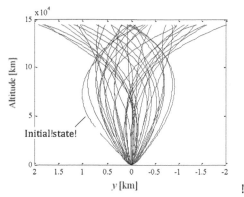

Figure 6-18. Dynamic behavior of flexible tether with no apex anchor (initial shape is sinusoidal wave).

Now, the absolute nodal coordinate formulation (ANC) method is applied to the space elevator system to consider the transverse *and* longitudinal deformation of the tether. The dynamic formulation has been discussed in detail by Uchiyama *et al.* (2013). The method is a finite element non-incremental formulation introduced to study flexible multi-body applications. This section provides the dynamic equations of a finite element in matrix form. Figure 6-19 shows the parameter definition on tether element. The global position vector $\mathbf{r}$ at arbitrary point on the tether shown in Figure 6-19 is defined as

$$\mathbf{r} = \mathbf{Se} \qquad (6.55)$$

where $\mathbf{S}$ denotes the global shape function that has a complete set of rigid-body modes, and e is the vector of tether element nodal coordinates.

$$\mathbf{e} = \begin{bmatrix} e_1 & e_2 & e_3 & e_4 & e_5 & e_6 & e_7 & e_8 \end{bmatrix} \qquad (6.5)$$

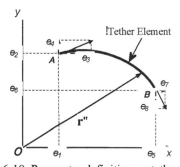

Figure 6-19. Parameter definition on tether element

The global displacement e_1 and e_2 are components of the vector at point A. Components of the vector at point B are expressed by e_1 and e_2. The vector of the global slope of the element nodes is split into two components along nodal coordinates as shown in Figure 6-19. It is assumed in that a cubic polynomial describes un-deformed and deformed components of the displacements.

The kinetic energy of the element is

$$T = \frac{1}{2}\int_V \rho\, \dot{x}^T \dot{x}\, dV = \frac{1}{2}\dot{e}^T M_a \dot{e} \tag{6.57}$$

where M_a is mass matrix defined by the following equation:

$$M_a = \frac{1}{2}\int_V \rho\, S^T S\, dV \tag{6.58}$$

Here, S is a global shape function expressed with the Bernoulli-Euler assumption.

Assuming isotropic materials, the strain energy due to the longitudinal deformation can be expressed as

$$U_l = \frac{1}{2}\int_0^l EA\varepsilon_l^2\, dx \tag{6.59}$$

where E is young's modulus and A is cross section of a tether. It is supposed that the deformation of a tether element is sufficiently small and the length of the element is linear distance between A and B as shown in Figure 6-.

The vector of the generalized elastic force due to longitudinal deformation of the tether element can be defined as

$$Q_l = K_l e \tag{6.60}$$

where K_l is the stiffness matrix.

The apex anchor is connected to the tether by a pin joint. The vector of nodal coordinates in terms of the apex anchor is defined as

$$e_c = \begin{bmatrix} e_{c1} & e_{c2} & e_{c3} & e_{c4} & x_c & y_c & \theta_c \end{bmatrix}^T \tag{6.61}$$

where e_{c1} to e_{c4} denote the nodal coordinates at the node between the long tether and the apex anchor that is treated as a rigid body. The parameters x_c and y_c represent the position for the center of mass of the apex anchor and the angle of the apex anchor is expressed by θ_c. The motion of the apex anchor is then taken into account in formulating the dynamics of the space elevator

The dynamic behavior of space elevator system that consists of a long tether and an apex anchor is investigated numerically. The case of a 40,000km tether is simulated. The apex anchor with mass $1.2\,10^6$ kg is assumed to be rigid. The only external force considered is that of gravitation. Figure 6-20 shows the results of a numerical simulation where the initial condition is a 1km transverse displacement of the apex anchor. The red line in Figure 6-20(a) denotes the initial state of tether, which has zero initial velocity. The first mode of the system is observed under this condition, and its time period is again about 47 hours. The transverse oscillation is hardly damped in this case. Figure 6-20(b) shows the time response of longitudinal deflection of the tether. It clearly shows that the higher mode due to longitudinal vibration of the tether comes to converge. Also, the order of magnitude of the initial induced longitudinal vibration is small (about 6 meters). The oscillation in this figure is gradually attenuated coupled motion between the flexible tether and the apex anchor.

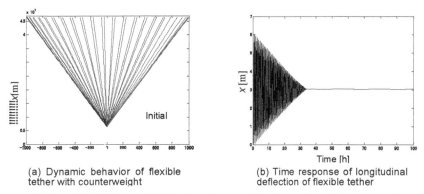

(a) Dynamic behavior of flexible tether with counterweight

(b) Time response of longitudinal deflection of flexible tether

Figure 6-20. Dynamic behavior of space elevator system with apex anchor

6.5.5 Comments on Stability and Damping

As this section has shown, the nominal space elevator system consisting of a deployed tether and apex anchor is a stable one for linearized stationally vibrational modes. If the tether is disturbed from equilibrium in any way, it responds by tending back to its equilibrium state. The primary mode (that of pendulum oscillation) is stable for the same underlying reason that a typical space tether system is stable: gravity gradient torque. Furthermore, the elastic behavior of the tether is stable as well for obvious reasons.

While the dynamics of the tether are of a stable nature, the various modes are somewhat coupled. As a general rule, certain modes of oscillation can excite others. The presence of an apex anchor causes higher modes to be excited by lower ones, and minimizes the extent to which higher mode oscillations excite the pendulum mode.

Perhaps the most important realization concerning dynamic behavior is that all modes of oscillation are visco-elastic with the exception of the pendulum mode. This means that the eventual state of any complex dynamical state of the system is undamped steady state pendulum vibration. Elastic modes will dampen, while the fundamental mode will not.

It is well known that the lateral librational motion of space tethers is coupled with the longitudinal motion of a mass on the tether in non-linear resonance. The extraordinarily huge space elevator system contains a large number of flexible modes. It is therefore noted that further study with regard to unsteady vibrational modes and nonlinear motion is necessary. Control will then be sometimes necessary for safe operation of the space tether system.

6.6 Induced Dynamics

6.6.1 Introduction

This section examines some of the many environmental factors that will impose loads on the nominal space elevator system, causing it to deflect from its nominal configuration. The nature and magnitude of such induced dynamics are examined for many causes of excitation. Of particular interest are the effects that climber transit has on the space elevator system. Such an excitation may not seem external, but climbers are not part of the nominal system and do indeed affect its dynamics significantly. First, an analytical solution is found for constant rate climber ascent and descent when the tether's elasticity is neglected. Then, numerical simulations that include tether elasticity are presented. Based on these results, climber transit guidelines are proposed: the aim here is to minimize the effect that climber transit has on the structure.

Other excitations that are part of the space elevator system include forced motion at each of the ends: the marine node and the apex anchor. These may actually be thought of as means of control rather than excitations. They are discussed, but not in great detail. Then, three excitations that are actually external to the space elevator system are considered: aerodynamic effects, lunar gravitational effects, and solar gravitational effects. Finally, the extent to which a moving tether affects the orbit of a launched satellite is discussed.

6.6.2 Climber Transit with Rigid Tether Model

This section will make reference to the rigid tether model (Figure 6-11) and governing equations for it (Eq. (6.) – (6.21)) that were presented in section 6.5.2. An analytical expression for $\alpha(\tau)$ may be found for a climber transit with constant speed.

If a climber goes from non-dimensional location D_i to D_f on the tether with constant non-dimensional velocity V_c, its position, velocity and acceleration are given by

$$D_e = V_c \tau + D_i$$

$$D'_e = V_c$$

and

$$D''_e = 0 \tag{6.62}$$

In reality, the climber will experience some form of ramp up and down in velocity. However, if the climber is to move a long distance, this ramp up and down time will be short in comparison to the cruising time. Thus, to simplify the analysis, climber acceleration and deceleration are approximated as being instantaneous. For a climber with uniform motion, Eq. (6.21) has a closed form solution. Ignoring higher order terms, the variation in libration angle in response to a constant rate climber transit is given by:

$$\alpha(\tau) \cong \left(\alpha_0 + \frac{2\bar{M}_e V_c D_i}{W^2} \right) \cos(W\tau) + \frac{1}{W} \left(\alpha'_0 + \frac{2\bar{M}_e V_c^2}{W^2} + \bar{M}_e V_c D_i \alpha_0 \right) \sin(W\tau)$$

$$-2\frac{\bar{M}_e V_c}{W^2}(V_c \tau + D_i) \tag{6.63}$$

Here, W is the non-dimensional natural frequency of the rigid tether when a climber is in transit with constant speed. It is slightly less than the nominal value ω, and is given by

$$W^2 = \omega^2 - \bar{M}_e V_c^2 \qquad (6.64)$$

where

$$\bar{M}_e = M_e \Big/ \left(M_c + M_p \hat{l}_3 \right) \qquad (6.65)$$

α_0 and α_0' are the initial libration angle and rate, respectively.

From Eq. (6.63), the libration angle response is the sum of oscillatory terms and a linear term in time. The linear term is a direct consequence of the Coriolis force, which acts on the climber as it undergoes longitudinal motion within a rotating frame. The oscillatory terms decay when the climber ascends, but grow when it descends. This result is due to the rate-dependent term that is present in the governing equation. However, because this term is small, the decay/growth of the oscillations that occur during a climber's ascent/descent is small enough to be neglected. It may be concluded that the space elevator dynamics due to an ascending *or* descending climber are well behaved. This good behaviour is attributed to the fact that the climber mass is small with respect to the rest of the space elevator structure and that the tether itself is not actually being deployed or retrieved.

Equation (6.) is useful for devising climbing procedures. By substituting the transit time $\tau = \tau_f = \left(D_f - D_i \right)\big/ V_c$, it may be noted that the non-oscillatory component of the libration introduced by a uniform ascent or descent is of the order of $\bar{M}_e V_c D_f \big/ W^2$ radians. For an ascent, the rotation angle is negative, thus in the direction opposite to that in which the Earth spins (westward), whereas descent pushes the tether eastward. The libration is proportional to the climber mass, the cruising velocity and the final altitude of the climber, all of which have upper bounds. If all three of them approach their respective maximum values, the induced rotation will be of the order of 10^{-3} radians. Milliradians of libration translate to hundreds of kilometres of displacement for the higher sections of the tether, and thus may not be ignored. In general, minimizing the climber mass and cruise velocity serves as a general guideline for minimizing climber transit effects. Of course, transporting a significant amount of payload at a reasonably fast speed over a long distance is the purpose of a space elevator, and thus, inducing milliradians of rotation about the base is, to a certain extent, an inevitable consequence of operation.

When the climber is stationary, the libration angle is excited only by the initial conditions. It then behaves much like a pendulum, oscillating about its vertical equilibrium position with an amplitude that is defined as the residual libration. If $\alpha(\tau_f) = \alpha_f$ and $\alpha'(\tau_f) = \alpha_f'$ at the moment a climber arrives at its destination, the libration that ensues is given by:

$$\alpha(\tau) = \alpha_{res} \cos \left(W\tau - \psi \right) \qquad (6.66)$$

where

$$\alpha_{res} = \sqrt{ \alpha_f^2 + \left(\alpha_f' / W \right)^2 } \qquad (6.67)$$

and

$$\psi = \tan^{-1}\left(\alpha'_f / W\alpha_f\right)$$

(6.68)

The complete closed-form solution for the response of the libration angle to climber transit can be shown by considering both Eqs. (6.) and (6.). Again, let $\tau_f = \left(D_f - D_i\right)/V_c$. Then, the response to a climber having constant speed V_c, beginning its motion at D_i when $\tau = 0$, and arriving at D_f when $\tau = \tau_f$, is well approximated by:

$$\alpha(\tau) = \left(\alpha_0 + \frac{2\bar{M}_e V_c D_i}{W^2}\right)\cos\left(W\tau\right) + \frac{1}{W}\left(\alpha'_0 + \frac{2\bar{M}_e V_c^2}{W^2} + \bar{M}_e V_c D_i \alpha_0\right)\sin\left(W\tau\right)$$

$$-2\frac{\bar{M}_e V_c}{W^2}\left(V_c\tau + D_i\right) \qquad\qquad 0 \le \tau < \tau_f$$

$$\alpha(\tau) = \alpha_{res}\cos\left[W\left(\tau - \tau_f\right) - \psi\right] \qquad\qquad \tau_f \le \tau$$

(6.69)

This response applies to both climber ascent (positive V_c) and descent (negative V_c) at constant rate. The shape of this response may be seen in section 6.6.3 for ascent and descent in Figures 6-21 and 6-24, respectively. While those graphs refer to transverse displacement of the apex anchor, this displacement is governed primarily by the libration angle.

6.6.3 Climber Transit with Elastic Tether Model
Before assessing the response of the *elastic* tether system to an ascending climber, it is worthwhile to note that the simple act of mounting a climber causes the elastic space elevator structure to deviate from its nominal state. This happens because the point load of the climber causes a tension discontinuity in the tether, which leads to a strain discontinuity. Effectively, a climber mounted near the marine node will decrease the strain within the tether below it, and cause the whole structure to shift downward ever so slightly. Just as a climber in transit leads to a transverse disturbance in the tether, so does longitudinal motion of the tether itself. Thus, mounting a climber on the tether instils a very small sway in it.

From a stress point of view, the tension in the portion of tether above the climber is largely unaffected, while that below the climber is reduced significantly. If the space elevator is to remain a structure, this portion of tether must not be entirely un-tensioned; this constraint sets the upper bound for the mass of a mounted climber.

Analysis for a space elevator system with climbers moving along a flexible tether is complicated by the strong effect of the Coriolis force acting on the climbers combined with the coupled motion of the tether itself, which experiences variable tension. Though several studies have revealed certain aspects of its dynamics, the dynamics of space elevators have not been fully clarified by a realistic model as of yet. Space elevator contests on the ground may help to fill in some of the gaps of knowledge that exist within the spectrum of space elevator dynamics.

The dynamic equations of a flexible *space tether* system equipped with a climber have been derived and analyzed via numerical simulation by Fujii *et al.* (2008). This problem is made more difficult by the fact that the climber must be constrained to move on the tether whose ends are *both* floating in space. It is easily seen that the flexible tether is deflected by the Coriolis effect on the climber.

As already seen, a constant rate climber transit causes a rigid tether to rotate significantly. Climber transit effects are now assessed again, but the model used includes a flexible tether. The work presented in this section is based on the paper by Ohkawa *et al.* (2010). Readers may wish to refer to other papers including that of Williams (2009), which describes a modelling strategy for dealing with powered and propelled bodies moving along space tethers, Modi *et al.* (1993), where the planar dynamics of a space station based tethered elevator system are assessed, and Woo and Misra (2010), which analyzes the dynamics of multiple climbers on a partial space elevator.

The effect of rider transit on the motion of the flexible tether is considered as a disturbance. The dynamic model is formulated for a space elevator system that consists of a flexible tether, an apex anchor, and a climber. The dynamic model is expressed by a distributed parameter system. The tether is assumed to have constant mass density along its length, i.e., not tapered, in order to simplify the flexible tether analysis. The analysis may be adapted to assess a tapered tether model.

The equation of motion for the climber is described by

$$m_e \ddot{\mathbf{r}}_e = \mathbf{F}_e + m_e (\Omega^2 - \frac{\mu_E}{r_e^3}) \mathbf{r}_e \qquad (6.70)$$

where m_e denotes the mass, $\mathbf{r}_e$ the position vector, and $\mathbf{F}_e$ the thrust, respectively, of the climber. The command is set to be velocity and then the thrust changes depending on the value of the command velocity. It is assumed that the reaction force of the thrust is transferred to the system as friction force at the position described by the Dirac delta function. The climber may, alternatively, be driven by a motor along the tether. The necessary acceleration to increase the velocity by $\Delta \mathbf{v}_e$ for a constant time is

$$\ddot{\mathbf{r}}_e = \frac{\Delta \mathbf{v}_e}{time} \qquad (6.71)$$

The thrust of the climber is obtained as follows:

$$\mathbf{F}_e = m_e \left\{ \frac{\Delta \mathbf{v}_e}{time} - (\Omega^2 - \frac{\mu_E}{r_e^3}) \mathbf{r}_e \right\} \qquad (6.72)$$

The velocity profile of the climber is then prescribed. The climber is assumed to be driven, ascending or descending, with a constant velocity along the flexible tether between the earth surface and the synchronous orbit.

Numerical simulations reveal that the time periods of the first modes of the tether system vary non-linearly with respect to its length when there is an apex anchor. In contrast, the time periods of higher modes of the system increase in proportion with the tether length. The constant speed rider motion excites the lower modes of the flexible tether. As was the case for rigid tether analysis, the vibration amplitude is nearly proportional to the elevator speed.

Figure 6- shows the dynamic behavior of the system with the elevator ascending at a constant speed of 300km/h along a 40,000-km-long tether. The initial tether shape is taken to be a straight line in this simulation. The black dots in Figure 6- indicate the climber. When ascending the tether, the climber moves to the right at the beginning of the numerical simulation due to the Coriolis force. The elevator reaches the geostationary orbit after about

120 hrs.

Figure 6-22 shows the dynamic behaviour of the space elevator system *after* the climber reaches the geostationary orbit. Figure 6-23 shows the time response of the free end of the tether, where the apex anchor is connected. The effect of climber transit on the dynamic behaviour of the tether cannot be ignored. The vibration amplitude after the climber has ascended is about 200 m in this case. This amplitude of oscillation is far less than that discussed in the previous section. This is due to numerous reasons. One reason is that its tether length is significantly shorter than that of the previous model that was analyzed (40,000km vs 100,000km). Another is that the climber in this case is headed by a thrusters in the velocity profile along the tangent of the flexible tether element as shown in Eq. (6.).

Figures 6-924 to 6-26 show the numerical simulation results for a climber descending at a constant speed of 300km/h from the geostationary orbit to the surface of the Earth. At the beginning of the numerical simulation, the Coriolis force acts on the flexible tether in the left direction. Higher modes of the tether are excited as the climber descends. Figure 6-27 shows the relationship between climber speed and the vibration amplitude after the climber has ascended or descended at a constant speed. In all cases, the vibration amplitude after the climber has ascended is equal to that after the climber has descended. The figure shows that the vibration amplitude after ascent or descent of the climber is nearly proportional to the climber's speed.

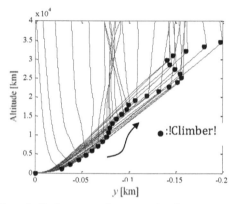

Figure 6-21. Effect of climber ascending at 300km/h on a 40,000-km-long space elevator system.

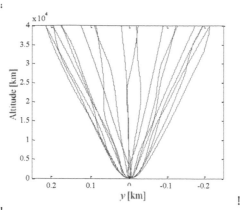

Figure 6-22. Response of space elevator system
after elevator reaches geostationary orbit

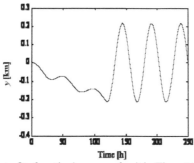

Figure 6-8.   Displacement of tether tip (apex anchor) in Figs. 6-21 and 6-22

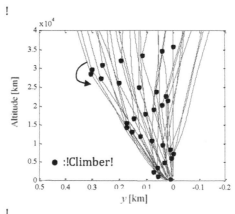

Figure 6-9. Effect of climber descending at 300km/h on
40,000km space elevator system.

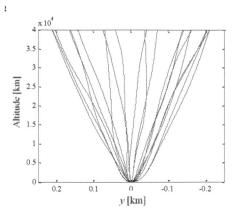

Figure 6-25. Response of space elevator system
after climber reaches Earth surface.

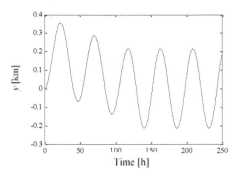

Figure 6-26. Displacement tether tip (apex anchor)
in Figures 6-24, 6-25

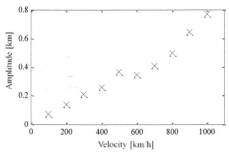

Figure 6-27. Vibration amplitude as a function of climber speed after ascent or descent at a constant speed on a 40,000-km-long space elevator system.

Finally, two more works concerning the dynamics of climbers on the space elevator are brought to the reader's attention.

Dynamics of the space elevator due to operation of a climber is studied by Lang (2006) using the Generalized Tethered Object Simulation System. The dynamic response is studied in a variety of climber operation contexts including: initial lift-off dynamics, nominal transits, transit resumes, and transit arrests. The study characterizes effects on the ribbon's transverse, longitudinal, and libration mode oscillations due to start-up, cruise transits, and motion arrest. This study points out the potential effects of simultaneous rider interactions with both a very low effective end-to-end spring-rate of an elevator ribbon of full length, and the high spring rates associated with shorter ribbon sections near the ground at liftoff. This manifests itself in a variety of climber operations, but most dramatically in the process of both accelerating and decelerating a climber on the ribbon, especially in near-ground operations such as liftoff. The longitudinal string modes of vibration were found to be easily excited under climber acceleration and deceleration. Bobbing mode frequencies of the apex anchor, as well as climber mass can manifest in response to climber activity. Stress wave propagation effects are also observed.

The propagation of disturbances along the upper-tether of the Tether Elevator/Crawler System has been analyzed by Lorenzini and Cosmo (1990). Both longitudinal and transverse waves are investigated as the waves propagate from the station to the elevator, and beyond to the upper-platform. Perturbations propagate along the tether of the system from the station to the elevator and beyond, to the upper-platform. However, a small value of viscous material damping (1-5% damping is estimated for kevlar tethers) is sufficient to significantly abate the longitudinal waves with a frequency above 1-2 Hz. It is concluded by the analysis that, for both longitudinal and transverse waves, the elevator attenuates the perturbations propagating from the station to the upper-platform. This conclusion may suggest a way of designing a passive attenuator for transverse waves to be placed between the elevator and the station.

6.6.4   Climbing Guidelines to Minimize Effects
The previous sections have described the space elevator's response to climber transit. In summary, the Coriolis force excites the pendulum mode as well as some elastic modes. Of greatest concern is the pendulum mode, which is undamped. The amplitude of this vibration is proportional to the mass of the climber, its velocity, and how far it climbs. It is desirable to minimize the effects of climber transit without placing any additional constraints on these parameters. Below are a few climbing procedures that accomplish this (for further details, see Cohen and Misra (2009)).

The simplest way to minimize the effect of a single climber transit is by decelerating the climber to rest very gradually as it nears its destination. The slower speed causes a smaller Coriolis force, such that the tether begins to rotate back to equilibrium. Gradual deceleration over the course of days instead of hours reduces the amplitude of oscillation significantly (factor of around ten). However, this adds time to the already lengthy process of transporting payload, and is thus not ideal.

Another option for a single climber transit is to *use* the Coriolis force to return an oscillating tether to equilibrium. A climber ascent introduces negative libration: if the ascent begins at the moment the tether is at its maximum positive libration, it can restore equilibrium in the tether. Similarly, beginning a descent at the moment of maximum negative libration can restore equilibrium. However, this method is also not ideal as it imposes a specific mass for the climber (as well as a specific climbing speed).

The most general and ultimately important climbing guideline to consider is the proper phasing of multiple climbers. It is expected that climbers will undergo transit at regular intervals. For the dynamics of the tether, it is desirable that these transits result in destructive interference – that is, they introduce individual responses that cancel each other out. If p identical climbers are sent from one location to another on the tether with the same motion profile, the net induced pendulum vibration will be zero if the time between transits ($t*$, in days) is given by

$$t* = (pn + 1)/pW \qquad (n = 0, 1, 2 ...) \qquad (6.73)$$

where W is the non-dimensional natural frequency of the pendulum mode. While the various integers n represent multiple spacing options, $n = 0$ is the shortest option, and is also the only one that results in non-oscillatory *in-transit* dynamics. Equation (6.) must be considered when planning climber transits. Just as optimal climber intervals can negate the net effect of climber transit (destructive interference), improper phasing can add the adverse effect of each individual climber (constructive interference).

Finally, a single climber transit can induce zero net libration if its motion profile is specifically chosen as shown by Williams and Ockels (2009). The optimal (fastest) way to achieve this involves reversing climber direction for a short period of time. Clearly, there are several ways that climber effects can be minimized or even negated. The Coriolis force on the climber can actually serve as a control measure for the space elevator.

6.6.5 Marine Node and apex anchor Forced Motion

Forces may be exerted at the marine node and the apex anchor: the marine node can achieve thrust as does any large ship, while the apex anchor may do so in the fashion of any spacecraft. The marine node must be mobile so as to displace the entire space elevator (deviations perpendicular to the equatorial plane) in an effort to dodge space debris. apex anchor impulses are costly and should be avoided if possible. Still, the ability to exert a force at the free end may be helpful in certain situations, such as restoring equilibrium in the system.

Out of plane motion of the marine node has not been analyzed as of yet. Equation (6.) governs the *in-plane* motion of the base. Some analyses have shown that space elevator dynamics have a negligible effect on the marine node. Contrastingly, the marine node, which has a mass that is several orders of magnitude larger than that of the tether and apex anchor, will be able to tow them along. Out-of-plane forced motion of the marine node will lead to out of plane oscillation of the tether. A parametric analysis relating the out of plane forced base motion to the induced out of plane libration amplitude would be useful. It would yield, for example, the maximum acceleration that the marine node can have so as not to induce too large an out-of-plane wobble. Such a study would also reveal the time delay between mobile base displacement and displacement of the tether at various altitudes.

Similarly, the structural response to apex anchor forced motion has not been studied. Impulses at the apex anchor are not envisioned during regular space elevator operations. However, such impulses will be critical for the deployment of the structure, which shall be discussed in section 6.7.

6.6.6 Aerodynamic Effects

Basic analyses for aerodynamic effects on the space elevator have been carried out (Cohen (2006) and Lang (2005)). Obviously, such forces act only in the atmosphere, and are most significant in the lower atmosphere. Although the region of application represents a relatively small portion of the tether length

(< 0.1%), the effects are non-negligible.

Numerical simulations reveal that sustained high winds lead to a fairly dramatic bubble of transverse displacement in the tether at the marine node. Ultimately, this results in a tether departure angle that is nearly horizontal. The amplitude of the local bubble that forms is on the order of tens of kilometres for sustained winds in the tens of m/s. The particular displacement is dependent on the effective width of the tether in the region. This is difficult to predict with any accuracy because the particular direction of the wind can vary, as can the particular orientation of the tether (it can twist).

The local bubble of displacement near the base can translate into excitation of the pendulum mode. If a sustained aerodynamic load contributes exclusively to pendulum mode excitation (rigid tether model), the structure rotates about a diverted angular position with an amplitude on the order of milliradians. This implies that for anticipated space elevator values, aerodynamic torque has a similar magnitude to that of a climber transit. However, as the flexible tether responds dramatically in the lower region to high winds, aerodynamic loads can impose significant additional stress on the tether in this region. For this reason, it may be desirable to reinforce (thicken) the bottom 100km of tether. As this is such a small percentage of the tether's length, it represents a negligibly small change to the area profile of the tether.

6.6.7   Effects of External Disturbances

Perturbing forces and their influences on the orbit of a satellite have been well studied. The reader may refer to Sidi (1997). The way in which perturbing forces affect the space elevator system must be studied, in particular, as it extends beyond the GEO altitude. The perturbing forces on the space elevator include:

1) The g2 terms of the earth gravity arising from the non-homogeneity of Earth. This disturbance is well known, and varies in space around the planet. Chosen locations along the equator in which to station space elevators must be stable from a J2 point of view.

2) Gravitational loading by celestial bodies such as the sun and moon. These gravitational perturbing forces can disturb the motion of the system. It appears critical that gravitational effects of the sun and moon are well understood. Preliminary results indicate that design changes to the space elevator may be required so as not to be too excited by the sun in particular. One possible design includes a large GEO station. Adding a very large mass at the geosynchronous altitude will add significant inertia to the system, while not affecting its nominal stress profile. In addition, certain control measures may be required for the space elevator in view of solar gravitational effects.

3) The solar pressure exerted by the sun and interference with magnetosphere and/or ionosphere at the upper altitude. These disturbances differ significantly from the others in that their effect is dependent upon the chemical make-up of the tether material. For example, it may or may not be electrodynamic and the extent to which it responds to radiation is not yet known. These excitations are actually sometimes *used* to control the dynamic motion of space tether systems. Such control measures may prove helpful for a space elevator.

Further detailed studies are encouraged for how such perturbing forces may affect a space elevator that is 100,000km in length.

6.6.8   Effects of Tether Motion on the Orbit of a Launched Satellite

All of the various excitations to the space elevator that have been discussed previously will combine via superposition to yield a perpetually dynamic structure. *Some* motion of the structure will be inevitable. The effect of a reasonable amount of motion on the orbit of a launched satellite has been examined by Cohen and Misra (2013).

When a payload is released from a climber, Figure 6-28 shows the Earth orbit that the payload will be in if the tether is static at the time of launch. It is noted that all orbits with the exception of that resulting from geosynchronous altitude release are elliptical.

The orbit of a launched satellite will be altered to a small extent if the tether is oscillating at the moment of payload release (slight modifications to the orbits shown in Figure 6-28). If the tether is oscillating with an amplitude on the order of milliradians (a reasonable amount for expected excitations) at the time of payload release, the semi-major axis and eccentricity of the resulting orbit will be affected by the order of tens of kilometers, and 10^{-3}, respectively. The flight path angle of the payload's intended orbit may also experience a small deviation.

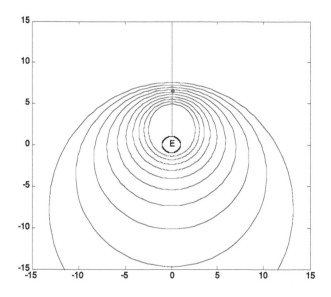

Fig. 6.28: Natural Earth orbits for payloads released from static tether

6.7 Deployment Dynamics and Construction

6.7.1   Introduction

Two different approaches have been proposed to deploy the initial elevator ribbon. They differ in terms of the starting point and maneuver strategies. One starts with a spacecraft at GEO and deploys the ribbon downwards, while the other starts at a spacecraft at LEO and deploys the ribbon and the ballast mass upwards (Lang, 2010). It is clear that the initial configuration plays an important role in the construction of the space elevator system.

Dynamics of the space elevator during its deployment has been studied by a small number of investigators. It has been shown by Takeichi (2010) that when the space elevator ribbon is deployed downward from a spacecraft in GEO, the space elevator will gradually lose altitude and may fall to the surface of the Earth before achieving full deployment. He subsequently proposed an orbital control strategy during deployment (Takeichi, 2012). Later, Keshmiri *et al.* (2012) conducted a study in which deployment of the space elevator was carried out using an optimal deployment scheme.

This section attempts to give some details associated with the deployment dynamics. A dynamics model is described briefly and some numerical results are presented. A simple optimization problem is defined and dynamical behavior associated with various deployment strategies is discussed.

6.7.2   Simple Deployment Dynamics Model:
A space elevator system consisting of a main spacecraft, a sub-satellite and a rigid ribbon is shown in Figure 6-29. The system is assumed to move in the equatorial plane. Neglecting the librational motion, the dynamics of the system can be described by three generalized coordinates r, l and q. Of course, if the system in constrained to have a prescribed orbital motion, clearly it will have only one degree of freedom: l.

Let us assume that the main satellite and the sub-satellite are point masses with mass M and m, respectively and the ribbon mass per unit length is r.

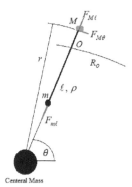

Figure 6-29. Schematic of a space elevator system undergoing deployment

It may be noted that during the retrieval, M changes with time and is given by

$$M = M_t - m - r\,l \qquad (6.74)$$

where M_t is the total mass of the system and is fixed. The equations of motion can be obtained by using the Lagrange's method. After some manipulation, these equations can be written as

$$M(\ddot{r} - r\dot{\theta}^2) - \frac{\rho\dot{\ell}^2}{2} + \frac{M\mu}{r^2} = F_{Mr}$$

$$Mr(r\ddot{\theta} + 2\dot{r}\dot{\theta}) + m(r - \ell)\left[(r - \ell)\ddot{\theta} + 2(\dot{r} - \dot{\ell})\dot{\theta}\right] + \rho\ell(r - \ell/2)\left[(r - \ell/2)\ddot{\theta} + 2(\dot{r} - \dot{\ell})\dot{\theta})\right] + \frac{\rho\ell^3}{12}\ddot{\theta} = rF_{M\theta} \quad (6.75)$$

$$m\left[(\ddot{r} - \ddot{\ell}) - (r - \ell)\dot{\theta}^2\right] + \rho\ell\left[(\ddot{r} - \ddot{\ell}) - (r - \ell/2)\dot{\theta}^2\right] - \frac{\rho\dot{\ell}^2}{2} + \frac{\rho\mu\ell}{r(r - \ell)} + \frac{m\mu}{(r - \ell)^2} = F_{mr}.$$

In the above equations, F_{Mr}, F_{Mq} and F_{mr} are the applied control forces, the first two at the main satellite and the third at the sub-satellite. These equations can be solved numerically. Figure 6-30 shows the variation of the radial distance of the upper mass (R_M), that of the lower mass (R_m), that of the centre of mass of the system (R_C), that of the centre of gravity (R_G) and that of the centre of orbit (R_O) for a typical constant rate uncontrolled deployment. All distances have been non-dimensionalized by dividing by the geostationary radius. It is clear that the entire system gradually loses altitude as deployment progresses, as has been observed by Takeichi (2010). Hence, it is essential to deploy the ribbon using some type of a control scheme. Figure 6-31 shows the variation of the abovementioned radial distances obtained by Keshmiri *et al.* (2012) using a deployment scheme in which the deployment rate is constant and the centre of orbit is maintained at the geostationary altitude. This deployment is not acceptable either, because the lower mass does not reach the surface of the Earth. Successful deployment requires control and non-uniform deployment.

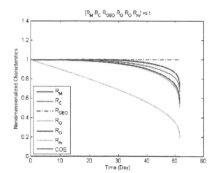

Figure 6-30. Characteristics of a non-fully controlled constant rate deployment of the sub-satellite

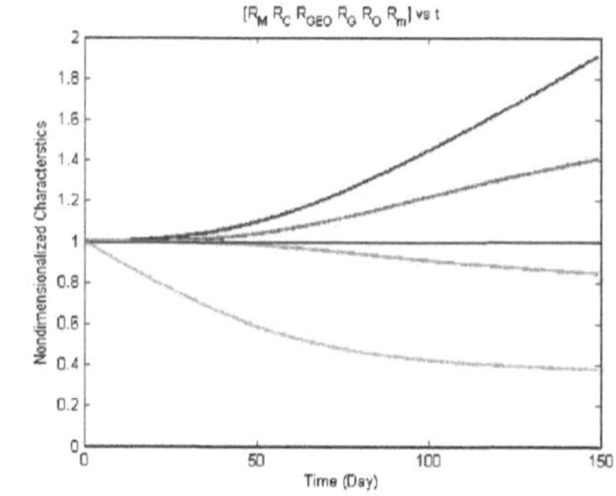

Figure 6-31. Characteristics of fully controlled and fixed constant rate deployment of the sub-satellite

The results shown above correspond to the deployment of the sub-satellite from the main satellite initially positioned at the geostationary orbit, with the following values of the various parameters:

$$M_o = M(t) + r\,l(t) = 10,000 \text{ kg}, \ m = 100 \text{ kg}, \ r = 10^{-4} \text{ kg/m}, \textit{ldot} = 5 \text{ m/s}.$$

6.7.3 Optimization

Figures 6-30 and 6-31 show, in a sense, two extreme strategies for the deployment of the ribbon. One can think of a cost-effective strategy for the deployment of the sub-satellite and the ribbon. For example, one can think of minimizing a cost function defined by

$$J = \int_0^{T_f} \left(\left|\hat{F}_{Mr}\right| + \left|\hat{F}_{M\theta}\right| + \left|\hat{F}_{mr}\right|\right) d\tau. \quad (6.76)$$

The cost function defined above is proportional to the total fuel consumption. The optimization can be carried out using various techniques. A near-optimal procedure has been described by Keshmiri *et al*. (2012). They considered three different scenarios consistent with the system dynamics as follows:

Case 1: The system is kept in circular orbital motion with R_o (t) = constant.
Case 2: The system orbits around the Earth with constant angular velocity during the deployment while its centre of orbit undergoes circular orbital motion only at the initial and final stages of deployment. In other words, although the whole system rotates around the Earth with constant angular velocity, it can slide up and down along the radial direction.
Case 3: The system has no constraints during the deployment phase. However, the deployment starts from a geostationary orbit and the centre of orbit returns to this orbit at the final instant.

Figure 6-32 shows the deployment dynamics corresponding to the three cases mentioned above. The duration of deployment is 60 days. It is clear that the fuel cost, characterized by J, is the lowest for case 1 when R_o is kept constant. The non-dimensional deployment rate, i.e., the ratio of the deployment rate to the length of the ribbon at any instant, is shown in Figure 6-33. It may be noted that, except in the beginning, this ratio remains fairly constant for all three cases, implying that the optimal deployment is more or less an exponential deployment. The non-dimensional control forces that must be applied at the upper and lower masses during this optimal deployment are shown in Figure 6-34 (for case 1). It has been found by simulation that the forces required as well as the cost function are an order of magnitude higher if the deployment rate is constant.

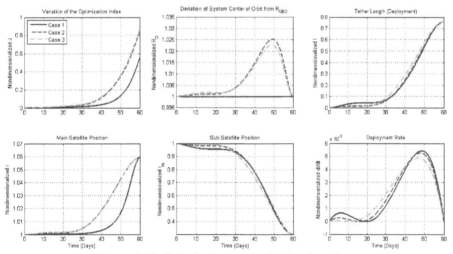

Figure 6-32. Optimization results for the given three cases

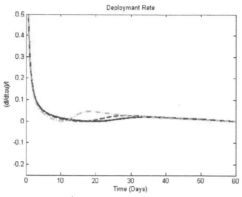

Figure 6-33. Change of $\dot{\ell}(t)/\ell(t)$ during the three deployment strategies

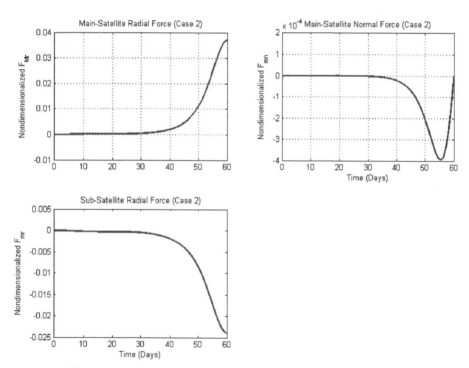

Figure 6-34. Non-dimensional control forces in the near optimal solution

6.8 Space Elevator Severance
6.8.1 Introduction
This section examines a very important issue in the design and development of space elevators, namely, severance. The space systems engineering approach will weigh the potential methods of damage, design against this threat, and lower the risk to a manageable level. Space tether missions have had their fair share of failures, including severance of the

tether on TSS-2 [see tether history E-3]. However, by design, the space elevator tether is expected to survive for the length of its operational life. Consider the example of the tethered satellite experiment (TiPS) designed to specifically address survivability issues of tethers in space. The TiPS system was launched in 1996 and had an expected lifetime of six months. The tether is reported to have been severed in 2006, ten years after its launch and nine years after mission completion. The tether survived significantly longer than had been predicted because of complete design.

In spite of such successes, severance presents a potential hazard to other spacecraft in LEO or GEO. It is necessary to investigate the dynamics of a severance incident so that more detailed studies can be undertaken to address any potential issues that a preliminary analysis might uncover. It is the goal of this section to investigate, through numerical simulations, the potential impact that tether severance could have on surrounding spacecraft and other space elevator tethers and to initiate discussions of systems approaches to lessen the risks. Two case studies will be discussed.

6.8.2   Initial Concept for Remediation
As the design of the space elevator is a system of systems, the severance of the tether will be approached as another risk to manage. There will be many trade studies and risk reduction approaches laid out in the future for the threat of a severed tether; however, at this point the following assumptions will be used in the threat analysis:

- Most likely sever from space debris will be below 2,000km. The chapter on this threat (chapter 10) will show that the probability of collision is a manageable risk and should **not** hinder the development of the space elevator.
- A sever could occur above LEO from climber explosion or a flaw in the tether, although this is a much lower risk.
- There will be a very capable apex anchor to significantly assist in reducing the impacts of a severed tether. The apex anchor will have a large and continuous thrust capability to keep it in its appointed location. In addition, the apex anchor will have continuous communications to the HQ&POC as well as the tether operations centre to enable quick and decisive actions.
- There will be a large GEO Node capability that will have the ability to grasp the tether and stabilize, to some extent, the tether from GEO to the apex anchor. This will be a fully capable satellite system with thrust capability and connectivity to the HQ&POC and tether operations centre.

These mitigation efforts will be analysed in future studies and discussed at great length. The resulting tether severance operational responses will then be incorporated into the design requirements across the space elevator infrastructure. As this section of the chapter progresses, these concepts can be leveraged to understand the risks and how to mitigate them.

6.8.3   Mathematical Model
In order to begin examining the behaviour of the space elevator tether following severance, it is necessary to introduce a mathematical model of the tether. A variety of space elevator models have been presented in the literature. The one utilized in this chapter has historical precedence (Williams, 2009). It has been used successfully to analyze the behaviour of real tethers in space, such as the YES-2 mission. The model is fundamentally the same dynamic model as earlier in this chapter, except that the climber is omitted from it. There are a myriad of possible configurations for the tether and climber at the time of severance, and these may

impact the results. Future studies will reflect the full transportation infrastructure design with up to seven climbers active on the tether. Future detailed studies into proposed mitigation techniques would utilize Monte Carlo analysis to take into account a wide variety of initial tether/elevator configurations. For this preliminary analysis, the initial tether configuration is the radial equilibrium configuration, which represents the mean of expected tether/elevator configurations.

6.8.4 Simplifications to Equations of Motion

The equations of motion presented in the previous studies referenced and in this chapter apply to a tethered elevator system in an arbitrary orbit and are convenient when considering the motion of the tether relative to the apex anchor. In this section, focus is on the effects of the tether following severance of the tether, and thus a coordinate frame attached to the apex anchor is not convenient or intuitive. Therefore, the model can be expressed in an alternate coordinate frame attached to the nominal geostationary orbit of the system. The origin of the new coordinate system is not attached to any of the masses, and therefore does not restrict the validity of the model or impose any unnecessary assumptions. The coordinate frame is shown in Figure 6-35.

By considering the forces acting on each of the masses, m_j, in the rotating frame shown in Figure 6-35, we have

$$\ddot{x}_j = \frac{1}{m_j}(F^s_{x_j} + F^d_{x_j} + F^g_{x_j}) - \ddot{R} + \dot{\omega}_z y_j + 2\omega_z \dot{y}_j + \omega_z^2 R + \omega_z^2 x_j$$

$$\ddot{y}_j = \frac{1}{m_j}(F^s_{y_j} + F^d_{y_j} + F^g_{y_j}) - \dot{\omega}_z R - \dot{\omega}_z x_j - 2\omega_z \dot{R} - 2\omega_z \dot{x}_j + \omega_z^2 y_j \qquad (6.77)$$

$$\ddot{z}_j = \frac{1}{m_j}(F^s_{z_j} + F^d_{z_j} + F^g_{z_j})$$

where the motion of the reference coordinate system is prescribed as

$$R = \frac{a(1-e^2)}{1-e\cos v},$$

$$\omega_z = \sqrt{\frac{\mu}{a^3(1-e^2)^3}}(1 + e\cos v)^2 \qquad (6.78)$$

and a is the orbit semimajor axis, e is the eccentricity, μ is the gravitational parameter, n is the orbit true anomaly, $F^s_{x_j}$ represents the x-component of the tension force on the jth mass, $F^d_{x_j}$ represents the x-component of the damping force on the jth mass, and $F^g_{x_j}$ represents the x-component of the gravitational force on the jth mass.

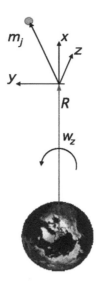

Figure 6-35. Geostationary rotating coordinate frame.

6.8.5 Tether Radial Equilibrium Configuration

The determination of equilibrium configurations for the space elevator is important, because it establishes the initial conditions required for the numerical model. Without appropriate initial conditions, a large multibody system undergoes essentially random oscillations, corrupting the simulation. For tethers with short lengths, it is possible to use approximate solutions for the elongation of the tether to specify the positions of the lumped masses along the tether axis. For tethers with very long lengths, more accurate techniques are necessary to prevent large longitudinal oscillations. If longitudinal equilibrium is not achieved prior to commencing a simulation, then this also induces lateral disturbances due to Coriolis coupling. Unfortunately, unlike other cable systems, the tether does not settle to an equilibrium position quickly due to the coupling between tether librational motion and longitudinal motion.

There are two approaches that can be used to determine the tether equilibrium configurations. The first is a direct approach, where the positions of the masses are iterated upon until the net acceleration is equal to zero for each mass. This approach can be susceptible to divergence and long computation times if the number of masses is large. A good initial guess is also required. An alternative approach is to specify only the position of the tether end mass and then invert the equations of motion sequentially to obtain the position of the tether end point (assuming a fixed length tether). The residual tension on the space-facing side of the apex anchor is driven to zero (i.e., there is no tether on the space-facing side of the apex anchor).

The latter approach, known as the inverse shooting solution, is more convenient because a minimal fixed set of unknowns is used irrespective of the number of masses used to model the tether. In addition, the optimal mass distribution of the tether can also be obtained in a straightforward manner during the iteration. Consider the arrangement shown in Figure 6-36. Assuming that the position of m_1 is specified as x_1, we can obtain the required tension force to maintain equilibrium from Eq. (6.77):

$$m_i(\ddot{R} - \omega_z^2 R - \omega_z^2 x_j) = T_i - T_{j-1} - \frac{\mu m_i}{(R+x_i)^2}$$
(6.79)

For the end mass we have

$$T_1 = m_1(\ddot{R} - \omega_z^2 R - \omega_z^2 x_1) + \frac{\mu m_1}{(R-x_1)^2}$$
(6.80)

Figure 6-36. Inverse procedure for determining equilibrium.

For any subsequent mass, the tension in the lower segment is written as T_{j-1}, allowing the next tension to be determined. The position of each subsequent mass is obtained from the tension using the relationship

$$T_i = \frac{EA_j}{L_i}(x_{i+1} - x_i - L_i)$$
(6.81)

where E is the Young's modulus, and L_j is the unstrained segment length.

An approximate solution for the distribution of mass required to support the system can be obtained from the tension T_j, by first computing the required cross-sectional area

$$A_i = \frac{T_i \nu}{\sigma_{ct}}$$
(6.82)

where F is the factor of safety, and S_{ut} is the strength of the tether. In order to properly account for the mass distribution on the tether, it is necessary to perform a two-loop iterative process. The inner-loop iterates on the mass distribution until convergence. The mass of each bead is approximated using the cross-sectional area of the lower tether element on the first iteration of the inner-loop

$$m_j = \rho A_{j-1} L_j$$

(6.83)

Subsequent iterations of the inner-loop use

$$m_j = \frac{\rho}{2}\left(A_{j-1}L_{j-1} + A_j L_j\right)$$

(6.84)

for each element. When the element masses are updated, the tension distribution changes, requiring the cross-sectional area to be updated using Eq. (6.82). As the inner-loop iterations proceed, the change in element mass is monitored until it converges to within a prescribed tolerance (10^{-9} summed across all elements).

For the tether to be in equilibrium after the shooting process, it is necessary for the tension T_{N+1} in Fig. 6- to be zero. One way to achieve this is to start at the apex anchor end and shoot towards the desired anchor point. This has the advantage that the apex anchor mass can be specified to a desired value. However, it means that there will be a residual tension, in general, at the anchor point. The problem with having a nominal residual tension at the anchor point is that if the tether severs, the higher tension will result in the apex anchor moving into a higher energy orbit (see analysis below). The alternative approach is to simply calculate the required apex anchor mass such that no residual tension is present, i.e.,

$$m_n = \frac{T_{n-1}}{\left(\omega_z^2 R + \omega_z^2 x_N\right) - \mu/(R + x_n)^2}$$

(6.85)

The solution process outlined above improves in accuracy as the number of elements used to model the tether increases. This design gives a constant stress tether, equal to the design stress. The factor of safety needs to take into account the changes in tension induced by tether swinging or elevator motion. In general, elevator motion will induce pendulum motion. However, the exact mass distribution is something that needs to be considered in detailed analyses of the entire system. In this chapter, the tether is sized by placing a large mass at the anchor point equivalent to the maximum required elevator mass. For the purposes of this section, this approach gives a realistic mass and tension distribution along the tether. It is used to specify the initial conditions and mass distribution required for numerical simulation of the severance dynamics.

6.8.6 Tether Severance

There is the potential for the elevator tether to break due to a variety of reasons. It is not the purpose of this section to analyze the causes of severance, nor their probability of occurrence. Instead, the primary focus is on the post-severance system response. Therefore, no cause of severance is modelled. This is a simplification, but is not expected to alter the conclusions substantially. Take, for example, the possibility of severance by space debris. Contact with large fast moving space debris will result in an impulse applied to the remaining tether, which would affect the resulting motion. Here, this is neglected. Tether severance is simulated simply by removing an elastic element corresponding to the severance location from the dynamic model. The tension and damping due to the element are set to zero. This section considers only a single point of severance to reduce the complexity of the analysis.

The elevator tether is modeled in the Simulink environment. This enables fast simulations via compiled code to be undertaken. A fixed time step 4th order Runge-Kutta algorithm is utilized for time propagation. The time step is set to 0.1 sec. The tether is discretized into 2,000 elements for the purposes of this analysis. Simulations were also conducted with 5,000 elements, but due to the length of the simulation runs and amount of data being logged, 5000 elements was considered excessive. A 2000 element simulation runs approximately 10 times real-time. Data is logged to file at 10 second intervals. The simulation length is set to 24 hours to allow for a full cycle of the fundamental mode of vibration of the original system. Each simulation produces 1 GB of log data for analysis. The severance point was systematically varied as a percentage of the tether length. It was severed at intervals of 1 % of the tether length, from 1 to 99 %. However, for the purposes of this chapter, two cases are shown: 30,000km (approximately 70% from apex anchor) and 1,900km altitudes (illustrated with a 98% sever).

6.8.7 Apex Anchor Motion

The motion of the apex anchor following a severance event depends on the final system configuration and the position of the point of severance. Consider the motion of a point mass from the point of view of its orbital energy

$$\varepsilon = \frac{V^2}{2} - \frac{\mu}{r}$$

(6.86)

where V is the orbit velocity, and r is the orbit radius. If we define the radius for geostationary orbit as r_g, then the orbit velocity of a point on the elevator tether at radius r is given by

$$V = r\sqrt{\frac{\mu}{r_g^3}}$$

(6.87)

For an escape (hyperbolic) orbit, the orbital energy must be positive, so, from Eq. (6.86), we have

$$\frac{\dot{r}^2\mu}{2r_\mu^3} - \frac{\mu}{r} > 0 \tag{6.88}$$

or

$$\frac{r^3}{r_\mu^3} > 2 \Rightarrow r > 1.2599 r_\mu \tag{6.89}$$

Thus, in principle, for tethers longer than approximately 47,000km, the apex anchor will enter into an escape orbit following severance. This conclusion depends somewhat on the actual mass distribution of the tether and where the severance point is located. If the center of orbit of the resulting free mass is less than approximately 47,000km, then the system will enter into a highly elliptic orbit rather than a hyperbolic one. This feature of the system is actually one of the advantages of the space elevator system, i.e., the ability to put payloads into different orbits after releasing them from the tether. However, the cost of this is that in the event of severance, the apex anchor will require immediate onboard propulsive assistance to prevent it from entering into an escape orbit. Simulations have verified that the apex anchor does indeed enter into an escape orbit for the configuration studied here.

6.8.8   Case Study 1: Severance of Bare Tether @ 30,000km altitude
When the tether breaks, a tension wave moves along it until it hits the boundaries. The apex anchor no longer has the reaction of the tether tension to maintain its position, and it therefore moves into a different orbit as described above. The simulation results show that the resulting orbit of the apex anchor is strongly influenced by the position of the sever point. The effect is due primarily to the variation in the total mass release, which is a function of the severance point. When the sever point is very close to the apex anchor, the mass released is roughly equal to that of the apex anchor, and the center of mass is nearly coincident with the apex anchor center of mass. As the sever point moves down the tether, the total mass increases and the center of mass of the released mass is at a lower orbital position at the time of release. Figure 6-37 shows the initial response of the apex anchor and the remaining attached tether following severance at 30,000km. The release of the system into a higher energy orbit is evident.

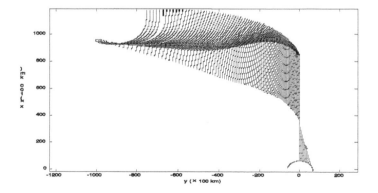

Figure 6-37.   Time lapse of tether motion following severance at 30000km, as seen in rotating
coordinate frame (shown at 3.5 minute intervals for 7 hours).

For an elastic tether, the results show that after severance occurs, the apex anchor and remaining attached tether commences a slow rotation. The speed of the rotation is a function of the point of severance, or equivalently, the length of tether attached to the apex anchor. For short tether lengths, the rotation speed is faster than for longer tether lengths. This may be directly related to the fact for shorter lengths, the apex anchor is ejected into an escape orbit. The rotational speed of tethered satellite systems is directly related to the eccentricity of its orbit (Williams, 2006; and Williams *et al.*, 2004).

The most problematic result of the tether being severed is the fact that the lower portion of the tether recoils and tends to wrap around the Earth. The simulation clearly shows that when the tether is severed close to the apex anchor, the Earth-side of the tether does not simply fall back to Earth. Instead, due to induced Coriolis forces that occur as a result of the large linear tether velocity following severance, the tether tends to fall to one side. The tether continues falling until it wraps completely around the Earth. Once the tether starts to contact the Earth (or indeed the atmosphere), it is unlikely that the mathematical model is fully representative. For example, no heating of the tether due to re-entry is modelled. Thus, it is possible that the tether burns up and therefore does not have the chance to wrap completely around the Earth.

Nevertheless, the tether far away from the atmosphere does indeed sweep out a large area in low Earth orbit during the recoil. This is perhaps the most hazardous part of the severance. The potential for collision with other spacecraft in LEO, or indeed, other elevator tethers is likely to be high.

Figure 6-38 shows the motion of the remaining tether below the sever for a 30,000km altitude severance. [Note: motion to the right is from the South Pole view] The laydown of the tether from this altitude is forward (to the East) and "soft," in that it does not stretch out full length, but tends to "bunch up" as it lays down. As shown the reach for the laydown is only about 20% of the circumference of the Earth at the equator or approximately less than 8,000km.

6.8.9   Case Study 2: Severance at an Altitude of 1,900km
The previous case study dealt with a high severance point on a bare tether. This section chooses a "representative" severance point and examines other effects on the severance dynamics. If the tether severs due to impact from a large piece of space debris, the most likely place will be in LEO. A representative severance position is therefore selected at an altitude of 1,900km. In this section, we seek to compare the effects of different scenarios on the severance dynamics. In particular, we focus on the response of the apex anchor and remaining attached tether, and the lower portion of the tether as it "falls" back to Earth.

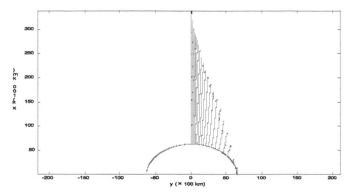

Figure 6-38. Close-up of the evolution of severed tether at Earth end for severance at
30000km (shown at 3.5 minute intervals).

The case of severance at 98% [1,900km altitude] of the tether length from the apex anchor is
selected as the baseline case with which to compare tether responses. We examine the
dynamics of the baseline tether severance prior to adjusting the system parameters. The
response of the apex anchor and remaining attached tether is shown in Figure 6-39. A direct
comparison against Figure 6-39 highlights the early findings that the lower the severance
point on the tether, the less orbital energy gained by the apex anchor and remaining tether.
Thus, for the lower and more likely severance position, the lower the requirements for apex
anchor thrusting to counteract the change in orbit.

The response of the lower portion of the tether is shown in Figure 6-40. The tether profile is
shown at 10-second intervals from the moment of severance. It shows that the tether initially
reacts by recoiling along the Nadir pointing direction. The tether accelerates quickly along
the Nadir direction primarily due to the large tension forces in the tether at the instant of
severance. Additional acceleration following the large transient acceleration is provided by
gravitational acceleration. The tether falls to the East (positive y-direction) due to the
Coriolis forces acting on the tether. This may be advantageous because it allows the tether to
present a larger cross-sectional area to the atmosphere (to either help slow the descent or to
burn the tether). It takes the tether approximately 500 sec to fall back to Earth (this is the
fastest possible time because it does not take into account atmospheric retardation). The
tether reaches a speed of over 2km/s in the first 10 seconds following severance. At the
instant prior to hitting the Earth's surface (or appreciable atmosphere), the tether has a speed
along the Nadir pointing line of over 5.7km/s. The rapid build-up of the tether velocity
caused by the large potential energy stored in the tether is potentially very difficult to
counteract. Similar recoil speeds are achieved by the tether on the apex anchor side of the
severance point. However, the tether does not continue to speed up, but slows down due to
the counteracting effect of gravity on the tether. One obvious conclusion is that severance at
an altitude of 1,900km tends to lays down the tether "softly" eastward for a shorter distance,
most likely less than 100km, as shown in Figure 6-.

177

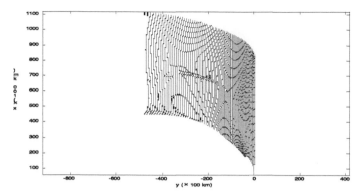

Figure 6-39. Time lapse of tether motion following severance at 1,900km, as seen in rotating coordinate frame (shown at 3.5 minute intervals for 7 hours).

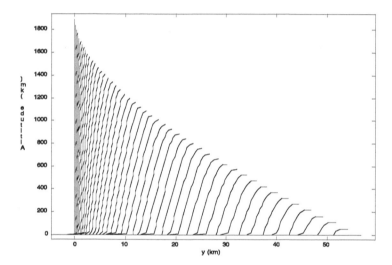

Figure 6-40. Time lapse of lower portion of tether following severance at 1,900km, shown at 10 sec intervals.

6.8.10 Effect of deployment on system response

One possible means for mitigating the effect of tether severance that has been suggested is to deploy additional tether from the apex anchor and attempt to reattach it at the anchor. This approach assumes that severance occurs at a low altitude, such as LEO. Tether deployment is simulated by incrementing the tether length closest to the apex anchor until it exceeds a specified length, at which point a new mass is introduced in the mathematical model. The new mass is given initial conditions so as to maintain consistent longitudinal dynamics of the existing elements. The speed of deployment is shaped according to

$$
\dot{L} = \begin{cases} \frac{1}{2}\dot{L}_{max}\left(1 - \cos\left(\frac{\pi t}{t_{max}}\right)\right) t < t_{max} \\ \dot{L}_{max} t \geq t_{max} \end{cases}
$$

(6.90)

which commences deployment at zero speed and ramps up to the maximum rate by time t_{max}. All simulations assume it takes 10 minutes to reach maximum deployment rate. Maximum deployment rates of 50, 100, 150, and 200 m/s are simulated.

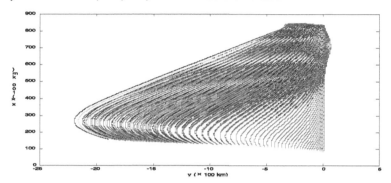

Figure 6-41. Effect of deployment from apex anchor on tether response following severance (black - no deployment case, green – 50 m/s, blue – 100 m/s, magenta – 150 m/s, red – 200 m/s), showing tether profiles at 110 sec intervals for 100 minutes.

The results from numerical simulations for all deployment speeds are shown in Figure 6-41. Comparison to the case of tether severance without deployment is also given. Figure 6-41 clearly shows that although deployment does affect the overall tether response, it is relatively minor. Higher deployment speeds have a larger perturbing effect on the response, but even a deployment rate of 200 m/s is insufficient to overcome the recoil. The main cause of this deficiency is that the potential energy stored in the tether results in a recoil much larger than can be mitigated by tether deployment, i.e., the tether accelerates to speeds of over 1.5km/s very quickly. Therefore, unless a deployer capable of working at speeds above 1.5km/s can be made, deployment alone will be an ineffective strategy in a rapid replacement scenario.

6.8.11 Effect of climbers on tether response

In this section, we consider the effect that the presence of climbers has on the tether response to severance. To simulate the effect of climbers, the tether is augmented with 5 climber masses of 5,000 kg each, distributed along the tether. The location of the climbers are as follows: 1) 1, 2) 25, 3) 50, 4) 75, 5) 99% of the tether length. Thus, there is 1 climber below the severance point on the Earth-side, and 4 climbers above it.

The response of the Earth-side tether is shown in Figure 6-42. The presence of a climber below the cut has only a minor effect on the tether response as it falls to Earth. In particular, by comparing Figure 6-42 with Figure 6-40 it can be seen that the climber acts like a node for the elastic oscillations. Some of the tether tends to "bunch" up at the climber position.

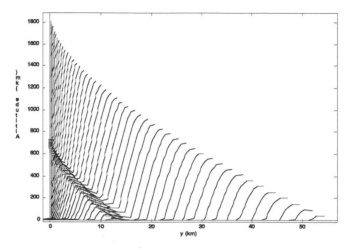

Figure 6-42. Time lapse of lower portion of tether following severance with 1 climber below the severance point, shown at 10 sec intervals.

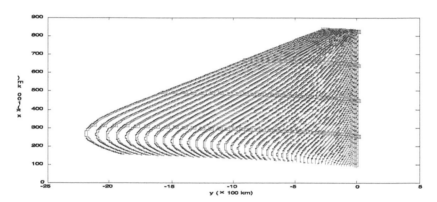

Figure 6.43. Response of upper tether following severance. Black is a bare tether, red is tether with climbers.

Figure 6-43 shows the response of the upper portion of the tether (apex anchor side) with climbers attached. The response of a bare tether is also shown for comparison purposes. It is evident from the response that the climbers have only a very minor effect on the overall dynamics. Thus, the loss of tension caused by severance dominates the tether response regardless of the presence of climbers on the tether.

6.8.12 Possible Mitigation Strategies

The simulation results illustrate that, due to the very large tension forces involved, when the tether is severed the free ends of the tether at the sever points recoil at rapid speeds. This is advantageous for the Earth-side of the tether since it will minimize the interaction of the tether with LEO spacecraft, and also contribute to its burning in the atmosphere. It is not desirable for the apex anchor-side of the tether, since it is desirable to reattach the tether to the anchor as soon as is possible. Unfortunately, the results indicate that this cannot be done by simply reeling out more tether from the apex anchor. Once the tether is cut, the apex anchor and remaining tether can move into an escape orbit if the sever is high enough. This will need to be counteracted.

One option is to use thrusters on the apex anchor to prevent movement of the apex anchor before the tether is reattached to the anchor. This approach is simple – if cheap propellant can be brought up on the space elevator, it is a good option. It is an option that needs investigating. It may also require that the climbers have thrusting capability to aid in straightening the tether, although the simulation results show that the tether does not tend to wrap around the apex anchor. Other alternatives could involve using lower propellant levels to change the orbit, or attempting to connect the free end of the tether with an anchored tether as it passes through perigee (in the case where the system does not enter an escape orbit). System designers will need to investigate all possibilities to devise a contingency plan in the unlikely event that the tether does indeed sever. It is not the purpose of this section to investigate mitigation strategies, but to merely highlight potential issues. Time will enable the gravity gradient forces to support stabilization if the location of the apex anchor can be maintained with thrusters. After all, the massive apex anchor and 98% of the massive tether are still in orbit with only a small loss of mass at the lower end point.

6.8.13 A Potential Mitigation Approach for Case 2, Sever at 1,900km
The engineering team will strive for a "bridge that does not fall down – as all designers do." The space elevator design team will go to extraordinary efforts to ensure that the risk is understood and defeated. The expectation of the space elevator community is that good design and operational procedures can make severance a risk that must be assessed, and designed against, but one that will not happen! However, if the unthinkable occurs, there are some mitigating approaches and emergency responses that could help the situation.

- Recognize: The laser rangefinders which are triangulating the exact locations of the individual elements of the tether would recognize that the tether has severed (along with dramatic change in tension at both ends) within an operationally short time period [on the order of minutes]. The anchor will detect the tension wave first in the case of a LEO severance point.
- Most Probable Altitude of Cut: 800km altitude is the most dense space debris environment [although the one year study for ISEC in 2010 does not predict sever, rather a long life for space elevators, even in the current and reasonable future LEO space debris environment].
- Assume: Five tether climbers, one below cut.
- Immediate Response:
  Step 1a: Upon sever, the apex anchor immediately thrusts in the direction towards the GEO Node to maintain the artificial orbit previously held. The fuel in the storage tanks are ready to respond to the emergency [previously brought up cheaply on the space elevator]. This thrusting will compensate for the tension lost which holds the apex anchor in its standard location.
  Step 1b [simultaneous]: The GEO Node "grabs" the tether and provides a stable force up and down without motion. A thruster will be available to maintain position and modify dynamic motion resulting from sever of the tether.
  Step 2: Start letting out tether at GEO Node until tether is again attached to base station. This is possible as pre-located tether has been "rolled up" into the GEO Node storage reel during the assembly of the tether. As the assembly of the space elevator

used the bootstrap method of Dr. Gassend, the last 2,000km of developmental tether that was rolled up is very capable [it contributed to the assembly of the full space elevator]. This is the tether that would be rolled out in an emergency manner to enable the connection at the ocean base station. Gravity gradient forces will stabilize the tether below the GEO Node and enable this process.

- Design Criteria: All tether climbers, when falling back to the surface, must be designed to self-destruct when entering the atmosphere. The high potential energy provides heat to separate elements into consumable parts [Note that this criteria will require re-examination when the human element is entered into the system].
- Recognize: Send a ship out to "reel in" the space elevator lower tether which would have "softly" laid down to the east and north of the base station [probably not in a straight line, but clumped – bunched/grouped together]. The tether climber would have disengaged prior to atmospheric entry.
- Recognize: The four other tether climbers would provide some stability to the tether while it is reeled out in reaction to the sever.
- Recognize: The apex anchor will want to move towards a higher elliptical orbit, but the reeling out of tether and thrusting will limit the motion and the re-attachment will stabilize the space elevator rapidly.
- Recognize: A new idea centers around the leverage of a GEO space station. If that station can "grip" the space elevator at that altitude, the resulting satellite would change the dynamics and make the lower reactions of the tether more stable and the upper reactions of the tether far less dramatic. Instead of two free ends [which occurred when the tied down end of the Earth station was lost], the new GEO station could grasp the space elevator tether and endure some forced motion [depending on mass ratios], but really stabilize the resulting motion of the tether. A thrusting capability will help stabilize the motion above the GEO Node and minimize any motion below the node.

The whole arena of space elevator severance is one that will be studied extensively as the program moves ahead. Obviously, if the worst occurs [cut near apex anchor], then the tether climbers and the tether would fall down and cover much of the equator with a one meter wide material. One interesting aspect is that two of the climbers could be in orbit and should release their grips on the tether.

6.8.14 Summary of space elevator severance

Detailed simulations of the behaviour of the space elevator tether following severance have been performed. The resulting motion for severance when the system is in a nominal Earth-oriented configuration is largely predictable in a large-scale sense. That is, the apex anchor and remaining tether attached to it is released into a higher elliptical orbit. The closer the severance point to the apex anchor, the higher the final orbit. A high enough sever point results in the apex anchor entering into an escape orbit. The Earth-side of the tether recoils due to the sudden loss of tension. The induced velocity creates Coriolis forces that result in the tether deviating from the local vertical. The tether therefore does not fall back to Earth in an ideal manner, but tends to sweep out an area in LEO and eventually wraps itself around the Earth. The tether may be burnt during the re-entry, but there is a potential risk to LEO spacecraft that needs to be mitigated by detailed study and contingency planning. Finally, reeling the tether out from the apex anchor has minimal impact on the post-severance dynamics, as does the presence of several climbers distributed along the tether. However, the new concepts of a massive GEO Node facility with the capability to grasp the space elevator tether in a rapid manner and a thrusting capability at both the GEO Node and apex anchor change the dynamics significantly. These suggested mitigation approaches must be studied extensively.

The engineers and designers of the space elevator must consider the extreme cases during their design processes as part of the risk assessment. This would include heat sensitive material to re-entry velocities to break up the tether into manageable portions. However, bridge builders complete the design and are often quoted as saying, "Not on my shift." Engineering skill, material science, and persistence should enable the space elevator to survive – even when faced with unique and intimidating hypotheses. Risk mitigation is an essential part of the development process, especially in mega-projects that have not been accomplished before.

6.9 Dynamics Summary
Dynamic analyses concerning the deployment, operation, and even potential severance of a space elevator have been conducted over the past ten years.
The deployment of such a structure represents a fairly unique dynamic challenge. Though many space tethers have been deployed, none have been so long that the mass of the tether itself drastically affected the dynamics. Research has shown that the originally proposed deployment scenario, where the apex anchor ascends while the Earth end of the tether descends, contains a certain inherent instability. Specifically, the overall structure tends to lose altitude during the deployment. However, with active control (thrusting capability) at both free ends of the structure, a successful deployment has been shown to be feasible.

Concerning the tether's design, it has been shown that the cross-sectional area profile that ensures uniform stress throughout the tether is a bit different than that originally derived in 1975. The modification that must be made accounts for the nominal elongation that takes place once the structure is in its operational configuration.

Modal analyses of the nominal structure have been carried out for various tether lengths. Such studies reveal that the nominal configuration of the space elevator is stable. The first mode of vibration of the structure is a rigid body mode (pendulum mode), and is stabilized by gravity gradient torque. For a 100,000km tether with a taper ratio of six, this mode has a period of about six days. This mode of vibration is particularly significant as it is undamped. Longitudinal and transverse elastic mode shapes are sinusoidal in nature; the first few of these modes have periods on the order of hours.

The presence of climbers on the tether affects its tension profile, and, subsequently, to a small extent, its position profile. The action of climber ascent and descent causes the tether to be excited due to the Coriolis force. The principal tether mode that is excited is the pendulum mode. A typical climber ascent from the marine node to the apex anchor will induce a librational amplitude on the order of milliradians. A number of passive and active control climbing schemes that aim to minimize climbing effects have been devised. The simplest such measure involves specifying a gap between multiple climbers. Other excitations to the structure, such as aerodynamics, have been studied, though to a lesser extent than that of climber transit.

Finally, the dynamics of tether severance have been investigated. In the event of a tether break, the Earth side falls towards Earth, while the space side drifts away. Certain measures to salvage the space side have been investigated; the most promising option of those considered involves active thrust at the apex anchor as well as at a GEO node. It is also noted that the portion of the tether that falls towards the equator bunches up as it does so.

There remains a substantial amount of advanced dynamic studies of the space elevator to be carried out in both theory and practice. Little research on tether torsion (twisting) has been done, and certain excitations such as those due to lunar and solar gravitational loading must be investigated further. Due to the extreme size of the structure, theoretical analyses may reveal certain design considerations that have yet to be conceived. One item that must be explored in the future is the variation of the Earth's rotation.

Some of the practical issues associated with space elevator dynamics, particularly those near the surface of Earth, may be better understood through the climbing of real tethers (e.g. 1km tether at the Space Elevator Games).

Operational space tethers continue to shed light on the challenges that a space elevator will face. They also give confidence that a space elevator can be successfully deployed and operated.

Findings

Finding 6-1:   If the necessary tether to apex anchor mass ratio is not maintained, the structure will not maintain nominal equilibrium: it will find a slightly modified equilibrium configuration – one where the stress profile is no longer constant.

Finding 6-2: The nominal space elevator system consisting of a deployed tether and Apex Anchor is a stable one for linearized stationary vibrational modes.

Finding 6-3: The space elevator dynamics due to ascending or descending tether climbers are well-behaved.

Chapter 7
Systems Design for Environmental Effects

7.1   Background
The design of a complex transportation infrastructure requires a "systems" approach with its discipline. The process is well defined and basically enables a successful approach. When properly implemented, systems engineering will: (AIAA/INCOSE, 1997).

- Provide a structured process for integrating and linking requirements, schedule, decision milestones, and verification -- it works best when the project team is committed to the systems engineering process.
- Enable the project team to work to a single, integrated, set of requirements and processes.
- Enable integration of the system at the requirements and design stages (before sunk costs) rather than waiting until hardware and software are available.
- Reduce unplanned and costly reengineering necessary to resolve omissions and integration difficulties.

Successful systems engineering procedures follow a natural sequential approach (AIAA/INCOSE, 1997) as shown below:

- Plan and organize the technical aspects of the project.
- Analyze the problem posed by the stakeholders.
- Assess and evaluate alternatives, which may satisfy these needs and expectations, and select a balanced solution for each systems element as well as a balanced solution for the system as a whole.
- Ensure implementation of the balanced solution (design to the end product)
- Verify the solution satisfies the stakeholder's requirements.

The objectives of this chapter are to initiate discussion on threats to the transportation infrastructure. Two of the initial steps follow the systems approach: (1) Identify the risks and (2) evaluate alternatives. The approach chosen will address the space elevator arena with two risk reduction thrusts;

- Risk Reduction Thrust A - Tether: Discuss the various threats to space elevator tethers and describe three proposed risk reduction options. One of the basic issues with understanding the tether is the lack of technical information about the characteristics of the one-meter wide CNT based tether. Such items include friction coefficient, resistivity, conductivity, elasticity, capacitance, and responses to sunlight and to the vacuum and atomic oxygen aspects of space.

- Risk Reduction Thrust B - Climber: Define the various threats to the tether climber and describe three proposed alternatives towards risk reduction. One of the significant keys here is that a tether climber is no more than a spacecraft with unique velocity vectors. As such, historic space lessons learned should be applicable and lead the designers towards a systems approach for survivability.

This chapter will first list the known hazards inherent in space flight with comments about the severity of the threat and the applicability of the threat to the major space elevator segments; tether and climbers. The chapter will then discuss thrusts A and B with risk reduction approaches. A key to this whole discussion is that a good systems approach should enable the space elevator infrastructure to thrive in the hostile environment of space. The environment being discussed stretches from the surface of the ocean to well beyond the major magnetic fields of Earth. At the end of the chapter a matrix is shown to illustrate the complexity of many major segments and diverse environmental effects.

7.2   Environment Threats
Meteors and micrometeorites
Meteors and micrometeorites are ubiquitous in space and need to be accounted for. The odds of being hit are extremely small; so, the design philosophy is to treat them like space debris - manoeuver for the big meteors and accept the hit from smaller micrometeorites with repair of the tether and climbers as routine.

Space debris
This includes current or expired spacecraft, rockets and their fragments (see Chapter 8 for a good discussion of this topic). This is a special issue as it is a significant concern and there was a year-long study conducted resulting in a report entitled "Space Elevator Survivability Space Debris Mitigation." (Swan, Penny and Swan, 2010).

Space environment
The space environment covers x-rays, gamma rays, atomic oxygen, energetic particle radiation, cold/heat and the like. This category of threats stretches across many specific phenomena that have been dealt with for 50 years for orbiting spacecraft. Many procedures have been established to ensure that the spacecraft launched today have the best chance of surviving until their missions are complete.

Electromagnetic effects
The effects are largely from space electric and magnetic fields. There are some unique aspects that could affect the operations and survivability of the space elevator infrastructure. The magnetic fields are continuously changing in magnitude and direction as the Earth rotates and encounters the bow shock of the solar wind interaction with Earth's magnetic field.

Atmospheric environment
The atmospheric environment includes winds aloft, hurricanes, tornados, lightning, etc. This category of threats affects the tether and the climber in the lower reaches of the climb. As such, secondary approaches can be taken such as protection with light-weight boxes that will not be taken all the way to GEO, but only through the atmosphere as protection for the fragile spacecraft and solar arrays.

Human environment
By human environment is meant aircraft, ships, terrorists, etc.   The human element is always difficult to comprehend and the rationale of someone who wants to harm major transportation infrastructures is hard to understand or predict. However, the threats exist and must be dealt with in a manner that doesn't make operations onerous and does not allow unacceptable threats. Armed guards will probably be required to patrol the sea, the air and the logistics trail to ensure that no terrorist or accidental tourist impinge the operations of the space elevator.

Finding 7-1: The environmental threats to a space elevator are not significantly different from historical threats to orbiting spacecraft, reflecting on the differences in motion – orbiting around the Earth vs. rotating with the Earth. Similarities will be obvious for Human transportation and when designing for the atmospheric portions of the space elevator. The large scale of the space elevator crosses many environment regions which increases complexity.

7.3   Risk Reduction Thrust A – Tether
Threats to the space elevator tether encompass all those mentioned above; however three are very serious: winds, electromagnetic effects, and terrorism.

Winds *(Winds affecting the tether)*
Winds are a challenge to the space elevator. In temperate latitudes, jet stream winds can exceed 100 meters/sec between altitudes of 9 and 15km (Barry and Chorley, 2009). Figure 7-1 shows global average wind speeds against altitude. The high speeds above the stratopause are of little consequence because of the extremely low density. Figure 7-2 takes the atmospheric density ρ into account to reach an estimate of global average wind pressure ρv^2, where v is wind speed. Maxima may be three times as great as averages; that worst case effect can be demonstrated by multiplying the pressure scale by nine.

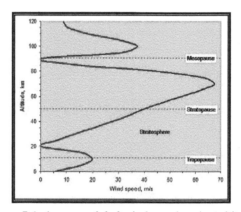

Figure 7-1. Average global wind speed against altitude

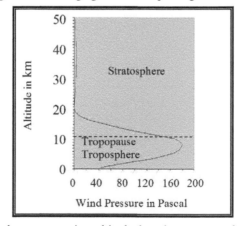

Figure 7-2. Wind pressure against altitude, based on average global wind speeds

Near the equator, there are only seasonal jet streams over Africa near latitudes of 15° N or S, and they do not occur over the equatorial oceans. Figure 7-3 shows that equatorial wind speeds are generally more moderate than the global average (Jiang et al., 2004), although more detail is needed on the extremes.

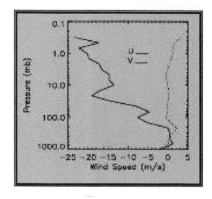

Figure 7-3. Wind speed against atmospheric pressure in the equatorial Western Pacific December-March 1991-92

Wind pressure on the tether

Previous calculations (Knapman, 2005) have shown that the maximum wind pressure that may be encountered in the stratosphere is about 1000 N/m². Chapter 5 discussed this issue in depth. The conclusion was that Marine Stage One will lead to movement of the tether from winds and more tension will be placed upon the tether. However, if there is a High Stage One platform, the pressures are less on the tether as shown in Figure 7-4.

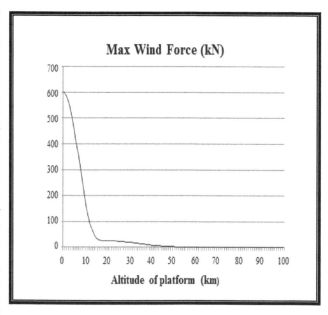

Figure 7-4. Estimated maximum wind force encountered by the tether above the platform for various platform altitudes

Solution to winds aloft

The efforts of this study group have come to some conclusions relating to the future operations of space elevators, they are. The first is that the operations are simplified and the cost of the system is lowered if the spacecraft, called the tether climber, operates on solar array power alone. This means that the fragile craft must be delivered above the winds in a protective box or initiated from High Stage One. Chapter 4 [tether climber] describes a simple concept while Chapter 5 describes alternatives for Stage One. High Stage One illustrates the advantages of elevating the platform above the winds while Marine Stage One enables the "boxed satellite" to reach altitude. A solution to winds aloft for the tether climber is to "skip" the atmosphere and start at altitude. The initial solution for the tether, when dealing with winds aloft, is simply to plan for the movement of the tether from winds on the surface all the way to the stratospheric winds. Having a meter cross-section for 20km will provide quite a "sail" for the environment; but, there are no real requirements to maintain the tether in any specific location other than being attached to Stage One. Releasing the tether from the bottom or reeling it in at the bottom will apply forces to the tether to move it through wind in a predictable manner that will ensure the system remains operational.

Finding 7-2:   Incorporating the concept of initiating the tether climber at altitude enables the tether operators to successfully monitor, move and adjust the space elevator tether depending upon the environment, including winds. As such, winds aloft become an operational planning challenge, not a risk to the program.

Electromagnetic effects from space electric and magnetic fields

The choice of running a carbon nanotube based tether from the surface of the Earth to well outside of the Earth's magnetic field is shown in Figure 7-5. A simple breakdown of these issues include electromagnetic phenomenon in the atmosphere (usually lightning); the electromagnetic occurrences in the upper atmosphere and lower space, including blue jets, sprites and elves; and, finally, electromagnetic connections with natural fields of the Earth as it rotates around its axis. In addition, as the space elevator tether extends beyond the bow shock of the Earth's fields, the electromagnetic fields from the sun must be understood and characterized. Some interesting questions come to mind; the first one being: Can we use this energy for propulsion? At the present time, the question has not been addressed seriously and seems to be one that could very well enable a simpler and more robust space elevator. Alas, no one has researched that relationship and the question remains one of vast potential. This portion of the chapter will break the discussion of the threats to the tether into three sections: atmospheric, high altitude, and magnetic fields in free space.

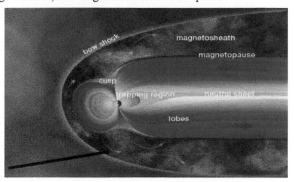

Figure 7-5. Earth's Bow Shock with Space Elevator [Jorgensen, 2004]

Atmospheric

Many people have studied the frequency of lightning strikes around the world and have discovered that there are multiple locations that do not have significant strikes or cloud-to-cloud electric releases. As a result, space elevator designers are recommending a quiescent location in the Pacific west of the Galapagos along the equator (Edwards, 2003). In addition, for the lower reaches of the atmosphere, lightning arrestors have worked for centuries. In modern times, additional approaches for releasing the energy prior to strikes have been developed such as laser ionization of the air to provide a path for the energy to reach the ground. As such, if Marine One is the choice in Stage One, lightning arrestors and ionization lasers would be standard equipment to keep the tether safe from atmospheric effects. If Stage One is the High Stage One, the lightning phenomena become the concern of the structure going to 40km, not the tether.

High altitude

Choosing a site with few electrical storms means that high-altitude electrical phenomena are also likely to be infrequent. Locating the transfer platform at 40km altitude will still expose the main space-elevator tether to elves, sprites and gigantic jets; but, carbon nanotubes will conduct the current to the transfer station where it will be connected to the Stage One lightning conductor. These electrical phenomena occur at high altitude, as illustrated in Figure 7.6. Blue jets occur in the stratosphere, up to about 50km; sprites and elves are twice as high. Another phenomenon, the gigantic jet, was only discovered in 2001; they reach from the lower stratosphere up to 70km. All of these are associated with electrical storms in the troposphere. Electrical breakdown above thunderstorms was first predicted in the 1920s; but, the first documented visual evidence was obtained in 1989.

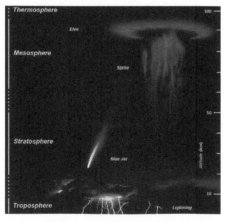

Figure 7-6. High altitude lightning and discharge phenomena [Scientific American]

As a result of these effects from electromagnetic discharges at altitude, the space elevator tether must be structured to handle massive current and voltage on limited occasions. This could be designed into the tether with a parallel lightning rod, multiple tethers separated by 100km or so, or a way to isolate the tether from the grounding phenomenon in a way that ensures that the energy does not deposit itself on the tether. This topic is still to be studied in detail and must be understood to a more detailed level to ensure a design that is safe and secure.

Free space

The third region, from 100km altitude to the Apex Anchor, deals with the tether running though a magnetic field with currents flowing. The key is to recognize that the Earth is turning around its axis and will bring the tether with it on its daily route. The issue is what happens when the long tether is continually crossing magnetic field lines that are changing direction [daily rotation], magnitude [noon constriction to midnight expansion of magnetic field lines] and energy levels [solar level of activity – 11-year cycle and individual solar event emissions]. The systems design team will need to look at this dynamic driving force and see how to place a carbon nanotube tether inside this dynamo while keeping it safe from significant effects. Some of the questions are: how much conduction should be allowed? How much insulation is required? How much current runs, and when? How do we take advantage of this current? As mankind has progressed further and further into space, challenges have surfaced that have puzzled the best designers. As a result, creative and innovative solutions have been incorporated into the systems design of spacecraft over the years hoping to ensure operational success. Consider that the current GEO communications satellite is prepared for a 15-year lifetime in this same environment where we did not know how it would survive in the beginning. All the effects of the electromagnetic and electric fields can be predicted once the design of the space elevator tether is laid out. The above discussed challenges are real and will have impacts upon the design of the tether; but, in the end, the success of the space elevator will come forward as the team solves these challenges one at a time.

Summary – Currents on the Space Elevator (Wright, 2013)

Electric currents generated within the ribbons of the space elevator are of interest for two reasons: 1) if they are large and variable they could pose a threat to the ribbon and the equipment attached to it; 2) if they are moderate and steady, useful power might me derived from them.

Previous estimates [Jorgensen, 2004] have shown that neither of the above cases apply, except in extreme situations. However it is useful to take a more detailed look at the sources of the currents and their time dependence. Two main sources were studied:

- currents induced by motion through the magnetosphere, and
- currents resulting from differential charging due to varying plasma densities along the ribbon.

Induced electromagnetic forces (EMF), using the Tsyganenko magnetosphere model [Tsyganenko. 2008] with the co-rotating dipole field of the Earth subtracted, and summing with the Volland-Stern [Volland, 73] model of the co-rotational and convection electric fields, the total time-dependent component of E along the ribbon was calculated. From this, and an assumed electrical resistance of the ribbon material, the detailed current flow along the ribbon was calculated as a function of distance along the ribbon. Figure 7-7 shows how the total electric field and its constituents vary along the length of the ribbon for a given orientation in space. In this case the space elevator is located on the equator at the Greenwich meridian during the vernal equinox of 2001.

Currents were found to be steady over large stretches of the ribbon, but not very large, with maximum values of 9 mA near the Earth. The power resulting from this is about 32 uW/m.

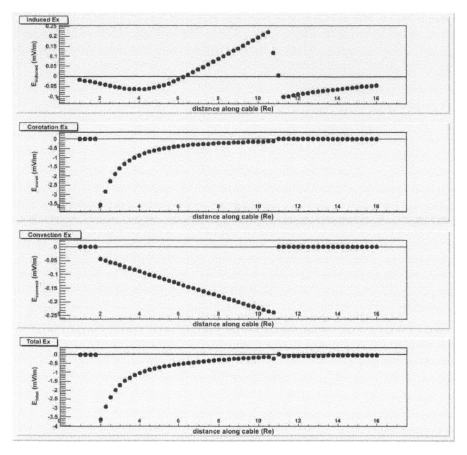

Figure 7-7, Constituents of total electric field along a ribbon of the space elevator at the vernal equinox 2001. From top to bottom: induced E from motion in magnetosphere, co-rotation E, convection E, total E.

Spacecraft charging resulting from the collection of plasma is a well-known hazard, but power generation from it has proven to be elusive. The charging of an astronomically large structure poses some interesting questions. Because the space elevator will pass through radiation belts and a number of other plasma currents of vastly different density, there is the possibility of differential charging, and hence current flow, over long distances. A quick estimate shows that these currents are small, of the order of 10^{-7} amp locally with a worst case of 5 mA, but that discharge from broken strands of the ribbon could be a concern. Estimates of charging time and equilibrium potential on the ribbon may be difficult to calculate due to the large scale of the conductor.

Finding 7-3: Electromagnetic effects on the space elevator tether must be studied in detail in the near future. The estimate is that the electric and magnetic fields and currents will not affect operations, but could enhance them.

Human environment [aircraft, ships, terrorists, etc.]
The important aspect of this threat is that the approach is a known entity. The space elevator infrastructure must be protected in the same manner as an airport. There must be controlled access to the area around the Marine Node. This can be handled with a private security force who have speedboats, airplanes, radar monitoring, anti-aircraft missiles, sonars, and, of course, large stretches of ocean to isolate the Marine Node. In addition, there will probably have to be submersibles to monitor the sea up close; but, the monitoring of the surrounding area can be routine similar to today's protection of an airport on an island. One other major concern is loading something on the space elevator that could be explosive. This would have to be a primary rule of design for customers. Monitors at the various gateways of the space elevator infrastructure are the last resort for compliance.

Finding 7-4: This large transportation infrastructure must be valued and protected as airports around the world are currently. Physical protection, personnel monitoring, and active sensors should ensure that the human element does not affect operations of the space elevator.

7.4   Risk Reduction Thrust B – Climber
Here the various threats to the tether climber are defined and three proposed alternatives towards risk reduction are described. One of the significant keys here is that the tether climber is no more than a spacecraft with unique velocity vectors. As such, historic space lessons learned are applicable and lead the designers towards a systems approach for survivability. The three areas of concern are radiation issues, thermal effects, and spacecraft charging.

Radiation in space
Spacecraft have been protecting themselves from radiation from the first days of space exploration. The first American satellite discovered the radiation belts and led to the realization that the environment was hostile to normal electronics and to humans. The solutions are many and the success rate follows the operations procedures of the space systems design, assembly, test, and orbiting. Each of the historic orbits has a special set of radiation issues that dominates; but, all radiation types can affect the space elevator tether climber in each of the altitude regimes. As a result, the space systems designers must use the worst case scenario and then design the systems to withstand that level of radiation. In the vernacular of the space designer, the tether climber must be designed for the natural environment.

The problem in this case is that the tether climber will be working inside all of the orbital regimes that were definitive of other missions. Low Earth orbits have always been protected by the Earth's magnetic fields, while GEO orbits are fairly benign. However, solar flares and the resulting effects from those high-energy emissions from the sun are the exception. The radiation includes ions, electrons, and all of the speed-of-light phenomena such as x-rays, gamma rays, UV, and even optical light frequencies. A recent Scientific American article even talks about Gamma-rays and anti-matter being created in the upper atmosphere moving towards space (Dwyer and Smith, 2012). As a result of this broad based threat, designers must design in multiple approaches to ensure survival. The good news is that NASA and all its contractors [as well as all other nations' space agencies] have tables describing the types of radiation, the magnitude of each type, and the region of danger for each. As the space elevator tether spans those regions [LEO, MEO, GEO, interplanetary], designers for the tether climbers will have to have robust solutions to radiation hardening and radiation tolerance.

Finding 7-5: Radiation is not a problem for tether climbers, as the designers will incorporate this threat into the design requirements and ensure operational success through any radiation environment. Historic precedence supports this conclusion as the space community runs spacecraft in all the regions where the space elevator will be operating. However, when people are included in the tether climb [after some years of robotic success], the radiation problem becomes an order of magnitude more difficult. There are many ways to reduce the radiation and shorten the trip, which will have to be incorporated when the human element is added.

Thermal effects

The systems approach to design for thermal effects has developed significantly over the last ten years as space systems have become more robust with multiple missions. When dealing with robotic spacecraft [the tether climber prior to people], the thermal issues are less stressing. The basic concept is to ensure that the extremes do not occur. Therefore, the transfer of heat must be planned with an understanding of the energy impinging upon the satellite [tether climber]. As the tether climber will be pointing at the sun to ensure solar arrays are maximizing collection, there will be a preferred side for heat creation. The problem becomes one of moving that heat to the cold side so that it may be radiated off the tether climber and into space. Traditional approaches have led to very good heat transfer mechanisms and heat radiation plates. In addition to the maximum situation when the tether climber is in full sunlight, the system has to deal with the cold of eclipse. As a result, there is also the need to create heat from electricity to make sure the tether climber does not freeze during eclipse. Each of these effects, too hot in the sun and too cold in eclipse, has been dealt with successfully. The design criteria are in the systems engineering handbooks and successful approaches have been identified. One key to remember is that the tether climber has moving parts in the drive train and must have temperature control to ensure continuous operations and no freeze-up during eclipse or melt down during full sun.

Finding 7-6: Design for thermal control has been a major element in space system survival in this hostile environment. The tether climber will leverage 50 years of historic lessons learned over 50 years and successfully manage its thermal characteristics in the long climb from the surface of the ocean to the Apex Anchor.

Spacecraft charging

There have been many books written on the topic of spacecraft charging. This was a major problem in the early days of space exploration and continued to plague designers for years as satellites became larger and more complex. At the present time, there is a very good set of rules to ensure operational space systems do not suffer from any build-up of electrical charge from the natural environment in space. This will indeed be a challenge for the tether climber and must be part of the systems design. In addition, as discussed in the previous thrust on the tether itself, coupling of the tether and magnetic fields could cause electromagnetic effects not previously identified. One of the basic rules for spacecraft charging is: "No loose pigtails and ground everything." As a result, even the extremely large International Space Station is working well without spacecraft charging affecting mission success. Once again, the space community must predict the effects of the environment on the new design and incorporate historical lessons learned to ensure future success.

Finding 7-7: Spacecraft charging will need to be addressed by the design engineer, who will leverage 50 years of experience with this issue. Spacecraft charging will need to be designed for, but is not a risk for tether climbers.

7.5   Additional Verification/Validation Requirements in Space

The transition from terrestrial manufacturing to the development for space requires some extra validation and verification steps. These challenges are shown in the following list:

- Radiation damage of the tether and climber electronics
- Radiation exposure to people riding the elevator
- Meteor damage to the tether
- Orbital debris damage to the tether
- Atomic oxygen erosion of the tether
- Lightning, hurricanes, hail, jet streams
- Induced oscillation
- Induced currents in the tether
- Terrorists attacking the system
- Airplanes and ships hitting the tether or end station infrastructure
- Thermal fluctuations
- Wear and tear on the tether
- Energy density stored in the tether
- Others if applicable

Each of the boxes in the following chart would be considered an important point for a future set of design requirements to ensure the system of systems works in the hostile environment. Major studies will be conducted to ensure the risks are identified in detail and mitigation plans are in place to resolve any issues early. Testing would be arranged to ensure many of these requirements are designed for – correctly.

	Tether	Apex Anchor	GEO Station	Tether Climber	Marine Node	High Stage One	Ocean Going cargo Vessel	Helicopter Transport	Operations Centers
Radiation damage of the tether and climber electronics	X	X	X	X					
Radiation exposure to people riding the Elevator			X	X					
Meteor damage to the tether	X	X		X					
Orbital debris damage to the tether	X			X					
Atomic Oxygen erosion of the tether	X			X					
Lightning, hurricanes, hail, jet streams	X			X	X	X			
Induced Oscillation	X	X	X	X					
Induced currents in the tether	X		X	X					
Terrorists attacking the system	X			X	X	X	X	X	X
Airplanes and ships hitting the tether or end station infrastructure	X			X	X	X	X	X	X
Thermal fluctuations	X	X		X	X	X	X		
Wear and tear on the tether	X			X					
Energy density stored in the tether	X			X	X	X			
Others if applicable									

Table 7–I. Integrated System V&V Requirements in Space

Chapter 8
Systems Design for Space Debris

8.1 Background
A major year-long study was conducted by the International Space Elevator Consortium (ISEC) addressing the issue of space debris. The quotation below was taken from the preface of the final report and lays the framework for this chapter. Much of the information presented and discussed herein comes from the ISEC study which was entitled, "Space Elevator Survivability Space Debris Mitigation."

"Will space debris be a 'show stopper' for the development of the Space Elevator Infrastructure? **The answer is a resounding NO!** The recognition of space debris risk with reasonable probabilities of impact is an engineering problem. The proposed mitigation concepts change the issue from a perceived problem to a concern; but, by no means is it a significant threat. This study illustrates how the development office for a future space elevator infrastructure can attack this problem and convert it into another manageable engineering problem." (Swan, P. *et al*, 2010).

Over the last 30+ years, the International Academy of Astronautics has been involved in research of space debris and how it influences the safety of flight and spacecraft / rocket design. Many of these analyses and recommended activities within the IAA permanent committee on Space Debris have been incorporated in this analysis. Both of this chapter's authors have contributed to the past discussions and eventually to their study reports on space debris. While these studies [lead by Mr. Bonnal and others] formed the basis of our analyses, a space elevator has the benefit of almost perfect knowledge of its individual element locations; thus, allowing for the space elevator centric approach used in the ISEC study.

The Big Sky theory of Space Debris, or the "what, me worry?" approach, has faded into the past as have Sputnik and the Saturn rocket. The space community now recognizes that the continuous growth (Figure 8-1) of objects remaining in orbit has led to an arena where space debris mitigation and removal becomes mandatory. Indeed, the space elevator community is concerned about space debris numbers and densities because of its dramatic growth over the last three years.

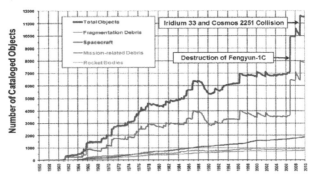

Figure 8-1. Continuous Growth of Space Debris

This chapter should raise the awareness of the problem to the space elevator stakeholders and all other users of the near Earth space environment. The chapter will deal with the historical breakout of space debris by altitude, show the probability of collision for segments of a space elevator, describe the decision approach for movement of a space elevator, bring together the conclusions for the threat against the infrastructure, and describe recommended actions to have remediation and removal requirements accepted by space faring nations.

8.2 Approach
There are three major parts of this chapter that describe activities of the space elevator with reference to space debris:

A)   Calculate Probability of Collision [sections 8.3 – 8.8]
During the analysis for the report, the team addressed many issues including:
- The probabilities of collision in Low Earth Orbit (LEO), in Geosynchronous Earth Orbit (GEO), and in Medium Earth Orbit (MEO).
- The growth rate as it threatens an operational space elevator.

To assess the risk to a space elevator, we have used methodology from the 2001 International Academy of Astronautics (2000) Position Paper on Orbital Debris:

"The probability (PC) that two items will collide in orbit is a function of the spatial density (SPD) of orbiting objects in a region, the average relative velocity (VR) between the objects in that region, the collision cross section (XC) of the scenario being considered, and the time (T) the object at risk is in the given region."

$$PC = 1 - e^{(-VR \times SPD \times XC \times T)}$$

Using this formula, we calculate the Probability of Collision for LEO, MEO, and GEO. Our focus is on LEO -- as fully two thirds of the threatening objects are in the 200-2000km (LEO) regime. Our analyses from the one-year study showed:

The threat from Space Debris can be reduced to manageable levels with relatively modest design and operational "fixes."

B)   Develop Decision Processes for Movement of the Space Elevator   [sections   8.9]
        Once the operations center has established routine operations of the space elevator infrastructure, there will be a continuous calculation of probability of collision. This will require constant coordination with organizations tracking space debris and continuous tracking of space elevator elements [1, 10, 100m (tbd) each]. A decision process must be established to trade risk for safety and control motion of the space elevator tether.

C)   Influence Future Space Debris Population   [sections 8.10]   The International Academy of Astronautics' "Position Paper on Space Debris Mitigation" recommends "zero debris creation" in LEO and GEO regimes. In addition, there is a movement to initiate removal of large space debris at the rate of five pieces per year. These and other activities must be encouraged and enabled along with the development of the space elevator. After the space elevator becomes operational, there should be additional activities assisting in the mitigation and removal of space debris. The space elevator will enable both cost effective debris removal and spacecraft protection.

8.3   General Threat Breakout

A systems approach to space elevator survival must address all threats from the expected environments. As such, a quick discussion on the other threats puts space debris in perspective, and were addressed in the last chapter. The space debris threats logically separate into five altitude regions (Table 8-I) and encompass all basic issues that must be evaluated. This ranges across many arenas, to include:

- Meteors and micrometeoroids
- Space debris (expired spacecraft and/or fragments)
- Operational spacecraft

Region	From (km)	To (km)
Super – GEO	35,880	100,000
GEO	35,680	35,880
MEO	2,000	35,680
LEO	Spaceflight limit (200km)	2,000
Aero Drag	Sea Level	Spaceflight limit (200km)

[GEO – geosynchronous orbit @ 35,786km; MEO-Medium Earth Orbit;
LEO – low Earth orbit: radius Earth = 6378km]
Table 8-I. Altitude Regions

Super GEO
There is very little human-created debris in this region, so the major threat consists of meteors and micro-meteoroids beyond the geosynchronous arc.

GEO Region
Problems in this region include the micro-meteorite issue and human hardware intersection. The advantage is that debris is mostly large and moving slowly when in, or close to, the "GEO Belt." The relative velocities are usually less than 10s of meters per second. However, current guidelines for GEO satellite removal call for raising their orbits at least 200km, and lunar and solar perturbations can cause inclination changes, raising the relative velocities of potential collisions with the space elevator. This leads to the conclusion that most of these dead satellites will have to be removed.

MEO Region
Few man-made objects reside in this region; and in the context of space debris, MEO resembles GEO. There are a small number of objects right above the lower limit of 2,000km altitude; less than 200 around the 12 hour circular orbit populated by navigation constellations [GPS with more than 36 satellites - GLONASS with more than 20 satellites - and the future Galileo with more than 24 satellites at 20,200km]; and, in addition, the Geosynchronous Transfer Orbit [12 hour, highly elliptical] retains rocket bodies after payloads are "kicked" into GEO orbit. The velocity differences between a space elevator and orbiting objects for this elliptical debris present a serious threat: however, the numbers are small. In addition, the lower portion of this region contains radiation belts.

LEO Region
Low Earth Orbit has a major problem with space debris, a modest problem with operational satellites, and a smaller problem with micrometeoroids. Most catalogued space debris exists in this region, filling all altitudes and inclinations, which results in equatorial crossings near any space elevator. Of the 15,000 objects tracked daily, approximately 12,000 are located in this region.

Aero Drag Region
The atmosphere will threaten the ribbon and integrity of the space elevator in this region as discussed in the previous chapter. The normal dangers of concern are: winds aloft, hurricanes, tornados, lightening, and human interference [aircraft, ships, and terrorism].

The primary concern for those studying space debris deals with "what is up there?" Space debris is defined as anything man-made that is in orbit and comes in multiple categories and sizes. There are large rocket bodies as well as large and medium sized spacecraft that are no longer functioning. There are functioning spacecraft - large, medium and small. And, there are pieces of junk - large, medium and small.

8.4 Space debris historical overview
This section will lay out a short history of how the global space community slipped into this situation while helping to define the population density and distribution. Table 8-II shows the four historical phases of space debris.

Phase	Years	Comments
Big Sky Theory	1957-1970	No concern because there is so much volume
What is up There?	1970-1989	Scientists/Military wonder what is up there
Collision Concern	1989-2009	Scientists/mathematicians worry about collisions
Collision Reality	2009-	The IRIDIUM-Cosmos Fragmentation

Table 8-II. Historical Phases of Space Debris

Big Sky Theory (1957-1970)
Space debris has long been an issue in the space operations. Exploding rocket bodies and batteries, cameras floating away from astronauts, and old, dead, satellites or rocket bodies all created worthless parts going at orbital velocities. The volume of space surrounding Earth is huge and for many years the issue of space debris was of no concern.

What is up There? (1970-1989)
During this phase, researchers attempted to determine what was really in orbit and to whom it belonged. Many radars and optical sites were placed around the world to help understand the dimensions of the problem.

Collision Concern (1989-2009)
During this phase many scientists and operators projected major concerns for the future; however, very little progress was made to reduce debris in orbit. Much was, though, accomplished in creating guidelines for design of spacecraft and rocket bodies culminating in

a document expressing the desire for "zero debris creation" as a goal. In addition, several space debris mitigation policies were implemented across space faring nations.

Collision Reality (2009-)
A collision between an active IRIDIUM and a dead Cosmos satellite was the watershed event that brought attention to the space debris issue. Projections show that the cascade of debris population is becoming a real problem. The community now recognizes that space debris reduction must be pro-active, not simply passive. Table 8-III lists eight major collisions that have so far been identified.

Year	Satellites
1991	Inactive Cosmos 1934 satellite hit by cataloged debris from Cosmos 296 satellite
1996	Active French Cerise satellite hit by cataloged debris from Ariane rocket stage
1997	Inactive NOAA 7 satellite hit by un-cataloged debris large enough to change its orbit and create additional debris
2002	Inactive Cosmos 539 satellite hit by un-cataloged debris large enough to change its orbit and create additional debris
2005	US Rocket body hit by cataloged debris from Chinese rocket stage
2007	Active Meteosat 8 satellite hit by un-cataloged object large enough to change its orbit
2007	Inactive NASA UARS satellite believed hit by un-cataloged debris large enough to create additional debris
2009	Active IRIDIUM satellite hit by inactive Cosmos 2251

Table 8-III. Satellite Collisions
[Complied by Dr. David Wright, Union of Concerned Scientists] (Weeden, 2009)

8.5   Space Debris Population
After over 50 years of space operations by numerous international players, more than 35,000 objects have been catalogued with over a third still in orbit. Figure 8-2 depicts the current population of objects as small as 10-20 cm for LEO [200-2000km altitude] and objects as small as one meter in Geosynchronous Equatorial Orbit (GEO). The minimum object size reflects the capabilities of the US Strategic Command's Space Surveillance Network (SSN). However, the LEO debris problem must be kept in perspective. The density is still quite small as there is only one large spacecraft item in low Earth orbit in each 750 x 750 x 750km cube and only one small piece of debris [10cm or larger] in each 90 x 90 x 90km cube.

The altitude distribution of debris must be understood when dealing with threats to a space elevator. The total length of the space elevator is not really at danger because most altitudes do not have any significant distribution-densities of debris. There is concern at GEO [where the large objects are not going very fast with respect to a space elevator] while at LEO it is much more important to understand the numbers because of increased densities and high velocities. This requires a methodology that addresses the differences in altitude and density. Figure 8-2 shows the growth in numbers of objects vs. time.

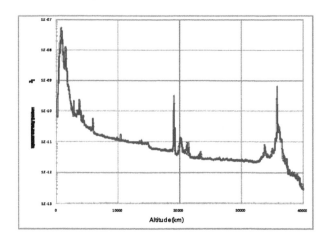

Figure 8-2. Growth in numbers of objects vs. time
(With permission from Debra Shoots, NASA Orbital Debris Program Office, May 2010)

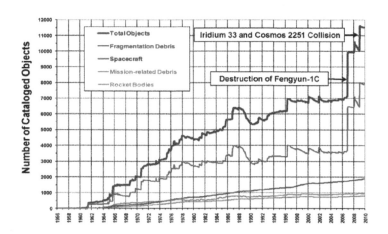

Figure 8-3. Spatial Density
(With permission from Debra Shoots, NASA Orbital Debris Program Office, May 2010)

This chart shows the dramatic increase due to the Chinese ASAT test and IRIDIUM-Cosmos collision. These numbers show how attitudes about space debris shifted through the four phases and reflect the current and future threat to a space elevator. A good rule of thumb is that the LEO numbers account for slightly greater than two thirds of the total objects. This is the area where we should focus on debris mitigation, such as "taking the hit" or collision avoidance actions. Again quoting from the IAA position paper, "Only about 6% of the catalogued objects are operational satellites. About one-sixth of the objects are derelict rocket bodies discarded after use, while over one-fifth are non-operational payloads. Pieces of hardware released during payload deployment and operations are considered operational debris and constitute about 12% of the catalogued population." (International Academy of Astronautics, 2000).

Lastly, the remnants of over 150 satellites and rocket stages that have been fragmented in orbit account for over 40% of the population by number. These proportions have varied only slightly over the last 25 years. Small and medium-sized orbital debris (size ranging from 1/1000mm to 20cm) includes paint flakes, aluminium oxide particles ejected during solid rocket motor booster firing, break-up fragments, and coolant droplets from leaking nuclear reactors."

It is important to estimate the densities of known and estimated [unknown] space debris to calculate the collision risk. Figure 8-3 shows densities of space debris per unit volume by altitude and is used to calculate the probability of collision.

8.6   Knowledge of Where Debris is (was):
As noted by Loftus and Stansberry (1993) "There are two distinct phases..." to the collision avoidance task: cataloguing objects and maintain full ephemeris for each. They go on to say "The minimum size of the objects one needs to track determines the frequency of the sensors to be used." Generally, one needs the wavelength of the sensor to be about 1/3 the diameter of the object(s) to be tracked. Obviously, antenna power and gain must be adequate as well. This means that to track a one centimetre size object, one needs radar in the X-Band at about 30 Ghz. For reference, the workhorse of the SSN, the FPS-85 at Eglin AFB in Florida, operates at 442 Mhz. (For more information on the Space Surveillance Network, visit www.au.af.mil/au/awc/awcgate/usspc-fs.space.htm).

The Joint Space Operations Center (JSpOC) is the terminus for the SSN's abundant and steady flow of information. It has large and powerful computers to store "observations" which include time tagged optical and radar measurements which sometimes include size estimates in the form of average radar cross section. The JSpOC computes and stores ephemeris for tracked objects. It also runs the Computation of Miss Between Orbits (COMBO) software to predict collisions for selected objects such as the International Space Station, which has a keep out zone of 25km. The Space Station has used those predictions to maneuver out of harm's way several times. As one would imagine, the accuracy of the ephemeris on tracked objects in the SSN database varies depending on the source and volume of the observations. Accuracy can be as good as a kilometer or two for objects that are tracked frequently by radar. Less frequently tracked objects can vary from a few kilometers to tens of kilometers. The large majority of catalogued objects have accuracies in the several kilometers to tens of kilometers range. Owners of operational satellites may know the locations of their satellites to much better accuracies. For example, Gravity Probe B and Global Positioning System (GPS) satellites are known to a few or a few tens of meters. Iridium is known to about 2 kilometers.

8.7   Knowledge of Space Elevator Element Location
By employing GPS receivers at multiple locations on the ribbon, taking measurements frequently, and utilizing powerful computers (Kalman filters), we would expect the knowledge of the location of the ribbon at those locations to be meters to tens of meters. An alternate could be small, extremely light weight, corner cubes placed every 10km [100km?] for a retro-reflective small laser range finder times three for location accuracy.

8.8   Probability of Collision

Quoting from the 2001 IAA Position Paper On Orbital Debris (International Academy of Astronautics, 2000), "The probability that two items will collide (PC) in orbit is a function of spatial density (SPD) of orbiting objects in the region, average relative velocity (VR) between the objects in that region, collision cross section (XC) of the scenario being considered, and time (T) the object at risk is in the given region.

$$PC = 1 - e^{(-VR \, x \, SPD \, x \, XC \, x \, T)}$$

This relationship is derived from the kinetic energy theory of gases which assumes that the relative motion of objects in the region being considered is random." This methodology was introduced in 1983, by Robert Penny and Richard Jones in their Master's thesis "A Model for Evaluation of Satellite Population Management Alternatives (Penny and Jones, 1983). This formula is also described in "Space Mission Engineering – the New SMAD" [Wertz, 2001]. As the catalogued population, lifetime, and satellite size increase, the PC will also increase. An example of cross-sectional area is 200-2,000km altitude of the ribbon in LEO. This leads to a cross sectional area 1,800,000m x 1m or 1,800,000m^2 or 1.8km^2. The relative velocity is the average velocity for the orbiting objects. In LEO, there are tens of thousands of tracked objects, so the calculation leads to valid estimates.

The probability of collision can be broken into separate illustrative cases. This chapter sets up the representation of several cases by altitude region [LEO cases A, B, & C; MEO case D; GEO case E] as identified in altitude density shells. In the LEO orbital region, two shells are 60km in thickness and represent the area where the tracked space debris is most dense [Case A] and average [Case B]. In addition, a third case in LEO deals with all the debris from 200-2000km altitude [Case C]. Another dimension for the description of LEO cases is the "untracked" (estimated) density [Cases A-u, B-u, C-u] where the numbers are estimated to be ten times the tracked numbers inside each case. A third dimension is the representation of operational spacecraft, which can maneuver as they are still being controlled by the ground [Cases A-c, B-c, and C-c]. Operational spacecraft numbers are assumed to be 6% of the tracked space debris. Case D represents MEO while Case E represents GEO. The cases are shown below:

Low Earth Orbit (9 cases)

- Case A: 60km ribbon segment [740-800km altitude] representing the peak debris density – highest risk case.
- Case B: 60km ribbon segment [1340-1400km altitude] representing an average debris density in LEO.
- Case C: 1800km ribbon segment [200-2000km altitude] representing the entire LEO environment.
- Case A-u, B-u, C-u: represent the untracked items in above described segments. Estimated to be ten times the tracked debris.
- Case A-c, B-c, C-c: represent the controlled satellites in above segments. Estimated to be 6% of the tracked debris.

Medium Earth Orbit (1 case)

- Case D: 200km ribbon segment [around 20,200km altitude] representing the navigation orbit environment [only tracked items are calculated].

GEO Orbit (1 case)

- Case E: 200km ribbon segment [35,680-35,880km altitude] representing the GEO environment [only tracked items are calculated].

As we noted earlier, the probability of collision is a function of the relative velocity (VR), the density of objects (SPD), the cross sectional area (XC) and time (T). This approach works well for LEO where the behaviour of Earth orbiting objects is very similar to the behaviour of gas molecules. It is less similar for MEO and GEO; however, we use the same methodology as we lack anything better.   We will use the formula PC = 1 – e(-VR x SPD x XC x T) for all eleven cases.

8.9 Decision to Move the Tether
The probability of collision for large space debris is small, but catastrophic. Space elevator operators must be able to predict the probability of individual satellite or rocket debris impacting the tether. This massive simulation would be an outgrowth of new conjunction analysis tools, such as recent improvements of Satellite Tool Kit or the next generation USAF software. There would be detailed inputs for space elevator operations teams with precise position knowledge of each element of the tether. As this is not required until at least 2030, the expectation is that knowledge of debris size and location will be much more precise and that some of the larger space debris pieces would have been removed. The next step would be to put the altitude and time track of the expected collision location and run a "projected dynamics response" to a stimulus. The stimulus would initiate a dynamics behavior such that a certain tether element would be moved X km [tbd] at the precise time needed. This stimulus could be from:

- Movement of space elevator Marine Node
- Movement of Apex Anchor
- Movement of tether at GEO Node
- Movement of tether climber [up or down]
- Lengthen or shorten tether at Marine Node
- Lengthen or shorten tether at Apex Anchor

Stimulus of the tether impacts its dynamic motion at one intended location and could also be constructively leveraged to damp out normal dynamics. The dynamics of the tether will be constantly monitored and the observed motion will be modelled in simulators to ensure safety and to allow immediate reaction if some dangerous dynamic mode resonates unintentionally.

8.10 Desired Impact on International Arena
The international space elevator development team must be involved with international organizations that control their destiny. This would include the frequency control by the International Telecommunication Union and the space debris community.   Similar to Motorola's early involvement in the international frequency allocation government process, the space elevator community must become involved in the space debris community and influence outcomes in the three categories shown below:

Orbital Debris Mitigation: The 2005 IAA Study recommended that:
- There shall be no new generation of operational debris.
- There shall be no risk of explosion following end of mission.

- Two orbital regions shall be protected... there shall be no orbital debris creation within these two protected region.

Orbital Debris Reduction: Recent international meetings [Washington DC Dec 2010, Delft 2011, Darmstadt 2013] have discussed the issue of space debris growth and have concluded that the dangers in LEO are significant for future utilization of this orbital regime. There are many recommendations at national and international levels to: "Remove five large pieces of junk each year." The space elevator community believes that is a great start; but, it is only a start. There should be other recommendations initiated as well:

- Each space faring nation that has created more than 100 pieces of space debris should sponsor removal of ten large pieces of debris each year. One way to do this would be to initiate a "Space Debris Removal Prize."
- Shorten the total time in orbit for a space system [operational and dormant] to 15 years, not 25.
- Do NOT allow cubesats/smallsats to be tossed into orbits with a greater than two year lifetime unless they have deorbit capability.

Space Elevator Operations supporting Debris Reduction:
After the development of an operational space elevator infrastructure, there are several things that can be accomplished by satellite designers to positively impact the space debris environment.

- Shielding – Designers can shield around critical components with more mass.
- Additional Redundancy – Designers can add redundancy to equipment to increase mean mission duration.
- Additional Fuel – Additional fuel would be available for maintenance, avoidance maneuvers, and EOL maneuvers.
- Sensors – Sensors could be added to help characterize debris impacts and debris flux.
- Larger structure – A larger structure would permit access panels for human or robotic on-orbit repairs, replenishment, and technology upgrades.
- Capture Friendly features – In addition to 3 axis stability and extra fuel, features might include grappling points or actual mating hardware to permit easy capture for removal from orbit.
- Allow "piggyback" for debris removal equipment – As is the case with expendable rockets, some satellites can catch a ride with another satellite to reduce their launch costs.
- Operational Tug – Organizing an ability to drop off and pick up space objects will enable a new look at design.

The bottom line from these options for space systems designers is that many different strengths of the space elevator can be leveraged to greatly improve the space debris environment.

8.11 Summary
After evaluating all of the eleven cases, the numbers show that LEO is the highest threat arena. We know this intuitively as the density of space debris is greatest at LEO and it has the highest differential velocities – two major drivers in the probability of collision equation. In addition, as the population density is not great at MEO and the volume is huge, MEO still falls into the "Big Sky Theory" of less worrisome. The GEO orbit has a restrictive band [Sir Arthur C. Clarke's altitude for station keeping at zero latitude] of limited population. This

leads to some concern from the numbers; however, the differences in velocities are so small that the danger is even smaller. Table 8-IV summarizes the concerns for all eleven cases.

Types of Debris	Case	Collision every
Untracked <10 cm		
60km stretch peak	A-u	60 days
60km stretch average	B-u	2.5 years
LEO 200-2000km	C-u	10 days
Tracked Debris >10cm		
60km stretch peak	A	2 years
60km stretch average	B	23 years
LEO 200-2000km	C	1.3 years
Cooperative Objects		
60km stretch peak	A-c	30 years
60km stretch average	B-c	400 years
LEO 200-2000km	C-c	5 years
Tracked Debris >10cm		
200km stretch-MEO	D	> 4000 years
200km stretch-GEO	E	400 years

Table 8-IV. Summary of Probability of Collisions

8.10 Findings
These results lead us to the following conclusions:

Finding 8-1: In the GEO altitude region space debris is not a problem.

Finding 8-2: In the MEO altitude region space debris is not a problem.

Finding 8-3: Untracked, small [<10cm] debris will, on the average, impact a space elevator tether in the LEO altitude region [200-2000km] once every ten days. Therefore, the tether must be designed for impact velocities and energies. Putting this into perspective, there are 1,800,000 one-meter by one-meter squares as targets for an impact every ten days.

Finding 8-4: Tracked debris will impact the total LEO segment [200 – 2000km] once every 100 days or multiple times a year if no action is taken. Once again, tracked debris lends itself to mitigation through long range planning and operational movement of the space elevator tether at the correct altitude and time. This threat then becomes manageable.

Finding 8-5: Tracked debris will, on average, impact a single 60km stretch of a LEO space elevator every 18 years and every five years in the peak regions if no avoidance action is taken. In addition, there are some operational satellites that might choose to lessen their risks by planning their orbit maneuvers to coincide with the prediction of conjunctions with the tether.

Finding 8-6: The threat from LEO Space Debris is manageable with relatively modest design and operational procedures. For small debris, tether design will enable survivability while for tracked debris, movement will prevent collision.

Chapter 9
Concept of Operations

9.1 Background

The International Space Elevator Consortium (ISEC) conducted a major year-long study addressing operations for a Space Elevator. The quotation below was taken from the preface of the final report and lays the framework for this chapter. Much of the information presented and discussed in this chapter came from the report entitled "Space Elevator Concept of Operations" (ISEC, 2013) with permission of the authors:

> *"While the development of Space Elevator tether and climber is a daunting task, their operation will leverage 50 years of satellite operations. The climber is essentially a satellite just like the thousands that have been launched to date. The classic "telemetry, tracking, and command" functions (TT&C) for the climber and tether operations will be the same as those for today's satellites."*

```
Operations for a Space Elevator
    Have No Showstoppers,
    Have Reasonable Costs, &
    Meet the Challenges.
```

This chapter presents an initial high level Concept of Operations for a single tether space elevator. The concept will be cloned for the follow-on space elevators with, of course, cost savings from the learning curve improvement. In addition, pairs of space elevators operating together could leverage the support infrastructure for more savings. The vision of a space elevator infrastructure is shown in Figure 9-1.

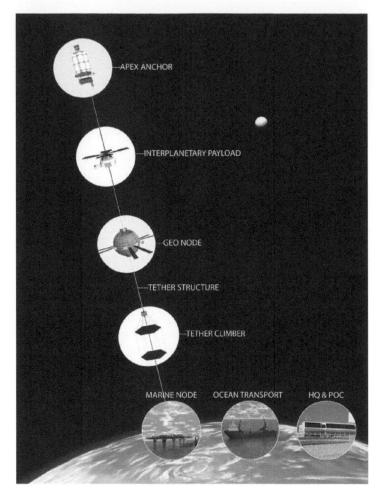

Figure 9-1. Space Elevator Infrastructure [chasedesignstudios.com]

Included in this chapter, in addition to a first look at an operations concept, are a visual operational view; a breakout of operations centers and major components of the space elevator; a look at the communications architecture; and, a sizing of support requirements in the sense of staffing.

9.2 Concept of Operations Definition

The development of an early operations concept ensures the team considers various aspects of the system of systems infrastructure and how the various functions match different facilities, locations and staffing during the design phase. This chapter will establish three parts of the operational concept and lay out the elements of a space elevator as a starting point for the community. These parts will be:

- Operational View #1 [top level view] of the system of systems.
- Breakout of the operations centers and their locations/facilities.
- Staffing and Cost Estimates.

2

A mission operations concept specifies how the mission operations system will meet mission objectives. This chapter frames the Concept of Operations (CONOPS) for a future space elevator. The CONOPS:

- Describes - in operator and user terms - operational attributes of the mission's on-orbit and ground-based elements.
- Provides derived requirements for the mission operations system in time for the initial systems requirements document.
- Emphasizes areas where trades can be made to minimize lifecycle costs and get better information from the mission.
- Requires different discipline experts [designers, users, operators] to communicate with each other.
- Assures that the operations organization provides a tested and certified mission operations system to meet requirements at the lowest cost.

9.3 Overview
The space community has developed a technique for looking at complex system of systems through a series of Operations Views (OV). Each one has a specific purpose and can be easily explained within the architecture community. They vary from simple top-level views (OV #1) to complex relationships, such as the communications architecture, and can be leveraged to illustrate the "white spaces" between different competing and conflicting functions and facilities. This Operations Concept will portray the OV #1 of the space elevator architecture as a starting point for understanding the complexity of the mission and execution of activities. Figure 9-2 is the Operations View for a Space Elevator. Each of the operations centers and elements is discussed in the paragraphs below, while Table 9-I shows a summary of the functions and locations.

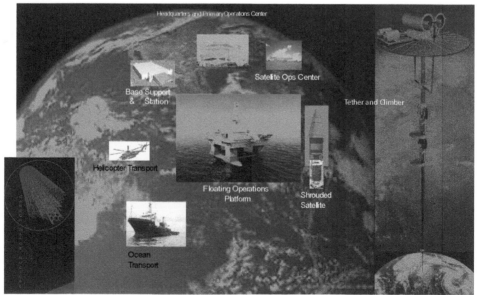

Figure 9-2. Space Elevator OV-1

3

Function	Location
Enterprise Operations Center	HQ & Primary Ops Center
Transportation Operations Center	HQ & POC
Climber Operations Center	HQ & POC
Tether Operations Center	HQ & POC
GEO Node Operations Center	HQ & POC
Marine Node Operations Center	Marine Node
Payload (Satellite) Operations Center	Owner's Ops Center

Table 9-I. Operations Centers of the Space Elevator

9.3.1 Headquarters and Primary Operations Center (HQ&POC)

The HQ&POC hosts key elements of conducting the business of transporting payloads to and from space. The business side will be the Enterprise Operations Center while day-to-day execution of activities will be segmented out to various operations centers co-located within the HQ&POC. The HQ will represent the corporation while the POC will consolidate operational functions of the system of systems. Table 9-II shows significant functions to be handled by the HQ&POC (Squibb, Boden and Larson, 1996; Larson *et al.*, 2009). A characteristic of this is that operations for a space elevator transportation infrastructure are segmented into multiple operations centers. This co-location is by design as two factors will dominate: (1) the communications architecture will allow 24/7/365 connectivity to anywhere in the infrastructure, and (2) co-locations should maximize efficiencies and minimize staffing demands. These operational activities will be conducted remotely, such as at the Marine Node, or in the future, at the GEO Node. The functions to be accomplished at the HQ&POC, in addition to the co-located operations centers, as shown in Figure 9-3, are:

- MP - Mission Planning
- APD - Activity Planning and Development
- MC - Mission Control
- DTD - Data Transport and Delivery
- NPA - Navigation Planning and Analysis
- CPA - Climber Planning and Analysis
- PPA - Customer Payload Planning and Analysis
- CDP - Climber Data Processing
- AMD - Archiving and Maintaining the Mission Database
- SEIT - Systems Engineering, Integration and Test
- CCS - Computers and Communications Support
- DMS - Developing and Maintaining Software
- MMO - Managing Mission Operations
- FMS - Financial Management

4

Headquarters and Primary Operations

		Corp. HQ	HQ TOC	EOC	Primary Operations Center — Climber	Primary Operations Center — GEO Node	Primary Operations Center — Tether	BSS*
Mission Planning	MP				x	x	x	
Activity Planning and Development	APD		x	x				x
Mission Control	MC				x	x	x	
Data Transport and Delivery	DTD			x				x
Navigation Planning and Analysis	NPA				x	x	x	
Climber Planning and Analysis	CPA				x			
Payload Planning and Analysis	PPA				x	x		x
Climber Data Processing	CDP				x		x	
Archiving and Maintaining Databases	AMD			x				
Sys Engr Integration & Test	SEIT	x		x				
Computers and Comms Supp	CCS	x		x				
Developing - Maintaining Software	DMS	x		x				
Managing Mission Ops	MMO			x	x	x	x	
Financial Management	FMS	x		x				

*might   Not be   co-   located

Table 9-II. HQ&POC Functions

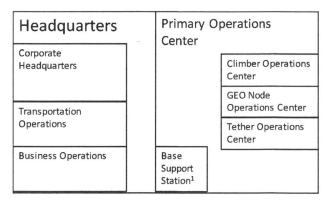

¹BSS could be not co-located

Figure 9-3. Layout of HQ&POC

The HQ&POC can be located anywhere; but, for the initial concept, it will be located in the greater San Diego, California area. It will have communications to all the other elements with an operations center staffed 24/7/365. Other sites closer to the Marine Node will be studied. Candidate sites must have both an international airport and a port on the Pacific Ocean. Stability of the government and overall security for personnel, equipment, and facilities will also be factors. The following sections discuss the various operations centers within the HQ&POC, address distribution of the operational activities, and look at staffing required. An organizational chart for the HQ&POC is shown in Figure 9-4 below.

5

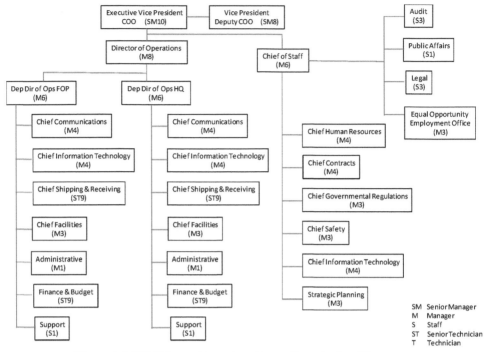

Figure 9-4. HQ/Primary Operations Center Organization Chart

9.3.2   Base Support Station (BSS)

If not co-located with the Headquarters, this will be the forward support base for operations. Its focus will be on processing supplies, satellites [climber payloads], and climbers for transportation to/from the Marine Node(MN). This will probably be located at a port for loading purposes. Staffing estimates are included with HQ&POC estimates.

9.3.3   Enterprise Operations Center (EOC)

This EOC is home for all business operations activities as well as administrative and logistics functions necessary for supporting operations of the space elevator infrastructure. This will be the location for the lead on all financial transactions [Financial Management function] within the corporate infrastructure throughout the various facilities and centers spread around the world. The corporation headquarters is located at the HQ&POC to ensure day-to-day cognizance of the space elevator's business environment. The Enterprise Operation Center will focus on revenue and expenses for operations across the corporation. Operations will range from strategic planning, for the enterprise, to the research and development needs of future implementations. Day-to-day operations across the enterprise will motivate sound business practices while conducting a transportation enterprise.

9.3.4 Transportation Operations Center (TOC)

All transportation aspects of the enterprise will be controlled from the TOC. This is where customer payloads and climbers will be tracked. Location and status information will be monitored from the factory to the BSS to the MN, and followed up the space elevator. The OGVs were discussed in more detail within chapter 5. Monitoring of returned payloads and climbers will also be done from here. Arrangements for the ocean going vessels will be

6

conducted as well as planning for air transportation. There will be two or more of these vessels for the transport of satellites, climbers, equipment, supplies, and personnel to and from FOPs. This will include picking up climbers at the descending tether FOP and delivering them to the ascending FOP. Occasionally, recovered satellites will be picked up for delivery to the BSS. The ocean going vessel must be capable to making the round trip [approximately 5 days each way at 30 knots] to the FOPs without refueling. Most likely, OGVs will be owned and operated by a vendor.

9.3.5 Climber Operations Center (COC)
This is the where tether climber operations are conducted. It is one of the main functions of HQ&POC. Its functions include activity planning for each climber, delivery of each to Marine Node, attachment to tether, climb activities, and maintenance of the various climbers on the tether and in process for being attached to or detached from the tether. It is likely that the center would keep track of all tether climbers that are finished raising, or lowering, cargo to altitude. Each climber will be fully instrumented for health and engineering status with connectivity through the climber's TT&C equipment and a supporting communication architecture. Climber operations will consist mainly of monitoring the health and status of the climber, such as; rate of climb, temperatures of the motor(s) and wheels, and other health and status data. In addition, the information of the customer payloads will be co-mingled with climber information and passed on to their operations centers in a periodic manner.

Some climbers will perform repair operations which will likely be a combination of autonomous and operator involved operations. The climber will be directed to stop and set its "parking brake" for periods of time due to solar array power generation limitations. Movement of the tether to avoid space debris might also require the climber to park for a while. After achieving the satellite's deployment altitude, the climber, likely using its own robotic arms, will assist in removing the protective covering from the satellite and positioning it away from the tether so any thrusting of the satellite will not harm the climber or the tether. This may be accomplished by the satellite itself autonomously or under control from the SOC. Deployment from the container will be analogous to deployment from the top of a rocket. One evolutionary path may lead to the situation where the climber is equipped with a robotic arm to perform shroud removal and satellite deployment. Such an arm would also be useful for receiving and securing satellites for a return to the earth.

The mission for the tether climbers will be varied and drive the actual movement. Initially, the climbers will go from the Marine Node to the GEO Node and then after off-loading the cargo, will probably be added to the mass of the Apex Anchor by raising to that altitude through a positive force when centripetal is larger than gravitational. Once operations has matured, the climbers will be re-usable and will decend as well as ascent. This allows the climbers to drop off customer payloads at the altitude/orbits of choice for individual missions. After deployment of the payload at a mission orbit, the climber will continue to rise to the GEO node where it will be de-mated from the tether and ferried to the other GEO node for the descending tether. It may be loaded with a satellite for return to the Earth's surface or it may pick up one on its descent. The climber, with payload, will ascend at a rate of meters to tens of meters per second while receiving energy from solar panels. This would enable a round trip of about two weeks. During periods when power is not available, the climber will remain stationary. Batteries on the climber and/or the satellite may be used to enable communication with the Floating Operations Platform (FOP) and to perform housekeeping tasks. In future operations, the climber may continue to higher altitudes with or without additional payloads and reaching altitude where it will act as part of the apex anchor.

7

When arriving at the FOP, the climber will be de-mated, inspected, and repaired, as necessary. If another satellite payload is ready for lift, it will be mated to the climber and the climber will be mated to the tether. Note, the satellite may be mated after the climber is mated to the tether. When the second tether is deployed, returned climbers will be transported to the partner FOP.

9.3.6 Tether Operations Center
Tether/ribbon operations will consist mostly of operations personnel at the HQ. Their principle responsibility will be to know the location and expected motion of each element of the space elevator. This responsibility is to understand how to adapt the natural motions [climber motion, initiation of climb, movement out of the way of space debris, and motion around the GEO node] for the operational needs. Knowledge of the three-dimensional location of all elements of a space elevators tether [assume an element is approximately five km long] is important to operations of the total system of systems. Each tether climber location will need to be known continuously and monitored as to speed and expected location in the near future. This will enable the tether operations crew to understand their situation at all times. Concern for space debris impact becomes critical to successful operations through location maneuvering. This will consist mostly of operations personnel monitoring the probability of space debris impacting a tether. US Strategic Command (USSTRAT) will send out advisories predicting close approaches between large objects and the space elevator tether(s).

Tether managers will decide whether to reel the tether in or out (and how much) to avoid possible collisions. Reeling out just a few meters of tether from the GEO host can impart tens of kilometers of lateral distance. The real time feedback of location of tether elements will assist the operations team in pre-planning, execution, and projection into the future. Looking at an altitude of 660 km:
- 10 meters spooled out from GEO results in a little over 26 km lateral movement in the LEO region
- 100 meters spooled out results in about 83 km
- 1 km spooled out results in about 265 km

Managers will also decide whether or not to re-position after the predicted collision event. Tether operations will include gathering of positional data for the tether(s) and reporting to USSTRAT. Note that debris avoidance can include re-positioning of the Marine Node terminus itself. In addition, the team will monitor the health of the tether and schedule repair functions to be carried out as well, including the "splicing" that might be necessary for construction of additional tethers.

9.3.7 GEO Node Operations Center
The initial GEO node will have only robotic operations. As such, the operations center will be remoted to the HQ&POC. In the future when humans operate at the GEO Node, the operations center will be handling all tasks assigned to the large facility in GEO. Off-loading and on-loading of cargo to the tether climber will be conducted at this zero-g location to facilitate delivery to the Geosynchronous Ring of operational satellites. The assembly facility will be capable of fully enabling satellites after their rise from the ocean to geosynchronous altitude. The satellites will then be "sent off" to their operational locations using either a tug or by their own power so that they reach their appropriate locations. This geosynchronous station could be used to off-load satellites going to the planets, initiate them for flight, on-load

8

them back to the space elevator and then watch them until they depart their climber in their high energy trajectories. A minor task is the de-mating of climbers from the tether and mating with a ferry for transport to another tether. In the future, refueling will be a principle mission at the GEO node as it is relatively inexpensive to deliver fuel via a climber rather than to launch with it. In addition, operations of the Apex Anchor will be controlled at the GEO Node Operations Center at HQ&POC. Apex Anchor operations will have major activity during construction with minimum activity once commercial operations commence. There may be some center of mass management that would reel the apex anchor in or out, along with active control of tether dynamic modes. Precise location knowledge will be important to enable the dynamics simulations to predict tether element locations accurately.

9.3.8 Marine Node

This is the virtual city on a floating platform in the eastern Pacific. The Floating Operations Platform will be the size of an aircraft carrier or large oil tanker. Its primary purpose is to function as terminus for the tether supporting mating and de-mating of satellites and climbers. It will have living quarters, kitchen, laundry, recreational, and medical facilities. It supports helicopter landings and loading/unloading from ocean going vehicles. The FOP hosts a local Operations Center for management of tether and platform operations. In addition, the center supports climber operations including operations/maintenance of the tether. A notional organization chart is shown in Figure 9-5.

The FOP can be a drillship which comes in two types: 1) It can be a ship which was designed and built to be a drilling vessel; or 2) It can be an older vessel which has been refitted with drilling equipment, or in our case, refitted to perform the functions of the FOP described above. Drill-ships are self-propelled, carrying a complete ship's crew while underway, as well as a crew of drilling operational personnel. Drill-ships are stabilized by either a standard anchoring system or by dynamic positioning of the vessel. Dynamic positioning is the use of a computer-operated inboard thruster system which keeps the vessel on location without the use of anchors. The FOP will be painted in red and white checkerboard to enhance visibility. It's position will be reported to oceanic and space centers to diminish the probability of collisions. It will have audible and visible warning lights and a keep-out zone for safety and security. More detailed discussions are provided in chapter 5 together with images.

9

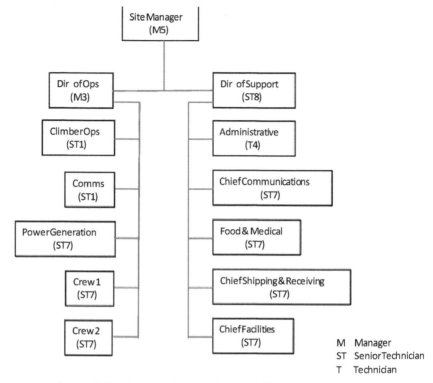

Figure 9-5. Marine Node Organizational Chart

9.3.9 Customer's Satellite Operations Center (SOC)
This is the satellite owner's Operations Center located at their facility. The satellite, while in transit, will be in contact with the GEO node, which will provide telemetry to the Customer's Satellite Operations Center.

9.4 Customer Satellite Flow Process - Space Elevator Cargo
The flow of a customer's satellite from their manufacturing facility to orbit is discussed as a six step process. These are the entities to be lifted to a predetermined altitude for release into their chosen orbit. Non-GEO releases will often require apogee lowering and inclination change maneuvers to achieve their desired operational orbits. This could be done with their own internal thrusters or through the use of a space tug.

Step One – Designing and Building: Satellite designs are initially expected to be similar to those for launch with rockets. New designs, with new materials such as CNTs, will evolve. If not already included, the satellites will have the ability to interface to the climber's data up/downlink to provide telemetry and command capability for the lift to orbital altitude. It will also be able to receive power from the climber.

Step Two – Move to FOP: Upon completion of system integrations at the satellite builder's factory, the satellite will be placed in a container to provide protection from weather that would be expected to be encountered during transportation from factory to San Diego International Airport. Upon arrival at the airport, the satellite, and any support equipment, will

10

be off loaded and transported to the Base Support Station in the greater San Diego area where it will be stored until ready to be taken to the FOP. The climber interface (power and T&C) may be used while in storage or while being transported. From the BSS, it will be trucked to the terminal for the ocean going cargo vessel (OGV). It will then be loaded onto the OGV, secured, and transported to the FOP in the eastern Pacific Ocean. Transit time will depend upon the OGV's speed and the weather. The container will be capable of being lifted by crane or forklift. This will allow wheeled movement in the BSS and on the deck of the FOP. The satellite will remain in the container until it is ready to be deployed in space from a tether climber.

Step Three – FOP Processing: Upon arriving at the FOP, the satellite will be lifted to the deck and wheeled to the location where mating [including power and communications] with the climber will occur. Weather or other situations may make it necessary to wheel it into temporary storage. At the appropriate time, the satellite, in its container, will be mated to the climber. The climber may have been mated to the tether already. If not, the climber and mated satellite will be mated to the tether. Testing will occur to confirm climber and satellite are in the desired state. This would include coordination with the base station, HQ, and possibly to the satellite's control center. Corrective actions will be taken as necessary.

Step Four – The Climb: The climber, with customer's satellite payload, will ascend while receiving energy from solar panels. During periods when power is not available, the climber will remain stationary ["parking brake set"]. Batteries on the climber and/or the satellite may be used to enable communication with the FOP.

Step Five – Release: At the desired altitude, the shroud on the satellite will be removed at the direction of the satellite owner. This may be accomplished by the satellite itself autonomously or remotely from the SOC. Deployment from the container will be analogous to deployment from the top of a rocket. One evolutionary path may lead to the climber being equipped with a robotic arm to perform shroud removal and satellite deployment. The satellite will then conduct the appropriate, and traditional, activities for satellite checkout for operations. The actual release should be low energy without "rocket-like" accelerations.

Step Six – Return: Initially, a robotic arm would be useful for receiving and securing satellites for a return to the earth. At this point, the climber may begin its return trip. In future operations, the climber may continue to higher altitudes, with or without additional payloads, and reach an altitude where it will be additional mass at the apex anchor. Operations for descending climbers will be similar to those for ascending. With gravity assisting, rates may be higher and monitoring of the braking function will dominate.

9.5 Communications Architecture
The space elevator infrastructure has a communication architecture that supports all the facets of operations. This would include the communications hub at the GEO node with its direct communications to all the elements of the space elevator system. The control of the climber switches from the FOP to the HQ&POC shortly after it begins to rise above the platform. The communications links are then set up with the GEO node and connectivity into all the other elements. The GEO node connects to the FOP and to the HQ&POC with high through-put links. In addition, all other elements of the space elevator system can connect through these links to the GEO node and tie-in with customers, satellite operators, elevator climbers, FOPs, ocean going ships, and personnel around the world. Figure 9-6 shows the communications architecture.

11

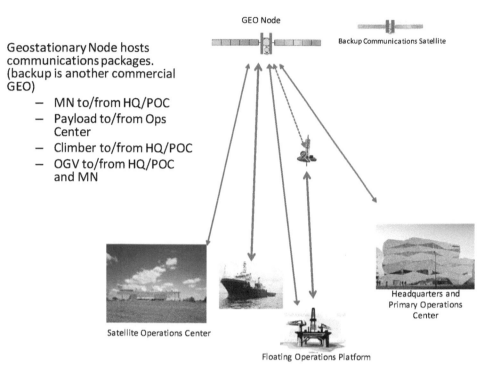

Geostationary Node hosts communications packages. (backup is another commercial GEO)
- MN to/from HQ/POC
- Payload to/from Ops Center
- Climber to/from HQ/POC
- OGV to/from HQ/POC and MN

GEO Node

Backup Communications Satellite

Satellite Operations Center

Floating Operations Platform

Headquarters and Primary Operations Center

Figure 9-6. Communications Architecture

9.6 Operations and Maintenance Staffing and Costs

The layout of the staffing and costs for a single space elevator infrastructure is shown in the following charts (Figures 9-7 to 9-11). Of course, this is a rough estimate based on 40 years of space operations experience and current estimates of equipment, staffing and other expenses. The bottom line is that this set of figures will give a good estimate of how to layout an operations infrastructure with a rough estimate of costs. The following figures show the staffing and O&M costs for the HQ and the FOP for a single space elevator tether. Each terminus would require additional staffing as a FOP. HQ would stay pretty much the same for the second tether and go up slightly for each additional pair.

Executive Vice President COO				1	Facilities		1
	Executive Asst			1		Sr Techs	5
VP Deputy COO				1		Jr Techs	5
					Admin & Support		1
Chief of Staff				1		Sr Techs	3
	Dep COS			1		Jr Techs	5
	Admin Asst			1	Finance and Budget		1
	Audit			1		Specialists	3
		Techs		2		Specialists	3
	Public Affairs			1	Climber Ops		1
	Legal			2		Engrs	2
	EEO			1		Techs	2
	Human Resources			1			
		Techs		2	Dep Dir FOP		1
	Contracts			1	Commun ications		1
		Contract Specialists		4		Specialists	3
		Contract Administrators		4	Informati on Technolo gy		1
		Govermental Regulations		1		Techs	3
			Specialist	1	Shipping and Receivin g		1
		Safety		1		Sr Techs	2
			Specialist	1		Jr Techs	4
		Information Technology		1	Facilities		1
			Engineers	2		Sr Techs	5
			Techs	4		Jr Techs	5
		Strtegic Planning		1	Admin		1
			Engineers	2		Sr Techs	2
						Jr Techs	2
Director Operations				1	Finance and Budget		1
	Dep Dir HQ			1		Specialists	3
		Communications		1		Specialists	3
			Specialists	3	Support		1
			GEO SAT OPS	3		Sr Techs	1
		Information Technology		1		Jr Techs	3
			Techs	3		Med Tech	1
		Shipping and Receiving		1			
			Sr Techs	2			136
			Jr Techs	4			

Figure 9-7. HQ O&M Staffing

13

			HQ & Base Support Monthly Costs			
Fuel	2000					$2,000
Food	0					
Supplies	3000					$3,000
Comms	3000					$3,000
Building Lease	17000	Assume 100 sq ft per person plus 25% for larger offices for management and conference rooms				
Warehouse Lease	5000	Assume large enough to store 2 weeks of supplies plus 2 climber and 2 satellites. Assume 5000 sq ft				
Single Lease	23000		per sq ft	100	$2,300,000
Electric	6000					$6,000
Water	300					$3,000
Monthly						$2,317,000
Annually						$27,804,000
		To build our own building @___ per square foot			250	$5,750,000

Figure 9-8. HQ O&M Costs

Executive Vice President COO				SM10	1	$250,000
	Executive Asst			ST8	1	$54,000
VP Deputy COO				SM8	1	$170,000
Chief of Staff				SM6	1	$110,000
	Dep COS			M5	1	$90,000
	Admin Asst			ST8	1	$54,000
	Audit			M3	1	$60,000
		Techs		ST7	2	$108,000
	Public Affairs			M1	1	$45,000
	Legal			M3	2	$120,000
	EEO			ST8	1	$54,000
	Human Resources			M4	1	$75,000
		Techs		ST7	2	$108,000
	Contracts			M4	1	$75,000
		Contract Specialists		ST7	4	$216,000
		Contract Administrators		ST7	4	$216,000
		Govermental Regulations		M3	1	$60,000
			Specialist	ST7	1	$54,000
		Safety		M3	1	$60,000
			Specialist	ST7	1	$54,000
		Information Technology		M4	1	$75,000
			Engineers	M3	2	$120,000
			Techs	ST7	4	$216,000
		Strtegic Planning		M3	1	$60,000
			Engineers	M1	2	$90,000

Figure 9-9. HQ Staff Costs

15

Position	Role	Grade	Qty	Cost
Director Operations		O8	1	$170,000
Dep Dir HQ		O6	1	$110,000
Communications		O4	1	$75,000
	Specialists	E7	3	$162,000
	GEO SAT OPS	E7	3	$162,000
Information Technology		O3	1	$60,000
	Techs	E7	3	$162,000
Meteorology		O3	1	$60,000
Shipping and Receiving		E9	1	$60,000
	Sr Techs	E7	2	$108,000
	Jr Techs	E4	4	$156,000
Facilities		O3	1	$60,000
	Sr Techs	E7	5	$270,000
	Jr Techs	E3	5	$170,000
Admin & Support		O1	1	$45,000
	Sr Techs	E7	3	$162,000
	Jr Techs	E3	5	$170,000
Finance and Budget		E9	1	$60,000
	Specialists	E7	3	$180,000
	Specialists	E3	3	$102,000
Climber Ops		O3	1	$60,000
	Engrs	O1	2	$90,000
	Techs	E7	2	$108,000
Dep Dir FOP		O6	1	$110,000
Communications		O4	1	$75,000
	Specialists	E7	3	$54,000
Information Technology		O3	1	$60,000
	Techs	E7	3	$162,000
Shipping and Receiving		E9	1	$60,000
	Sr Techs	E7	2	$108,000
	Jr Techs	E4	4	$156,000
Facilities		O3	1	$60,000
	Sr Techs	E7	5	$270,000
	Jr Techs	E3	5	$170,000
Admin		O1	1	$45,000
	Sr Techs	E7	2	$108,000
	Jr Techs	E3	2	$68,000
Finance and Budget		E9	1	$60,000
	Specialists	E7	3	$162,000
	Specialists	E3	3	$102,000
Support		O1	1	$45,000
	Sr Techs	E7	1	$54,000
	Jr Techs	E3	3	$102,000
	Med Tech	E7	1	$54,000
	Guard Sup	E8	1	$54,000
	Guards	E4	4	$39,000
			142	$7,534,000

Figure 9-9. HQ Staff Costs [continued]

16

Site Manager				1
	Admin/Support			1
	Operations			1
		Deck Officer		1
		Deck Hands		2
		Training		0
		Trainee		1
		Comms		1
		Comm Techs		0
		Power Gen		1
	Support			0
		Food Prep		0
		Medical		1
		Laundry		0
1	Crew			10
2	Crews			20
3	Crews			30

Figure 9-10, Single FOP O&M Staff

Site Manager			M5	1	$90,000	
	Admin/Support		T7	1	$54,000	
	Operations		M3	1	$60,000	
		Deck Officer	ST8	1	$204,000	
		Deck Hands	T5	2	$88,000	
		Training	ST7	0	$54,000	
		Trainee	T7	1	$44,000	
		Comms	ST7	1	$54,000	
		Comm Techs	T5	0	$0	
		Power Gen	T5	1	$44,000	
		Platform Maint	T5	6	$264,000	
	Support		ST8	0	$54,000	
		Food Prep	T5	3	$132,000	Shared among crew members
		Medical	ST6	1	$49,000	
		Laundry	T3	0	$0	Each does their own.
1	Crew			19	$1,191,000	
2	Crews			38	$0	
3	Crews			57	$3,573,000	
			Total		$16,674,000	

Figure 9-11. Single FOP O&M Costs

Summarizing the data from these five Figures above, we estimate annual costs in Table 9-III.

Yearly Operations Costs

HQ&POC Facilities O&M	28,000,000 build own facility for $ 6 million
HQ&POC staffing	7,500,000
Marine Node (2) Facilities O&M	30,400,000
Marine Node (2) Staffing	33,400,000
Total Yearly	$99,300,000

Table 9-III. Yearly Operations Costs

9.7 Findings and Conclusion
Below are the findings of the ISEC Report and, therefore, this chapter.

Finding 9-1: Operation of the space elevator will leverage over 50 years of experience in operating satellite systems. The tether climber, Apex Anchor, and GEO node are essentially satellites. Space elevator operations will be an easy extension of today's practices. Operations centers will look very much like today's satellite operations centers.

Finding 9-2: Operation of the space elevator will leverage more than a hundred years of experience in off-shore drilling operations. The Floating Operations Platform will likely be a modified drilling platform. Support to off-shore drilling platforms is a mature industry.

Finding 9-3: The operation and maintenance costs appear to be reasonable.

The conclusion from the study of future operations for a space elevator infrastructure is:

> Operations for a Space Elevator
> Have No Showstoppers,
> Have Reasonable Costs, &
> Meet the Challenges.

Chapter 10 Technology Assessment[1]

10.1 Background
This chapter has two major sections: Technology Assessment and Near-Term Research Projects. This chapter will assess the space elevator technologies by addressing the Technology Readiness Levels [TRL] and the risk versus consequence analysis. During the first half of the chapter, the technology assessment looks at the availability of technology today, the realizability of technology within a given time, and looks at the risk/trade of consequence and likelihood. The second half presents the research projects that should have immediate starts in 2013. There is a near-term need for basic understanding of the concepts to support a full-up development program.

10.2   Approach for Describing Technology Assessments
This chapter will identify the major segments of the space elevator that are unique to the system and discuss the technological challenges and their associated risk to the project. While pitfalls are expected, each technology seems to be achievable in the not too distant future. One key to the projection into the future is that the approach taken is that the technology will be "good enough." The designers of major space elevator segments will not wait for the "best" solutions depending on future materials. This technology assessment will be applied to the following major segments of the space elevator:

- Tether Material
- Tether Climber
- Apex Anchor
- GEO Node
- Marine Node
- High Stage One
- Dynamics Simulations
- Total Systems of Systems.

This study starts with a robotic space elevator with sufficient capacity to become a commercial success without requiring it to be human rated. This enables systems engineers to plan for the system with an appropriate safety factor [already discussed in Chapter 6 as safety factor of 1.4]. Each of the major segments of a space elevator infrastructure is shown in separate chapters. This included discussions on the components as well as any major constraints or requirements/specifications that are unique.

The following five-step process will be accomplished for each major segment. Each process step will help the reader understand future developments of space elevator sub-systems.

Step One: Availability of technology today and by 2030
Evaluations of the chosen segments define whether a similar system already exists in the world or not. If the technology of similar systems can be applied to a space elevator it reinforces the prediction that the segment will be real in the future. Lack of parallel developments from known systems leads to more risk.

---

[1] Space Elevator Roadmap Development Team in Japan (Japan Space Elevator Association, Nihon University, Tokai University and Earth-Track Corporation; Reviewed by Yoshio Aoki/Nihon University and Minoru Sato/Tokai University)

Step Two: Realizable time of technology within a given time
Estimate the approximate year a segment will be mature "enough," based upon reference documents/plans, such as the "Technological Strategy Map" from the Ministry of Economy, Trade and Industry of Japan" (JSTM, 2010). It does not require the development to be by the space elevator infrastructure team; but, it must be real in the sense of an estimate of the maturation of segment technologies.

Step Three: Expected year of availability for in-space segment
It is similar to Realizable Time; but, it is estimated directly for a specific segment of a space elevator. Additional information was gained from reviewing "NASA Space Technology Roadmaps and Priorities: Restoring NASA's Technological Edge and Paving the Way for a New Era in Space" (NTRM, 2012). Extrapolation from terrestrial technologies to space technologies requires additional verification and validation (V&V) periods. These V&V requirements were shown in the previous chapters dealing with each major segment.

Step Four: Current TRL and expected TRL by 2030.
NASA's TRL definitions provide a starting point for discussions on the topic of when will a technology be ready for the space elevator.

Step Five: A look at the consequence vs. likelihood of failure chart
This chart shows the impact and likelihood of a risk actually occurring. The impact is shown in a 1 to 5 range [5 being highest risk] while the likelihood shows the probability of occurrence. These charts are shown for each of the segments of the infrastructure.

The idea that the future can be laid out in a logical manner exists in the minds of all futurists. However, anyone who has lived through a development program for a new space system knows that surprises are frequent and the "unknown-unknowns" will keep arising. As such, NASA and others have found that using the Technology Readiness Levels is a method to estimate the difficulty of incorporating new technologies into space systems. Through long years of discovery through trial and error, major progress has been made and the space industry essentially knows how to build for this hostile environment. The space elevator system will provide a new series of surprises to developers; however, the space systems engineers will move forward through their understanding of the hostile environment, large challenges ahead, and rewards for success. The best estimates are just that - "estimates." As such, this cosmic study will provide at least two looks at estimated dates of material development and segment implementation. Each will be laid out with documentation and a realization that at any moment a major breakthrough could occur and change all the estimates. NASA, JAXA and ESA have been doing this for decades and leverage the following TRL's for guidance. The definition of each of the levels is given below:

• **TRL 1 Basic principles observed and reported:** Transition from scientific research to applied research. Essential characteristics and behaviors of systems and architectures. Descriptive tools are mathematical formulations or algorithms.
• **TRL 2 Technology concept and/or application formulated:** Applied research. Theory and scientific principles are focused on specific application area to define the concept. Characteristics of the application are described. Analytical tools are developed for simulation or analysis of the application.

- **TRL 3 Analytical and experimental critical function and/or characteristic proof-of-concept:** Proof of concept validation. Active Research and Development (R&D) is initiated with analytical and laboratory studies. Demonstration of technical feasibility using breadboard or brass-board implementations that are exercised with representative data.
- **TRL 4 Component/subsystem validation in laboratory environment:** Standalone prototyping implementation and test. Integration of technology elements. Experiments with full-scale problems or data sets.
- **TRL 5 System/subsystem/component validation in relevant environment:** Thorough testing of prototyping in representative environment. Basic technology elements integrated with reasonably realistic supporting elements. Prototyping implementations conform to target environment and interfaces.
- **TRL 6 System/subsystem model or prototyping demonstration in a relevant end-to-end environment [ground or space]:** Prototyping implementations on full-scale realistic problems. Partially integrated with existing systems. Limited documentation available. Engineering feasibility fully demonstrated in actual system application.
- **TRL 7 System prototyping demonstration in an operational environment (ground or space):** System prototyping demonstration in operational environment. System is at or near scale of the operational system, with most functions available for demonstration and test. Well integrated with collateral and ancillary systems. Limited documentation available.
- **TRL 8 Actual system completed and "mission qualified" through test and demonstration in an operational environment (ground or space):** End of system development. Fully integrated with operational hardware and software systems. Most user documentation, training documentation, and maintenance documentation completed. All functionality tested in simulated and operational scenarios. Verification and Validation (V&V) completed.
- **TRL 9 Actual system "mission proven" through successful mission operations (ground or space):** Fully integrated with operational hardware/software systems. Actual system has been thoroughly demonstrated and tested in its operational environment. All documentation completed. Successful operational experience. Sustaining engineering support in place. □The reality of developing a mega-project is that components of the design fall within all categories and different levels of "care and feeding" must be applied.

10.2.1 Tether Material Technology Assessment
The tether material was described in Chapter 3. The four steps to understand the future technological progress are applied in this section.

Steps 1 and 2 – Realizable time of the System
Based upon research for the "Strategic Technology Map 2010 by Minister of Economy, Trade and Industry of Japan" (JSTM, 2010), realizable time of each material characteristic for a Space Elevator as shown in Table 10-I.

Tether Materials (CNT)	Available in 2012	Realizable year	Remarks
Technology Mass production (Cost Reduction)	Not Available	2020	First to be accomplished for terrestrial uses. Needs to be "perfect" for the space elevator
Quality Control High crystallization	Not Available	2017	Needed for the space elevator
High Conductivity CNT	Not Available	2019	
Structure Control Position/diameter etc. control	Not Available	2014	Needed for the space elevator
Processing Deficit/repair in Nano level	Not Available	2020	Needed for the space elevator
Applications (Products) IT and communication Wiring Material for LSI	Not Available	2016	
CNT Display	Not Available	2020	Needed for the space elevator
Flexible Transistor	Not Available	2030	
Printable Post-CMOS circuit	Not Available	2040	
Environment/Energy High Density Super Capacitor	Not Available	2013	Needed for the space elevator
Electrode catalyst for fuel cells	Not Available	2015	
Body Armor	Not Available	2020	
Ultra-light weight and high strength structure for car/airplane	Not Available	2025	Needed for the space elevator
Artificial muscle for Robot	Not Available	2030	
Space Elevator	Not Available	2050	[Chapter 3 predicts much earlier Realizable Time]

Table 10-I. Tether material Realizable Time (Not for in-Space)

Step 3 – Expected available year for space material for Space Elevator System
The expected time for the space elevator depends upon the type of system of systems that is being projected (Table 10-II). This cosmic study is designed to look at a robotic version of the space elevator that can move materials off Earth and return payloads to the surface. Additional information for comparison is from the NASA Space Technology Roadmaps (NTRM, 2012). Human rating will probably be successful by the 2050 time period, or 15 years after the robotic only version.

	Expected year for Space Elevator System	Remarks
The Tether	2032+ 2060 for fully capable system [prediction from JSTM, 2010]	For robotic space elevator infrastructure (not human rated), it seems to be reasonable to expect it earlier. Many members of the study team expect the material to be ready for a space elevator by 2032.

Table 10-II. Tether Material Expected Year for in-Space

Finding 10.1: In all technological endeavors there are projections into the future. In the case of the space elevator, this study has recognized that there are two thrusts that must be taken:

Thrust ONE: Assume Tether Material is space qualified by 2035.
Thrust TWO: Assume Tether Material is available two decades later.

Each of these two thrusts has valid research projects leading to their estimates; however, no one can predict into the future, so this study will present both cases.

Step 4 – NASA TRL Level evaluation for the system by Roadmap Team (Table 10-III)

	TRL Level	TRL Level for 2030	Remarks
The Tether	2	7	Requires major space environmental testing to include in-orbit prototype systems level testing

Table 10-III. Material NASA TRL Level

Step 5 – Project Risk Position evaluation for the system by Roadmap Team (Figure 10-1).

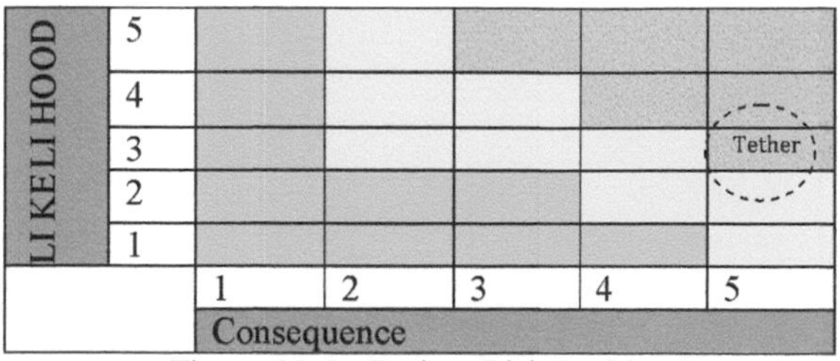

Figure 10-1. Project Risk Position Reporting

10.2.2 Tether Climber Technology Assessment

Steps 1 and 2 – Availability of the material [CNT] for the space elevator is based upon research for the "Strategic Technology Map 2010 by Minister of Economy, Trade and Industry of Japan" (JSTM, 2010). In addition, the realizable time for the CNT material is given as "expected year", with research also from the STM 2010 (Table 10-IV).

	Similar system's availability	Expected year	Remarks
Electric Power System	Battery and wiring from today's spacecraft	2012	existing
Electrical power supply	Solar systems routine today	2025	Based upon maximum use of CNT design and light weight materials Need major weight reduction and power increases for 2030 timeframe
Climbing Mechanism	Many systems today	2022	Mechanical design can be accomplished today; however, must be designed for specific tether design and space environment
Materials for Climber system	Could be done today, except for the mass reduction expected from CNT construction	Mostly available today	Major mass reduction to be accomplished by CNT design.
Command and Data handling, communication System	Available today	2012	Routine
Thermal radiation system	Available today	2012	Routine

Table 10-IV. Tether Climber System Availability & Realizability

Steps 3 and 4 – Expected available year for Climber System is shown along with the present TRL and future TRL (Table 10-V).

	Expected year for Space Elevator System	TRL Level	TRL by 2030	Remarks
Electric Power System	2012	5	9	
Electrical Power Supply	2025	5	9	Based upon maximum use of CNT design and light weight materials
Climbing Mechanism	2022	4	9	Mechanical design can be accomplished today
Materials for Climber system	Mostly available today	6	9	CNT's will be used to maximum mass reduction

	Expected year for Space Elevator System	TRL Level	TRL by 2030	Remarks
Command and Data handling, communication System	2012	9	9	routine
Thermal radiation system	2012	9	9	routine

Table 10-V. Tether Climber System Realizable Time

Step 5 – Project Risk Position evaluation for the System Climber (Figure 10-2).

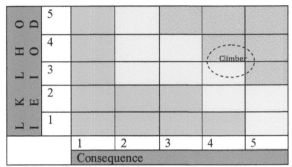

Figure 10-2. Project Risk Position Reporting

10.2.3 Apex Anchor Technology Assessment
Steps 1 and 2 – Availability and Realizable time of the Apex Anchor (Table 10-VI).

	Similar systems' availability	Expected Year	Remarks
Tether Dispenser	Available in terrestrial situations	2024	Can be adapted easily for hostile space environment. Should be proof-tested in-orbit during parallel prototype testing.
Satellite Components [propulsion, attitude control, power, communications, etc]	Routine	today	No real challenges except for the reel-in and reel-out of tether.

Table 10-VI. Apex Anchor System Availability

Steps 3 and 4 – Expected available year for Apex Anchor along with the NASA TRL Level evaluations (Table 10-VII).

	Expected Year for Apex Anchor	TRL	TRL by 2030	Remarks
Tether Dispenser	2020	4	7	Can be tested terrestrially and then in parallel prototype system level test in-orbit. Must be tested in orbit to raise the TRL so will be major component in parallel prototype system test.
Satellite Components [propulsion, attitude control, power, communications, etc]	2012	9	9	routine

Table 10-VII. Apex Anchor Realizable Time

Step 5 – Project Risk Position evaluation for the system Apex Anchor (Figure 10-3.)

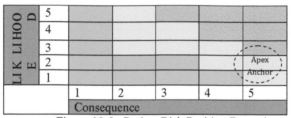

Figure 10-3. Project Risk Position Reporting -

10.2.4 GEO Node Technology Assessment

Steps 1&2 – Availability and Realizable time of the GEO Node

	Similar system's availability	Expected Year	Remarks
Tether Dispenser	Available in terrestrial situations	2024	Can be adapted easily for hostile space environment. Should be proof-tested in-orbit during parallel prototype testing.
Satellite Components [propulsion, attitude control, power, communications, etc]	Routine	today	No real challenges except for the reel-in and reel-out of tether.

Table 10-VIII. GEO Node System Availability

Steps 3 and 4 – Expected available year for GEO Node along with the NASA TRL Level evaluations (Table 10-9).

	Expected Year for Apex Anchor	TRL	TRL by 2030	Remarks
Tether Dispenser	2020	4	7	Can be tested terrestrially and then in parallel prototype system level test in-orbit. Must be tested in orbit to raise the TRL so will be major component in parallel prototype system test.
Satellite Components [propulsion, attitude control, power, communications, etc]	2012	9	9	routine

Table 10-IX. GEO Node Realizable Time and TRLs

Step 5 – Project Risk Position evaluation for the system GEO Node (Figure 10-4).

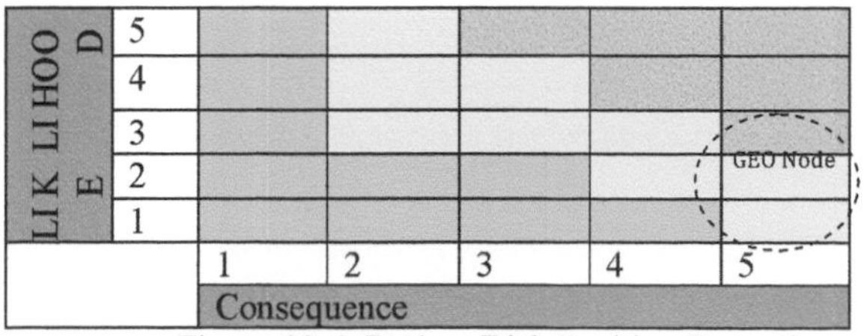

Figure 10-4. Project Risk Position Reporting

10.2.5 Marine Node Technology Assessment

Steps 1 and 2 – Availability and Realizable time of the Marine Node (Table 10-X).

	Similar system's availability	Expected Year	Remarks
Tether Anchor	Major design activity	2024	Similar to Bridge terminus; however, it must be proof-tested prior to the in-orbit parallel prototype testing.
Marine platform [stability, human support, power, communications, tether terminus, etc]	Routine	2020	Based upon Deep Sea Oil platforms

Table 10-X. Marine Node Availability

Steps 3 and 4 – Expected available year for Marine Node along with the NASA TRL Level evaluations (Table 10-XI).

	Expected Year for Marine Node	TRL	TRL by 2030	Similar to Bridge terminus
Tether Anchor	2020	5	8	Based upon Deep Sea Oil platforms
Marine platform [stability, human support, power, communications, etc]	2012	8	9	Routine, but Leveraging both deep sea oil drilling and Sea Launch platform designs

Table 10-XI. Marine Node Realizable Time and TRLs

Step 5 – Project Risk Position evaluation for the system Marine Node (Figure 10-5).

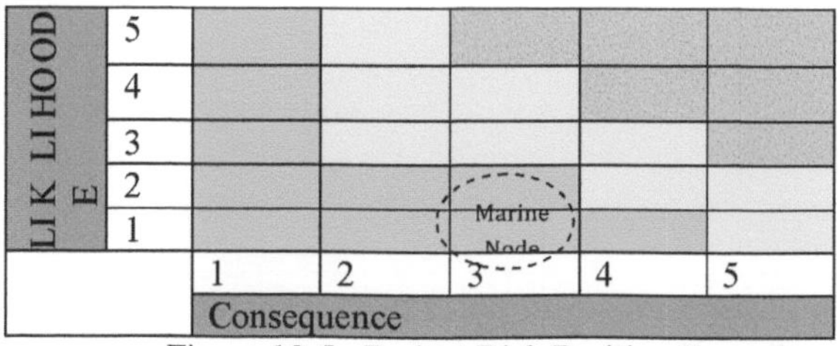

Figure 10-5. Project Risk Position Reporting

10.2.6 High Stage One Technology Assessment
Steps 1 and 2 – Availability and Realizable time of the High Stage One (Table 10-XII).

	Similar systems' availability	Expected Year	Remarks
Tether Anchor	2015	2025	Based upon deep ocean drilling platform
Platform at 40km altitude	N/A	2025	All components must be developed from concept
Altitude Support Infrastructure	N/A	2025	All components must be developed from concept
Transportation up/down	N/A	2025	All components must be developed from concept
Marine support	N/A	2025	All components must be developed from concept

Table 10-XII. High Stage One System Availability and Realizability

Steps 3 and 4 – Expected available year for High Stage One with TRLs (Table 10-XIII).

	Expected Year	TRL	TRL by 2030	Remarks
Tether Anchor	2030	4	8	Large reels are available today, but for CNT's will required development.
Platform at 40km altitude	2030	4	8	Prototypes must be developed.
Altitude Support Infrastructure	2025	4	8	Working in high-altitude will require much development of current technologies and testing for Verification and Validation.
Transportation up/down	2025	4	8	Unique and will demand major development, with V&V testing.
Marine support	2025	4	8	Essentially available today, with development for unique parts needed.

Table 10-XIII. High Stage One Realizable Time

Step 5 – Project Risk Position evaluation for the system Marine Node (Figure 10-6).

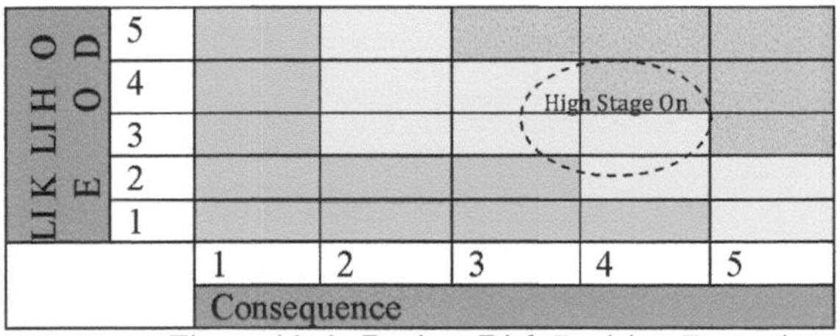

Figure 10-6. Project Risk Position Reporting

10.2.7 Dynamics and Deployment Simulation Assessment

The simulation for the dynamics and deployment of the space elevator, as described in chapter 6, are very mature and projected to be easily grown to simulate and model reality prior to flight. In addition, the parallel prototype full-up system in-orbit test will show the strengths and weaknesses of the computer simulation. There have been 30 years of space tether deployments and they model the computer simulations to a very reliable scale. There should be fewer concerns after the massive computer simulations expected and the in-orbit testing.

Step 1, 2, and 3 – Dynamics and Deployment Simulations are available today that take the details to quite a refined level. However, the key to the future is to show that the simulations can represent the key elements of the unique space elevator dynamics such as the 100,000km long first resonance and the motion induced by the movement of the tether climbers.

Step 4 – NASA TRL Level evaluation for the system for Dynamics and Deployment (Table 10-XIV).

	TRL Level	TRL by 2030	Remarks
Deployment	5	8	Maximum Simulations will be conducted by 2030.
Dynamics	6	8	Maximum Simulations will be conducted by 2030.

Table 10-XIV. Tether Deployment and Dynamics NASA TRL Level

Step 5 – Project Risk Position evaluation for the system by Roadmap Team (Figure 10-7).

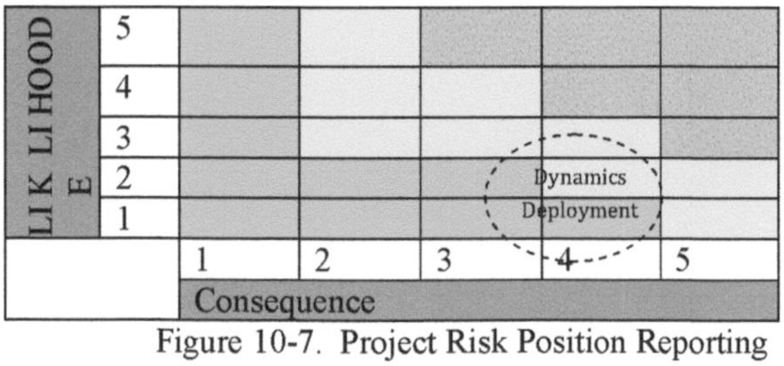

Figure 10-7. Project Risk Position Reporting

10.2.8 Integrated Systems Technology Assessment

The whole space elevator system consists of multiple major segments which will be shown as a system of systems. This complexity is usually handled at the time of deployment as they must all fit together and ensure that there are no "white spaces" between components that do not match. Many of the inputs are leveraging the NASA Roadmap Series (NTRM, 2012).

Steps 1 and 2 – The following table (10-XV) shows the systems level availability of major segments for the space elevator.

	Similar system's availability	Expected year	Remarks
The Tether	Material Exists (Not strong enough, not designed for space)	2035 + Estimates vary from 2035 to 2050 (JSTM, 2010)	Strength required for Space Elevator in long lengths in hostile environment. Needs significant testing. Estimate will vary with knowledge of material and progress in strength to weight ratio.
Apex Anchor	Satellites Exist	2020	Reel-out and control of tether must be tested in-orbit
Geosynchronous Station	Exists	today	Routine to develop
Tether Climber	Exists	2020	Satellite development is not a push; however, large light-weight solar panels will require development. Major design effort for system of climber; however, not out of the knowledge of current satellite designers. Should be tested in orbit.
Marine Node	Exist	2015	Routine except for the tether terminus. Should leverage large deep-ocean drilling platforms
High Stage One	Does not exist	2025-30	Major development – 14 year timeline. Not shown for other applications at the present time. Major breakthroughs needed in timely manner.
Ocean Going cargo Vessel	Exists	today	routine
Helicopter Transport	Exists	today	routine
Operations Centers	Exists	today	routine

Table 10-XV. Integrated System of Systems Availability

Steps 3 and 4 – Expected available years for in-Orbit Segments (Table 10-XVI).

	Expected year for Space Elevator System	TRL Level	TRL Level by 2030	Remarks
The Tether	2035+ with estimates varying to 2060 (JSTM, 2010)	2	7	Major development funding required. Terrestrial version will be available by 2030 in greater than 1,000km lengths with appropriate strength
Apex Anchor	2025	5	8	Reel-out in vacuum of long material will require design and testing of components in orbit.
Geosynchronous Station	today	6	9	routine
Tether Climber	2025	4	8	Major design effort, however, not out of the knowledge of current satellite designers
Marine Node	2015	8	9	Deep Ocean Drilling Platforms and Sea Launch platform can be a models.
High Stage One	2025-30	3	6	Major design and development effort. Major breakthroughs needed in timely manner for many of its major components.
Ocean Going cargo Vessel	today	9	9	Routine
Helicopter Transport	today	9	9	Routine
Operations Centers	today	9	9	Routine

Table 10-XVI. Integrated System Realizable Time and TRLs

Step 5 – Project Risk Position evaluation for system components: One axis is the estimate of a failure consequence to the system of systems (Figure 10-8). In addition, the other axis is for the likelihood of the failure occurring. This means that IF it fails [access vertical] it would have a consequence of an estimated magnitude scale [horizontal axis].

Figure 10-8. Project Risk Position Reporting

Finding 10.2: Based upon Thrust ONE, the space elevator should be available during the middle of the 2030 decade. Based upon Thrust TWO, the space elevator should be available after 2060. This is principally due to the availability of a tether material sufficiently strong to handle the longitudinal stresses inherent in a 100,000km long tether.

Finding 10.3: The remaining components of the space elevator have historical precedent and can be constructed as soon as needed with sufficient investment in design and production capability. The NASA Space Technology Roadmaps cover much of these major segments of the space elevator such as solar power, materials manufacturing, and nanotechnology.

10.3 Proposed Research Projects
The key to any development is the continual investment in technology and its products. The translation from research to realizable hardware is a difficult process and one that takes concerted efforts by teams of individuals with varied skills. As such, the space elevator infrastructure needs at least the following research projects initiated as soon as possible to ensure progress.

Research Projects Identified

Chapter 3 – Materials Research

Mat-1:   Requirements analysis to compare needed material
Mat-2:   Identification of alternate materials that could work
Mat-3:   Develop characteristics of CNTs for space elevator tether
Mat-4:   Understand process of "production" of 100,000km tether

Chapter 4 – Satellite and Climber Designs

Climb-1:   Design first production tether climber
Climb-2:   Design and test gripping mechanism and sub-system.
Climb-3:   Estimate solar cell characteristics necessary for climber:
            KW per kg, Radiation, heat, vacuum characteristics, Pointing approach,
            Power management for system distribution.

Chapter 5 – Apex Anchor, Marine Node & High Stage One Design Research

AA-1:   Design mission criteria for design
AA-2:   Identify approaches to supply "smart mass" to end of tether
AA-3:   Refine the thrust magnitude needed and how often
MN-1:   Identify "grappling" approach for initial attachment
MN-2:   Research reel technology for rapid and controlled activities
HSO-1:   Proof of concept demonstration of a bench-top working model
HSO-2:   Construction of progressively larger versions: 10m, 60m, 1km and 20km high

Chapter 6 - Further Research in Dynamics of Space Elevator Including:

Dyn-1:   Will boundary condition at ground station be fixed or free?

Dyn-2:	If fixed, how could the ground station sustain such a thin string end affected by the total dynamic motion of this extremely large and massive flexible structure?
Dyn-3:	Also define the yaw torsional motion required to control general motion of space tether.
Dyn-4:	Dynamics of a Space Elevator with a massive GEO Node [200,000 Metric Tons] acting as a "fixed" location.
Dyn-5:	Response to 800km sever with active control activities such as: massive GEO Node "grabbing" tether, GEO Node deploying tether rapidly to compensate for loss, GEO Node using active thrusting to control loss of lower mass
Dyn-6:	Active response to sever of tether from Apex Anchor such as: thruster assisted maneuvering for compensation of lost mass, rapid deployment of space tether from Apex Anchor to damp out dynamics responses

Chapter 7 – Environmental Threats

ET-1:	Categorize all the threats for the space elevator by magnitude
ET-2:	Specify the electromagnetic characteristics of the environment
ET-3:	Investigate the potential coupling of energy with tether climber for source of power.

Chapter 8 – Space Debris

SD-1:	Apply similar techniques to future estimates of densities
SD-1:	Investigate the policy and legal regimes to leverage
SD-3:	Study the removal of large objects from space

Chapter 10 – Technological Assessment

| TA-1: | Identify all risks and lay out risk mitigation plans |
| TA-2: | Identify all low TRL technologies and seek alternatives |

Chapter 12 – Legal perspectives

| LP-1: | Investigate the initiation of a space elevator corporation at the international level. |
| LP-2: | Investigate the creation of a UN organization to orchestrate the development of a space elevator transportation infrastructure. |

10.4 Findings and Recommendations

Finding 10.1: In all technological endeavors there are projections into the future. In the case of the space elevator, this study has recognized that there are two thrusts that must be taken:

| **Thrust ONE**: | Assume tether material is space qualified by 2030. |
| **Thrust TWO**: | Assume tether material is available two decades later. |

Each of these two thrusts has valid research projects leading to their estimates; however, no one can predict the future reliably, so this study will present both cases.

Finding 10.2: Based upon Thrust ONE, the space elevator should be available during the middle of the 2030 decade. Based upon Thrust TWO, the space elevator should be available after 2060. This is principally due to the availability of a tether material sufficiently strong to handle the longitudinal stresses inherent in a 100,000km long tether.

Finding 10.3: The remaining components of the space elevator have historical precedent and can be constructed as soon as needed with sufficient investment in design and production capability. The NASA Space Technology Roadmaps cover much of these major segments of the space elevator such as solar power, materials manufacturing, and nanotechnology.

Chapter 11
The Way Forward and
Technology Roadmaps[1]

11.1 Background
This chapter looks at potential roadmaps that could guide the development of a space elevator transportation infrastructure. The reality of the situation is that projecting for the future is at best an "art form," vs. solid engineering. In addition, other technological roadmaps are addressed to show parallel activities. As such, this chapter will be divided into three eight-year periods, or octennials. These three periods will define the approach for the road map for space elevators of the future. Octennials seem to fit the development of the material and they match the cycle time for full scale prototype developments of all the major components. The roadmap approach allows everyone involved to help provide a vision of a path to development of a mega-project crossing several decades. The timeline starts in 2014 and projects are in three periods.

Octennial One: 2014 – 2021   Parallel Prototype Testing
Octennial Two: 2022 – 2029   Flight Hardware Testing
Octennial Three: 2030 – 2037   Development to Operations

As one of the principal objectives of this report is to lay out a future approach to space elevators, the roadmaps are an important step in the process. Two previous roadmaps have been presented to the community: Dr. Edwards' schedule in his book (Edwards, 2003) and a LiftPort Group Road Map released in 2006 with a potential operations date of 2031 [with their own assumption on the CNT material refinements] (Laine, 2006). It is essential to remember that there are key assumptions in the development of a roadmap that must be understood as one reads the chapter, as listed below.

- The business model has not been selected by the investors, so the financial flow of funding has not been decided upon. The choices of government, public/private, or private investments will be decided upon as the project goes forward and the needs of the space arena are recognized by potential investors.
- Separate investment arenas will support different components of the project. The aspect of launch and movement from LEO to GEO by highly efficient ion engines could be developed by the government while space elevator components would be investments from the private arena.
- Future technology breakthroughs are projected by technologists of today who have an understanding of the potentials, but no ability to project "break-out" technologies. This was shown by the technological surprises surrounding the development of microchip, cell phones, cloud computing, or carbon nanotubes (CNT). The appropriate breakout technology, in this case CNTs, could cut a decade out of the development projected by today's technologists.

Another thing to realize while reading this chapter is that there are customary ground rules for roadmaps of future technology projects. They are:

---

[1] Space Elevator Roadmap Development Team in Japan (Japan Space Elevator Association, Nihon University, Tokai University and Earth-Track Corporation; Reviewed by Yoshio Aoki/Nihon University and Minoru Sato/Tokai University)

- Technological milestones are projected assuming that the funding is available. The team looking at each of the technological projects understood that minimum funding would be available at the beginning, with more funds following successes.
- The future flow of the project will not be calendar or schedule dominated. This roadmap will be strategic in character and will represent wide ranging investments of governments around the world as well as academic and industrial investments. This layout of the future must be both flexible and coherent in character to ensure quick responses to potential investor needs.
- The roadmaps must have a reasonable view of what can be accomplished in technological breakout arenas and normal maturation of components to ensure that the investors have a good understanding of where their early investments would be best applied.

In addition, comparison of the space elevator roadmap with other "official" technology roadmaps will increase the probability of coming close to appropriate estimates. In this case, a very good reference is the "Technology Strategy Map" (TSM) from the Ministry of Economy, Trade and Industry of Japan (METI, 2010). This forecast of general technologies to the year 2050 included many of the components of the space elevator technology development; however, they did not have in mind a simple space elevator that was robotic only and projected for the time frame of the middle of the 2030s. In addition, NASA (2012) presented multiple space technology roadmaps in its recent publication, "NASA Space Technology Roadmaps and Priorities: Restoring NASA's Technological Edge and Paving the Way for a New Era in Space." The development of a space elevator infrastructure will cross many timelines and require parallel tasking activities. As such, two roadmaps will be presented in the later part of this chapter [Section 11.5]:

Roadmap A: Assumption [based upon chapter 3] is that the tether material matures rapidly and supports a 2036 space elevator deployment.
Roadmap B: Assumptions support a space elevator deployment in the 2050s.

11.2 Overall Picture
This chapter will be broken into four sections so that the flow of the space elevator technological development can be explained. They are structured around eight year periods and result in two potential roadmaps to fully operational space elevators.

Section 11.3:   Technology Development - Parallel Prototypes
Section 11.4:   In-orbit Demonstration and Program Initiation
Section 11.5:   Two Potential Roadmap Approaches
Section 11.6:   Developmental Approach for Management

Space elevator development will depend upon many major processes as time goes by. Study participants of this Space Elevator Cosmic Study agree that there is a high probability that the system could be built as soon as the CNT material is refined enough for a 100,000km almost perfect one-meter wide tether. Separate technology projects supporting the other major space elevator components will be developed in parallel. However, these technological projects will not stress space engineers for their designs as they are developments based upon 50 years of spacecraft history. These projects will require sufficient testing and validation to ensure that the project holds together across all the segments (INCOSE, 2006). These are broken into the following major areas that are the domain responsibilities of the space elevator team:

- Encouragement and monitoring of material development for tension strengths at long lengths
- Climber design
- Power source [large area, light-weight, efficient solar cells]
- Deployment strategy with equipment design integration
- Marine node refinement
- Operations concept

In addition, there is technological growth in some areas that must be monitored as the space elevator project moves forward. These are:

- CNT material development for tension stress and long lengths
- Launch vehicle development to move 70 MT to LEO
- In-orbit raising of altitude by very efficient engines such as ion engines
- Assembly-in-orbit techniques and approaches
- Communications architectures for crowded spectrum [e.g. laser]
- International law and policy development

The first major section of this chapter discusses parallel prototype projects that would place the space elevator infrastructure in a very valid place to encourage investors for the project. It is reasonable to assume that the roadmaps would leverage the early parallel prototypes to ensure that the requirements of the customers are realized during the development. Verification and validation should be high on the planners' schedules to ensure that the roadmaps have on-ramps and off-ramps for the potential investors. One of the key assumptions that will follow the roadmaps of the near future is that the initial space elevator infrastructure will be totally robotic with the exception that humans might be at compatible locations to help assemble or re-fuel components in the far future. After the space elevator transportation infrastructure is mature, the need for human transport will be addressed to ensure that the tether and climbers become "human rated."

In addition to the following breakout of the first third of the space elevator roadmaps, there should be a parallel activity of academic research into significant topics that could have impact on the process. As such, there should be grants available for research projects that are identified by the participants of the space elevator development. A list of these was provided in the last chapter laying out recommendations for the future.

11.3   Technology Development – Parallel Prototypes
Key to developmental programs of an innovative transportation infrastructure is that it will be deployed as a total system prior to any utilization, similar to a bridge. The total system must be in place before revenue can flow and successful placement of satellites into orbits such as GEO or solar system investigation. The following is a series of prototype developments that are called "Parallel Prototypes," as they are to be run simultaneously. A preliminary set of technology developments must be accomplished early to lower the risk and increase the readiness of individual subsystems. Therefore, a series of technology developments must be initiated to develop, propose, and execute prototype subsystems.

The editors of this cosmic study believe that the major segments of the space elevator are all a natural progression of current space activities, except for the tether material as a long structure grounded on the Earth. This means that the first series of activities would be to take current space designs and transform them into a system of systems for a space elevator infrastructure. As such, these developments would lead to a systems level demonstration of an in-orbit flight prototype. This goal would become essential and will be THE MILESTONE that must be successful. As such, the pathway to this milestone, and then the roadmaps from there to full operations of the space elevator, have been broken down into three eight year periods. Each of these is explained below:

Octennial One: 2014 – 2021   Parallel Technology Prototype Testing
- Goal: Development of a testing program leading to full-up prototyping of major space elevator segments!
- Product: Mature components going to the in-orbit flight demonstration

Octennial Two: 2022 – 2029   Flight Hardware Demonstration
                                     & Major Program Initiation
- Goal: Full flight prototype testing in-situ leading to project initiation.
- Product: Successful orbital segments for space elevator and initial contract start for program initiation with approved funding.

Octennial Three: 2030 – 2037 Development to Operations
- Goal: Operational support of multiple climbers by 2035
- Product: Three pairs of space elevator operational by 2040.

Octennial One will be discussed below with all of the prototype plans while Octennials Two and Three will be shown in the roadmap development portion of the chapter. As the time frame moves out beyond Octennial One, the uncertainty increases and as such the detail is less. The two roadmaps show the alternative futures based upon the development of the tether material.

11.3.1 Octennial One: 2014 – 2021 Parallel Technology Prototypes
The following projects would be initiated in parallel to ensure that risk analysis was accomplished as each of the disciplines was significantly refined for specific leveraging toward a space elevator infrastructure. A parallel prototype developmental program must be established to lower risk and raise technology readiness levels (TRL's).

- Carbon Nanotube Specific Strength Demonstrations (Table 11-I)
- Tether Climber Design (Table 11-II)
- Initial Deployment Spacecraft (Table 11-III)
- Marine Stage One Prototype (Table 11-IV)
- High Stage One Prototype (Table 11-V)
- Dynamics and Deployment Simulations (Table 11-VI)

Table 11-I. CNT Specific Strength Demonstration

CNT Specific Strength Demonstration	
Goal	To produce a long tether sufficiently representative of a space elevator with the intent to use in space during the prototype demonstration.
Phase I	Establish Requirements
Objective	Define the space elevator tether with respect to tensile strength, thickness, density, width, woven structure, and produceability.
Schedule	2014-15 TRL at beginning: 2; TRL at completion: 2
Approach	Provide research centers around the world with "direction" for tensile strength, produceability, and zero defects.
Phase II	Prototype Acceptable Tether
Objective	Produce a 10km tether matching the in-orbit prototype demonstration needs with similar characteristics to the production tether.
Schedule	2016-19 TRL at beginning: 2; TRL at completion: 6
Approach	A competition for the desired tether. The winner receives support for on-orbit tests of material at the ISS (Shinobu, 2011)
Phase III	Establish Manufacturing
Objective	Once the producability of the tether is refined, produce a 1,000km tether in a similar manner to the future production so that in-orbit demonstration can be conducted.
Schedule	2020-25 TRL at beginning: 6; TRL at completion: 8
Approach	Once again, a competition for tether with characteristics of the operational space elevator.

Each of the following tables illustrates details of one of the prototype development projects designed to reduce risk and refine approaches.

Tether Climber Design	
Goal	**Develop TRL 9 Tether Climber for Baseline**
Phase I	**Requirements and Architecture**
Objective	Initiate the designs for both the Prototype flight vehicle and baseline tether climber. The architecture of the spacecraft called a tether climber to include all the components needed to reach the required speeds, reliability, safety, and customer needs.
Schedule	2015-16 TRL at beginning: 6; TRL at completion: 6+
Approach	The approach to this step is to leverage 50+ years of spacecraft design and requirements development.
Phase II	**Prototype Climber – Motor & Gripper**
Objective	Design the drive apparatus that is needed to lift the tether climber at appropriate speeds with other requirements illustrated during Phase I. This would include at least the required energy levels [electrical peak and average vs. altitude], the approach for gripping the space elevator tether, and the drive motor and gears required for various speeds.
Schedule	2017-19 TRL at beginning: 6+; TRL at completion: 8

Approach	The approach would be to leverage the tremendous design /manufacturing experience of the mechanical industry to include efficient and light electrical drive motors, track motors, opposing wheel material feed mechanisms, and other routine terrestrial approaches. The idea would be to produce in the laboratory, and test in several environments, the design to ensure it meets the requirements.
Phase III	**Prototype Production Climber**
Objective	To produce an initial spacecraft that is representative of the production climber and test in one-g and zero-g environments.
Schedule	2020-25 TRL at beginning: 8; TRL at completion: 9+
Approach	The end product would be a prototype tether climber to be used in the flight demonstration to show the key elements. This prototype production tether climber would be required to climb, descend, park, and execute simple tasks during the flight demonstration.
Phase IV	**Production Climber**
Objective	This space elevator production tether climber would be prepared to take the first trip up the baseline space elevator as needed.
Schedule	2025-29 TRL at beginning: 9+; TRL at completion: 9+
Approach	This production tether climber would have incorporated the lessons learned in the flight demonstration and be designed to satisfy both the owner of the space elevator [routine, safe, large capacity, reliable, rapid climb, robust] and the customer going to orbit [safe, reliable, timely].

Table 11-II. Tether Climber Design

	Deployment Satellite Design
Goal	**Develop TRL 9 Deployment Satellite for Baseline**
Phase I	**Requirements and Architecture**
Objective	Initiate a design for the deployments satellite. Architecture of the spacecraft called a deployment satellite will include all the components required to reach required orbits [LEO, transfer to GEO, GEO], reach operations status at GEO, initiate and control deployment of tether, initiate apex anchor, support building of the total tether, initiate commercial operations, and operate for 15 years.
Schedule	2015-16 TRL at beginning: 5; TRL at completion: 5+
Approach	The deployment satellite for the baseline space elevator will have to cross many disciplines during its lifetime. It will start out as a payload for a large launch vehicle as well as for the transfer second [or third] stage. When it reaches GEO altitude, it will have to maneuver to the appropriate GEO allocated slot, maintain that location through-out the development of the space elevator [requires energy – probably thrusting capability], initiate the deployment of the tether, control the dynamics of the tether through to operations, enable an apex anchor to support the system of systems, and then transition to operational status as needed.
Phase II	**Prototype Satellite – Reel and Deployment Mechanism**
Objective	The task of going from a payload in low Earth orbit to an operating space elevator based upon a Marine Node, Apex Anchor and GEO Node will be dependent upon the smooth, predictable, rapid and reliable deployment of the initial space elevator tether from GEO towards the apex anchor and the Marine Node. This will require a "large drum" of tether stored during the stressful launch and a deployment method such as a reel and brake.
Schedule	2017-19 TRL at beginning: 5; TRL at completion: 7
Approach	Terrestrial industry uses reels and deployment of tethers extensively, just not in the lengths the space elevator expects nor under the zero-g environment with radiation

	and thermal characteristics inherent in space. The approach will be to tie this project with the tether design process and ensure that the concept of deployment can be implemented with the strength of material expected out of Project CNT. The mass to GEO will be large, so the tasking of two [or three] space lift vehicles will be required with assembly either in LEO or GEO depending upon the approach chosen. The design criteria should have all operations conducted in the autonomous mode with continuous monitoring by the operations center at headquarters through the GEO communications node [perhaps a commercial relay for the initial phases]. Once the spacecraft, with a reel of tether and deployment apparatus, reaches GEO altitude and the allocated slot, the deployment begins. The tether deployment design will be tested with these prototype reels and computer controllers.
Phase III	**Prototype Deployment Satellite**
Objective	The prototype deployment spacecraft will be developed so that it can be tested in the space environment during flight demonstration. The flight demonstration will ensure that a significant length of tether is deployed under controlled conditions [1,000km], and then orbital control will be maintained.
Schedule	2020-25 TRL at beginning: 6; TRL at completion: 8+
Approach	The deployment satellite is key to the success of a space elevator. The complexity of the deployment can be reduced after in-orbit testing has proven out the simple approaches and suggested operational procedures to be utilized during the baseline space elevator deployment. This prototype spacecraft will have as close as possible to flight hardware on-board conducting the deployment of the tether with command and control being handled as training for the baseline.
Phase IV	**Production Satellite**
Objective	The production satellite must be ready to conduct operations as soon as the tether material manufacturing allows the lengths, strengths, reliability and projected lifetime needed.
Schedule	2025-29 TRL at beginning: 8+; TRL at completion: 9
Approach	Readiness for initiation of the space elevator would include its compatibility with launch vehicles, transfer stages, orbital maintenance at GEO and then deployment and control of the tether. Additional thoughts include the production of the second space elevator (and the third) with the same production satellite while it is on orbit and the first space elevator is completed.

Table 11-III. Deployment Satellite Design

	Marine Stage One Prototype
Goal	**To demonstrate that a small town in the middle of the ocean can operate Marine Stage One**
Phase I	**Establish Requirements**
Objective	To support the needs of the operational space elevator, an architecture and an operations concept must be developed leading to a System Requirements Document for Marine Stage One.
Schedule	2014-15 TRL at beginning: 7; TRL at completion: 8
Approach	Extrapolation from operations and support of a deep ocean drilling platform will be extensive as there are great similarities.
Phase II	**Architecture and Reel Design**
Objective	The ground reception of the hanging space elevator tether will add complexity to a relatively straight-forward marine operations node. The design of this architecture will tie with the tether development, tether deployment approach, demand for movement of the surface attachment, and needs of the potential customers.

Schedule	2016-17 TRL at beginning: 7; TRL at completion: 8
Approach	Bridge builders reel out tremendous lengths of cabling as well as manufacturing machines for business such as telephone lines or trans-oceanic cables. These proven techniques will be leveraged to ensure that Marine Stage One is designed within historic approaches.
Phase III	**Prototype Marine Terminus**
Objective	End up with a terminus that is simple, yet sufficiently laid out to support both owners [+ deployment team] and customers of the space elevator.
Schedule	2018-20 TRL at beginning: 8; TRL at completion: 8
Approach	Starting from the deep-ocean drilling operations will help Marine Node One understand the issues of working on the surface of an ocean a long way from support.

Table 11-IV. Marine Stage One Prototype

High Stage One Prototype		
Goal	**Establish High Stage One as baseline.**	
Phase I	**Laboratory Model [10 m high]**	
Objective	The objective of the laboratory model is to show that the concept works with appropriate speed of the high speed "bolts" and the projected mass of the tubes and support infrastructure.	
Schedule	2014-2015 TRL at beginning: 2; TRL at completion: 3	
Approach	The first step would be to lay out the design documents required for the High Stage One with emphasis on working backward to the modeling stage; then, exercise the work bench model to show a successful levitation design. The next step would be to show the vacuum technology and the benefits of that loss of friction.	
Phase II	**Scale Model of Production Baseline**	
Objective	This phase would be multi-level investigation. The first would be an outdoor vacuum technology model just 60 meters tall to ensure winds are compensated for and the velocity of the bolts are significantly challenging. The second one would be one kilometer high for scaling to the production version.	
Schedule	2016-17 TRL at beginning: 3; TRL at completion: 5	
Approach	The 60 meter test would be an identical model to the full production version except for size and velocity of the bolts. The next level of investigation and testing would be for a 1km high stage one. The objects would be to start discussing operations and development problems with this scale model. In addition, there could be revenue from this if placed in the correct location for skydivers, astronomers, or romantic hotels.	
Phase III	**Baseline test prototype version**	
Objective	This version would be constructed to be 20km high with almost operational hardware. The concept is that there should be revenue out there for this high location while preparing for space elevator operations.	
Schedule	2018-20 TRL at beginning: 4; TRL at completion: 8	

Table 11-V. High Stage One Prototype

Dynamics and Deployment Simulations	
Goal	Enable confident design, deployment and operations of multiple space elevator systems.
Phase I	Review Industry – Establish Requirements
Objective	The baseline simulation tool for all participants in the space elevator development program should be selected from the best of the industry during the year 2014, with improvements included throughout full program duration.
Schedule	2014
Approach	An exhaustive review of the literature and then a competition would be initiated that could define the baseline simulation capability.
Phase II	Establish Simulation of Baseline with Dynamics Management
Objective	The winner of the simulation competition would then be enabled within the space elevator development team, ensuring high credibility of deployment and dynamics simulations.
Schedule	2015-18
Approach	The need for a standard simulation tool for all of the major players in the development of space elevators is key to the teams meshing together and understanding the elements of the complex system of systems. The winning simulation will be employed as an industry standard for the space elevator baseline.
Phase III	Model Flight Experiment and Baseline
Objective	The winning standard will be used to model the flight experiment and ensure that key elements of the experiment are supported and the projected motion and reactions are as expected. The flight experiment should be able to validate the deployment scenario chosen during program development. In addition, variations from the recommended approach could be exercised to test cost-effective innovative ideas.
Schedule	2019-23
Approach	The space elevator development team will leverage an industry standard across all components of the program and will ensure that various team members from around the world either have the simulation or have access to the simulation in a timely manner to ensure consistency throughout program development, system deployment and operations. This will include the ability to manage the active dynamics of an operational space elevator tether system.

Table 11-VI. Dynamic and Deployment Simulation

11.4   In-orbit Demonstration

The overall objective of the pre-operational validation of space elevators will be a 1,000km tether in low Earth orbit centered at 3,000km altitude so that it would not be anywhere close to operational satellites or the majority of LEO space debris. This technology flight experiment prototype test of an "almost full up" space elevator would include the following components:

- 1,000km of tether representing operational 1-meter wide design
- Deployment satellite prototype launched into LEO and moved to test altitude
- Reel-out and reel-in procedures checked and practiced

- Apex Anchor characteristics represented at the top end
- Mass at lower end representing Marine Node with characteristics such as reel-in and reel-out of tether.
- Tether climber prototype with climbing gripper and motor
- Solar arrays producing needed energy supply for a full up climber
- Communications architecture tested with location of climber and tether segments routinely available to Op's Center
- Operations Center testing software for operations of space elevator to include dynamic control of tether motion.

In many cases, unique and revolutionary space systems only test in the terrestrial environment of one-g while simulating the vacuum and maximum to minimum temperature extremes. However, with so many important aspects of a space elevator needing testing, the prototype 1,000km in-orbit verification of requirements and validation of concept would be virtually demanded by investors. As such, the parallel prototyping of all the major components of the space elevator will lead to the in-orbit test in approximately 2025.

The objective of this in-flight prototype development test is simple (Table 11-VII): Show the Operations of a Space Elevator – in situ!

	Flight Prototype Demonstration
Goal	To demonstrate all the major components in space.
Phase I	Establish Requirements
Objective	The establishment of a space experiment to take equipment from modest level TRLs to space qualified has been a standard approach in the industry. As such, an experiment should be established to "proof-test" the concepts, prototype equipment, and methodology for full up operations of a space elevator baseline. The initial set of parameters could be structured around the concept described.
Schedule	2014-21 TRL at beginning: 4; TRL at completion: 7
Phase II	**Prototype Hardware**
Objective	Enable inflight hardware that would test the designs for the space elevator baseline. This would include all the components of the system of systems with the hardware, software, and operational procedures needed to implement the full up space elevator. The prototype hardware would be built for flight experimentation and would also be "proof-testing" of concepts, designs and procedures.
Schedule	2021-24 TRL at beginning: 7; TRL at completion: 8
Approach	Build flight-ready hardware and exercise it in an environment similar to GEO but easier to get to and less hazardous to operate. This in-flight testing program would enable the space elevator designers to have confidence in the equipment, processes and team.
Phase III	**Conduct Experiments**
Objective	Conduct experiments and record results for analysis and assistance in the final design of a baseline space elevator.
Schedule	2022-26 TRL at beginning: 7; TRL at completion: 9
Approach	Flight experiments will fulfill the requirements established for the inflight space oriented long tether testing.

Table 11-VII. Flight Prototype Demonstration

11.5   Two Projected Roadmap Approaches

The roadmaps are separated by the basic assumption of when the carbon nanotube based tether material will be ready for a space elevator of 100,000km. They are presented as Roadmap A and Roadmap B.

Roadmap A: Assumption [based upon chapter 3] is that the tether material matures rapidly and supports a 2035 space elevator deployment.

Roadmap B: Assumptions support a space elevator deployment in the 2050s.

Roadmap A: Supports a 2036 space elevator deployment. This first roadmap is the culmination of multiple individuals working together to project into the future. The rough schedule is that during the first eight years there are technology development projects; during the next eight years there are flight demo's in space; and, during the last eight years, the space elevator is built and initial operations begin by 2035. One concept that is proposed [and expanded upon in the financial chapter 14] is that the first phase is accomplished through grants and awards from many sources to include government and private. The second phase is based upon high risk investors, while the construction phase includes "bridge building" type investments and commitments. This roadmap shows the first elevator available in 2035 with the safety and backup one accomplished two years later (Figure 11-1).

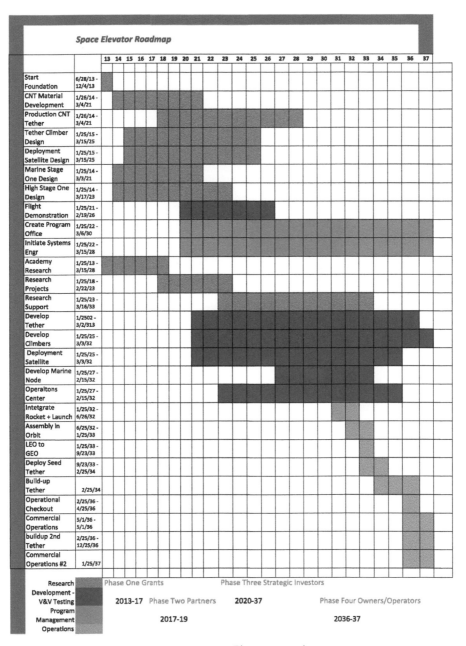

Figure 11-1. Space Elevator Roadmap A

Roadmap B: Assumptions support a space elevator deployment in the 2050s.

It is very difficult to make a 'roadmap' during this very early stage as a pre-concept exploratory research and feasibility study phase. This chapter describes space elevator developmental roadmaps to achieve the space elevator. The chart (Figure 11-2) estimates that the Operation Phase is later than the 2050s. To refine roadmaps with impartial analysis/judgment, the authors referred to other roadmaps that "foresee" the future technology trends which are required for a space elevator development. The most important thing for this early phase is to continue basic study of the space elevator and verify that this concept can be real in the future. A space elevator requires various technologies which are currently used and will be used in industrial and consumer markets in addition to technologies which are 'normally' used in the space industry. A great portion of technologies which will be used in the space elevator will be first used in the public welfare product field or the industrial field and then applied to space. This is one unique part of discussion of the space elevator.

Current space industries cannot make this system using their own technologies. In order to create the development roadmap of a space elevator, it is necessary to analyze the trend of the technical progress of various fields impartially and calmly, and to judge it. Therefore, we paid attention to the "Strategic Technology Roadmap" which the Ministry of Economy, Trade and Industry of Japan created (METI, 2010). After classifying this technological strategy map into the industrial fields "information and telecommunications", "nanotechnology and material", "a system and new manufacture", "biotechnology", "environment", "energy", "software", and "fusion strategy domain", a technological forecast out to the 2050s has been performed.

In addition there are three items that should be started in the near future:

(1) Project Office inauguration – In order to carry out smoothly each task from formulation of a basic operation policy to real operations, a project office needs to be inaugurated, and it mainly carries out the following tasks:

- International deliberation /enactment of laws
- Cooperation /public relations with the existing space industry
- Arbitrating the operations control rule between the space elevator and satellites
- Preparation of operational design and operational organizations
- Requesting research into the essential technology
- Contractor arrangements, project management and cash planning for space elevator construction - business plan
- Procedures as an international project [a- Conclusion of international recognition, understanding and agreement about the space elevator construction; b- International negotiation of the completion plan of space debris removal, and new generating control; c- Establishment of operation control rule with satellite communities, and achievement of the evasion technology; d- Preparation of operation facilities and rules for running; and e- Establishment of space elevator operating permission standards (biosphere security, vital care security, system safety, etc.)]

(2) The roadmap team discussed many things during this study, but if we need to choose one technological aspect to focus upon right now, we recommend the

following thing to do as a first step: development and verification of the simulation model of the tether dynamics.

(3) This roadmap chart also illustrates that the most important thing is the refinement of "Space Elevator System Requirements" which should be completed by the end of the 2010s. The main requirements would be based upon conceptual design and system definition after a basic concept is verified.

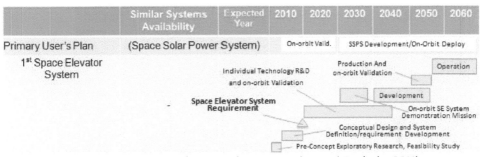

Figure 11.2. Summarized Space Elevator Roadmap B (Tsuchida, 2011)

11.6 Development Approach – Preparation for Baseline
This section has two parts: (1) Establishing a foundation and (2) Preparing for the program office with preparation for the final space elevator infrastructure baseline. The initial "real" step in this long road to a space elevator infrastructure is to establish a foundation that converts major contributions to actual projects through grants and incentive awards. This would enable the funding of risk reduction programs and parallel prototype development. The collection of funding for the foundation would then enable grants, endowments and incentive awards aimed at exciting projects as well as management of the various activities. The organization must be able to:

- Advocate space elevator infrastructure development
- Solicit early funds for parallel prototype projects
- Orchestrate awarding of grants – establishing parallel prototype projects
- Establish major incentive award programs recognizing global excellence
- Manage parallel prototype technology projects with risk ⬜reduction
- Establish small systems engineering team to "set the stage"
- Develop partnerships with global space elevator leaders
- Solicit funds for space elevator infrastructure development ⬜programs.

The next step is the transition to support a System Program Office and space elevator infrastructure customers. This activity should be initiated as soon as possible and hopefully completed during the year 2013. This would enable the initiation of parallel prototypes during the 2014 time period with aggressive schedules to reduce risk and increase knowledge of systems of systems complexity. The details are suggested here after:

	Preparation for Baseline
Goal	In parallel with all the development projects, including prototype equipment and procedures, there must be the basics of project initiation. This lower level of effort will lead to a team ready to initiate a mega-project lasting over eight years of development and centuries in duration [multiple replacement tethers of course].
Phase 0	**Create a Program Office to Support Program Initiation with Req's, Op's Concept, Life Cycle Cost with Customer Benefit Analysis, and Systems Engineering**
Objective	The development of a requirements document, sometimes called a systems requirements document [SRD], is essential to the initiation of a major project. In addition, and in parallel, the systems operations concept is necessary as a precursor to major funding expenditures ensuring consistent efforts and proper direction of energies.
Schedule	2014-25
Approach	A small sub-set of the members of all the parallel prototype teams must be involved in a team effort to pull together these two documents and then ensure that they are consistent throughout the development program.
Phase I	**Establish Baseline Requirements – Sys Req Doc [SRD]**
Objective	By the time this baseline space elevator development program is kicked off, preliminary SRDs must have been around for years. However, a final SRD must be refined as a baseline space elevator that developers hope to build and customers need for future businesses.
Schedule	2018-21
Approach	There are many requirement database software packages that can be leveraged to enable computer standardization across program offices. The Development Team will pick one and ensure that requirements are presented in a manner to be tracked for both validation as well as standard verification: first a SRD, and then a tracking system to ensure all are addressed and none are lost in the confusion.
Phase II	**Establish Risk Reduction / Opportunity Processes**
Objective	Even with the above mentioned parallel prototype projects, there will be risks identified that must be tracked, monitored, reduction plans developed and initiated. This will all be achieved through a standard risk reduction management plan exercised by the program management team.
Schedule	2019-22
Approach	In traditional space systems, programs routinely leverage the risk reduction plan. This will be implemented by the leadership team and monitored continuously as risk reduction efforts are implemented.
Phase III	**Mature Operations Concept**
Objective	During the development of the space elevator program, there will be a baseline operations concept that lays out the day to day (as well as long range) actions to ensure success. Early drafts will be leveraged as starting points and will be enhanced continuously over the development program.
Schedule	2021-25
Approach	Establish who does what to whom and when in a format that shares tasks around the world within the space elevator development team.
Phase IV	**Mature Life Cycle Cost**
Objective	Establish a life cycle cost (LCC) model that shows the expenses of developing the space elevator infrastructure with full visibility into all the components of the system of systems. In addition, the LCC will relate to benefits for the customer, ensuring that demand pull is present and investors are rewarded.
Schedule	2021-25

Approach	Establish a full life cycle cost model that deals with all phases of the program.
Phase V	**Support Internal and External Affairs**
Objective	Establish a small team to ensure that all legal and regulatory issues are addressed early to enable program execution.
Schedule	2021-25
Approach	Establish a team that ensures relationships are positive around the world.

Table 11-VIII. Preparation for Baseline

11.7 Findings and Conclusions

Roadmaps for space elevator development have been laid out, and they incorporate key testing of major components and equipment. The timelines are to be determined by funding and technological advances. The authors of this report have estimated what the future will be with respect to the funding issues, political realities, government involvements, and technological breakthroughs. The authors believe the space elevator will come to fruition; however, readers should understand that projection of the technological future is at best an art form.

Finding 11-1: The development of a space elevator infrastructure will cross many timelines and require parallel tasking of activities. Future roadmaps will lead to space elevators around the world, identifying and lowering risks, as well as moving technologies up the maturity hierarchy.

Finding 11-2: Parallel prototype developmental programs must be established to lower risk and raise technology readiness levels (TRLs). The successful program will then enable a construction company to initiate development of a space elevator infrastructure in the 2035 time frame.

Finding 11-3: A parallel prototype testing environment should lead to a full up, in-orbit, flight demonstration by 2023–25.

Finding 11-4: The CNT material development is pacing the prototype testing activities.

Finding 11-5: There are three activities that should be initiated as soon as possible: initiate a program office; establish a process for identifying requirements; and develop and validate a simulation of the space elevator dynamics.

Chapter 12
Legal and Regulatory Frameworks

12.1 Background
Here the relationship of the space elevator to the Laws of Space, Sea and Sky are considered. The space elevator will start out as a satellite with a unique identification number and permission to radiate from the UN. It will then stretch down through the arena of space law to the Marine Node [base anchor location] covered by Law of the Sea with transition through the aeronautical arena covered by Aeronautical Law. As such, the space elevator should establish the precedence of being a spacecraft, although a long one. The Marine Node will be floating on the ocean surface with multiple base floating platforms. One option in the design space also has a multi-leg structure supporting the bottom of the space elevator well above the atmosphere with an operations platform altitude at approximately 40km. This huge structure will then cross from the Apex Anchor at 100,000km radius and the Space Law region through to the Law of the Sea. This multiple dimensional legal regime puzzle will be broken down inside this chapter. The going in assumption is that land based space elevator concepts of the past [along the equator], would not be acceptable due to the risks of territorial ownership legal complexities. As a result, the Marine Node will be located outside of any territorial waters of the world. This chapter will outline the potential relationship between the legal regimes [sea, aeronautical and space] while discussing the projected space elevator infrastructure components in each region. Each of these regions is shown in Figure 12-1. As a guideline, we take the boundary between the atmosphere and outer space to be the well known Karman line, at an altitude of 100km.

12.2   Regime: Nation States
The legal regimes that a space elevator infrastructure must operate within reaches across the gamut of terrestrial law, aeronautical laws and treaties, law of the sea, and space law. This complexity is challenging and must be addressed early to ensure the appropriateness of technological choices crossing three decades. If the space elevator is established in the territory of any sovereign state, it would be very difficult to shut out the influence of that state, at least by the power of law. The experience of the cases of the Suez and Panama Canals clearly show the complexities.

Finding 12-1: The risk to the space elevator infrastructure from placing the base station inside a nation state's is too high to be acceptable.

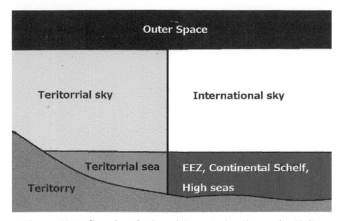

Figure 12-1. Crossing the Legal Boundaries [image by Kai]

12.3   Regime: Law of the Sea

In the past, the installation point for the ground base of the space elevator was deemed to the summit of a tall mountain in the equatorial zone. Recently, however, an installation point on the ocean has come to be considered as most suitable.   Therefore, in order to maintain the neutrality of the space elevator, the location of the base is better suited to a location that does not belong to any sovereign state. The United Nations Convention on the Law of the Sea [hereinafter called "the Convention of the Sea"] is an international agreement that resulted from the third United Nations Conference on the Law of the Sea, which took place from 1973 through 1982, in which over 150 States participated. The Convention of the Sea was opened for signature on 10 December 1982 and came into force in 1994. The Convention defines the rights and responsibilities of nations in their use of the world's oceans, establishing guidelines for businesses, the environment, and the management of marine natural resources. Nowadays, the Convention of the Sea is often referred to as the "Constitution for the Oceans."   It is almost impossible to change the Convention of the Sea for the needs or interests of the space elevator, because the Convention is a compromise of many countries. Even if it were possible to make any changes to the Convention, it would take decades. So, if we intend to establish a base for the space elevator in the ocean, we must search for such a possibility within the framework of the Convention of the Sea.

Territorial Sea

The history of the law of the sea is equal to the history of international law. Hugo Grotius (1583-1645), a jurist of the Netherlands, laid the foundation of international law and today is known as the "father of international law." In his book "Mare Liberum" (Free Sea), published in the spring of 1609, Grotius formulated the principle that the sea was international territory and all nations were free to use it for seafaring trade. Cornelius van Bynkershoek (1673-1743), also a jurist of the Netherlands argued in his book "De Dominio Maris" (on the rule of the seas), published in 1702, about the theory of sovereignty over the ocean. His theory is well known as the "cannon-shot rule". The rule said that a state has territorial sovereignty of that coastal sea within three nautical miles of land. Its name derives from the fact that in the 17th century this limit roughly corresponded to the outer range of coastal artillery weapons and therefore reflected the cannon-shot. This is the beginning of the concept "territorial sea". Of course, under the "cannon-shot rule", due to the progress of cannon technology, the breadth of territorial sea came to be claimed more widely - at first four nautical miles, then six nautical miles, and finally 12 nautical miles. Now, under the Convention of the Sea, the breadth of the territorial sea is determined to be 12 nautical miles.

Exclusive economic zone
In the past, the contrary concept of the territorial sea is high sea. Under the "Convention on the High Seas" established at Geneva on 29 April 1958, the term "high seas" means "all parts of the sea that are not included in the territorial sea or in the internal waters of a State" (Article 1). But the concept under the Convention of the Sea is very different from this. Under the Convention of the Sea, the term "high seas" is defined as "all parts of the sea that are not included in the exclusive economic zone, in the territorial sea or in the internal waters of a State, or in the archipelagic waters of an archipelagic State" (Article 86). Therefore, nowadays, the high sea means not only outside the territorial sea but also outside the exclusive economic zone (EEZ).

The concept of territorial seas and high seas arises from the long history of international customary law. In contrast, the EEZ is a concept which was formulated in the third United Nations Conference on the Law of the Sea, and as a result, it was created by the Convention of the Sea. This is the concept of a middle stage between territorial seas and high seas. This brings a structural change of the law of the sea. The springboard of the EEZ was President Truman's Proclamation of 1945 on the continental shelf and coastal fisheries. This Proclamation was the direct beginning of the continental shelf system, but the Proclamation set apart some Latin American countries which have almost no continental shelf. They thus searched for another way to protect their coastal fisheries. The first international instrument to proclaim a 200 nautical mile limit came into being on 18 August 1952 as the Santiago Declaration, which was signed by three Latin American countries that border the South Pacific: Chile, Ecuador and Peru. The Declaration reflects the desire of those states to develop the resources of their coastal waters.

The Santiago Declaration asserts that "owing to the geological and biological factors affecting the existence, conservation and development of the marine fauna and flora of the waters adjacent to the coasts of the declarant countries, the former extent of the territorial sea and contiguous zone is insufficient to permit of the conservation, development and use of those resources, to which the coastal countries are entitled". Therefore, the three governments "proclaim as a principle of their international maritime policy that each of them possesses sole sovereignty and jurisdiction over the area of sea adjacent to the coast of its own country and extending not less than 200 nautical miles from the said coast". The motivation for the establishment of the 200 miles territorial sea was economic. The reason for the current 200 nautical mile breadth of the EEZ derives from this Declaration.

The concept of the EEZ itself was the idea of the late Professor Frank X Njenga of Kenya, who brought up the idea in 1971 during the Asian-African Legal Consultative Committee (AALCC) in Colombo. It was ideally set up to protect the rights of coastal states, particularly developing countries with limited resources, to fully exploit the living resources of oceans off their coast and for their conservation and management, without interfering with other traditional international rights of the sea, such as the freedom of navigation and flight. The concept of the EEZ in the Convention of the Sea is an essential element of the package of compromises or trade-offs. This concept has received rapid and widespread acceptance in state practice and is thus now considered by some to be part of customary international law. In the Convention of the Sea, the important article in relation to the space elevator is Article

56 (Rights, jurisdiction and duties of the coastal State in the exclusive economic zone). The first section states: "In the exclusive economic zone, the coastal State has:

(b) jurisdiction as provided for in the relevant provisions of this Convention with regard to:
(i) the establishment and use of artificial islands, installations and structures;
(ii) marine scientific research;
(iii) the protection and preservation of the marine environment;"

It is not clear at this point of time which form the base of a space elevator shall have; but, it may have the form of an artificial island, installation or structure. And, under the provisions of this article, first section of Article 60 (Artificial islands, installations and structures in the exclusive economic zone) states:
"In the exclusive economic zone, the coastal State shall have the exclusive right to construct and to authorize and regulate the construction, operation and use of:
(a) artificial islands;
(b) installations and structures for the purposes provided for in article 56 and other economic purposes;
(c) installations and structures which may interfere with the exercise of the rights of the coastal State in the zone."

And the second section of Article 60 states: "The coastal State shall have exclusive jurisdiction over such artificial islands, installations and structures, including jurisdiction with regard to customs, fiscal, health, safety and immigration laws and regulations." In this provision of Article 60, artificial islands are designated to be handled differently to installations and structures. But the Convention of the Sea does not provide any clear definition of these three concepts. So it is very difficult to distinguish between the three concepts theoretically. And, in the state practice of each country, many countries have not made any distinction between these three concepts. Therefore, from the viewpoint of the space elevator, we must consider that there is no difference between territorial sea and the EEZ. As a result, we cannot establish the space elevator in the EEZ of a sovereign state.

Continental Shelf
Here we must consider the concept of the continental shelf. Some scholars think that the concept of continental shelf was absorbed into the EEZ concept. However, it is common belief that both exist still in parallel. Under the Convention of the Sea, the definition of the continental shelf is very complicated. However, it is defined basically in the first section of Article 87 as:
"The continental shelf of a coastal State comprises the seabed and subsoil of the submarine areas that extend beyond its territorial sea throughout the natural prolongation of its land territory to the outer edge of the continental margin, or to a distance of 200 nautical miles from the baselines from which the breadth of the territorial sea is measured where the outer edge of the continental margin does not extend up to that distance."

Therefore, to a distance of 200 nautical miles from the baselines, the EEZ and the continental shelf overlap. But if the continental shelf continues further, we must consider the problem of continental shelf itself. With regard to the continental shelf, the first section of Article 77 states that "the coastal State exercises sovereign rights over the continental shelf for the purpose of exploring it and exploiting its natural resources". Now, suitable points for the construction of the space elevator are very limited on the Earth. In that sense, the installation point itself has the character of national resources. Therefore, we must admit that if the space elevator were on the continental shelf, it would be under the sovereign rights of the coastal state. Article 80 of the Convention of the Sea is defined as "Article 60 applies mutatis mutandis to artificial islands, installations and structures on the continental shelf". Consequently, we cannot establish the space elevator on the continental shelf either, just the same as with the EEZ.

The High Seas

Here, we must consider about the freedom of the high seas. Article 87 section 1 of the Convention of the Sea declares:

> "The high seas are open to all States, whether coastal or land-locked. Freedom of the high seas is exercised under the conditions laid down by this Convention and by other rules of international law. It comprises, inter alia, both for coastal and land-locked States:
> (d) freedom to construct artificial islands and other installations permitted under international law, subject to Part VI;"

Of course, these freedoms to construct an artificial island, etc., are allowed to the extent of not infringing upon the freedom of the high seas of other countries. More exactly, "These freedoms shall be exercised by all States with due regard for the interests of other States in their exercise of the freedom of the high seas, and also with due regard for the rights under this Convention with respect to activities in the Area." (Article 87 section 2)   Ultimately, it shall be a matter of, what the word "due regard" means concretely. The legislative intent of this is that a particular country shall not unduly interfere with the lawful exercise by other countries. With regard to this point, the technical element of base mobility will be the decisive factor. As the base needs to move freely in a wide range in order to control the vibration of the cable or the upper part of the space elevator, the movements must not be so sudden or rapid that there is very little time to give any warning to avoid the base for the ships passing through the area or fishing vessels in operation [this would constitute an infringement of freedom of the high seas].

From the above it can be concluded, on the other hand, if the mobility of the base has enough predictability, that there are wide margins for the avoidance of any passing ships and fishing vessels in operation, it should not cause any particular problems for installation on the high seas (Figure 12-2).

Finding 12-2: The Marine Node of the space elevator will be in the ocean beyond the continental shelf and beyond any exclusive economic zone (EEZ) of individual countries. In addition, the Marine Node must be flexible enough to not infringe upon any nation's rights of movement.

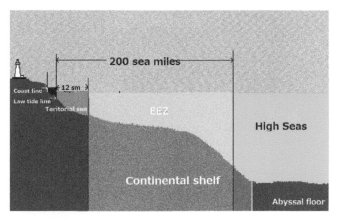

Figure 12-2: Recommended Location above High Seas [image by Kai]

12.4 Regime: Aeronautical Law
Similarly to the Law of the Sea, we must consider the problem of space elevator in relation to the Law of the Sky, under the framework of the Convention on International Civil Aviation (Chicago Convention). In the past, if people speak about the Law of the Sky, it meant only the Convention on International Civil Aviation.

The history of civil aviation law began with the Paris Convention of 1919. It was created for the purpose of freedom of flight. This convention has defined the concept "airspace" above the territory and the territorial waters. The airspace is the area under the "complete and exclusive sovereignty" of each state. Subsequently, the Madrid Convention of 1926, then the Havana Convention of 1928, and finally the Chicago Convention in 1945 were signed. In these conventions, the existence of "airspace" above the territory and territorial waters was recognized. However, the boundary between airspace and outer space is still unsure. This would be a serious problem in relation with the Bogotá Declaration, if the space elevator were not placed upon the high seas.

As a result, in relation to the civil aviation convention, legal issues which need to be considered seriously constitute only one. That is, every tower-shaped construction needs aircraft warning paint for the daytime and aircraft warning lights during the night. In the novels in which the space elevator appears, the cable of the space elevator was often drawn as a thin, almost invisible line extending towards the sky. But it constitutes a breach of the Chicago Convention. As the space elevator is the gate to the stars for all of mankind, there will be air traffic around the base after the completion of construction. Therefore, in order to ensure the safety of aviation, aircraft warning is a prerequisite condition.

Finding 12-3: As the space elevator is to be established stretching upward from the high seas on the equator, the undefined boundary between airspace and outer space is not a major problem.

12.5 Regime: Space Law
On 4 October 1957, the Soviet Union launched the world's first artificial satellite "Sputnik 1." The United Nations response to this was immediate. Barely two months later, on 12

December, the UN General Assembly passed a resolution "International cooperation in peaceful uses of outer space." Based on this resolution, the "United Nations Committee on the Peaceful Uses of Outer Space(COPUOS)"was established in 1958, and became a standing subsidiary organ of the UN General Assembly in 1959. "The Legal Subcommittee" is a part of the infrastructure of COPUOS. The first task undertaken by this subcommittee was to draft the Outer Space Treaty, which was adopted by the UN General Assembly on 19 December 1966.

We must consider whether the Outer Space Treaty is only a treaty or an established law of nations. The difference between the two is that a treaty is a law that binds only ratifying states, while an established law of nations is an international customary law that binds all states. It is hard to imagine that the basic purpose of this Treaty was to form a new established law of nations as the Outer Space Treaty was designed to take effect with ratification from as few as five countries (Article 14, paragraph 3). This resulted in its easy enforcement in October 1967.

Finding 12-4: The treaty, as the "Charter of Outer Space", established the principles governing the activities of states in the exploration and use of "Outer Space." As the treaty has been ratified by 100 countries to date, it can be said to have attained the status of an established law of nations [international customary law].

12.6   Who can establish a space elevator?

There are several legal issues surrounding the construction of a space elevator. It seems however, that the most fundamental problem is who can actually establish a space elevator. This issue has a close connection with the UN Outer Space Treaties. There seems to be three alternatives to the question of who can establish a space elevator:

- Possibility of a national institution of a particular state [e.g. NASA, JAXA]
- Possibility of a private enterprise [e.g. Arianespace, Boeing, Obayashi Corp]
- Possibility of an international organization [e.g. INMARSAT, INTELSAT]

Possibility of a national institution of a particular state
We must consider the principle of no occupation of outer space (Article 2 of Outer Space Treaty). If a particular state considers the establishment of a space elevator, this principle is bound to be discussed. The space elevator, as a semi-permanent fixed construction, could be seen as "occupation of the outer space" - although there is great motion at all times [GEO Node moving at 3km / sec with variations around the GEO node of tens of kilometers in motion.]   The UN, under the current Outer Space Treaty, identifies a satellite with a registration number while the International Telecommunications Union (ITU) Treaty allocates a slot to a GEO based satellite. Thus, when a particular state wants to establish a space elevator, it would not require a change or an exception in relation to Article II of the Outer Space Treaty. As such, a national institution of a nation state may elect to develop a space elevator through the approval of two UN organizations. On the legal side, the character of a space elevator project is a transportation business for people and materials. Public transport services usually have certain exclusivity. A space elevator project could essentially have strong exclusivity arising from its location.

Possibility of a private enterprise
With respect to the feasibility of this alternative, we must consider Article VI of the Outer Space Treaty. The Treaty says "States Parties to the Treaty shall bear international

responsibility for national activities in outer space…whether such activities are carried on …..
by non-governmental entities. The activities of non-governmental entities in outer
space…..shall require authorization and continuing supervision by the appropriate State Party
to the Treaty" [the principle of responsibility to focus on the state]. Even an international
company adopts the form of a coalition of domestic companies from many countries, unless it
is established on the basis of international treaty of some kind. Under this principle, a
domestic company can do nothing that the state cannot do.

Freedom of private sector activities is based on the constitutional freedom of business. This
freedom shall be allowed if the best results for public good can be expected on the basis of
market principles. However, as mentioned in the preceding paragraph, due to extremely high
levels of monopoly with regard to its geographical location of a single space elevator, the
establishment of a space elevator by a particular private company cannot be approved from
the principle of market conditions. Therefore, from the domestic viewpoint, the company that
owns the space elevator would be in violation of the antitrust laws, if there were only one
space elevator infrastructure. The current concept is to have multiple space elevator pairs
around the globe ensuring a non-monopolistic situation. Most likely, each of the pairs would
be owned by separate companies sponsored by separate countries. As such, the space elevator
infrastructure would be non-monopolistic and seen as an important series of transportation
entities.

Finding 12-5: Multiple space elevator companies will require the support and sponsorship of
sovereign nation state's.

Possibility of international organization
The authors believe that one of the best possibilities with respect to the establishment of a
space elevator is by an international organization - if possible, as a UN special agency.
Fortunately Article 6 of the Outer Space Treaty has clearly made an exception for
international organizations. The second sentence of Article 6 states, "When activities are
carried on in outer space… by an international organization, responsibility for compliance
with this Treaty shall be borne both by the international organization and by the States Parties
to the Treaty participating in such organization." Of course, this provision was not made in
expectation of the emergence of a space elevator. The earliest practical use of space in the
field of satellite communications were the "International Telecommunications Satellite
Organization (INTELSAT)" and the "International Maritime Satellite Organization
(INMARSAT)." Both have been established under the treaty for international organizations.

This provision is intended to correspond to it. Let us hypothetically name the international
organization for the space elevator as the "International Space Elevator Organization:
(ISEO)". The best form for ISEO to take would be as an organization similar to the
International Bank for Reconstruction and Development (IBRD). If it were to take the form of
IBRD, we could solve the problem of how to raise funds for the construction of a space
elevator. We need only background contributions from the each state Party to the Treaty. The
ISEO will be able to finance space elevator construction by procuring funds from the market,
and repay the loan from the income earned by providing transportation after the date of
maturity. This means that there would be no need to rely on taxes from the people of any
country. In addition, if ISEO could attain the status of a UN Special Agency, it would not
need to pay any tax for transportation activities. However, the challenge to create a UN
special agency cannot be underestimated.

International Space Elevator Treaty Creation

The authors suppose that it would be very hard to establish a UN international Space Elevator treaty through the traditional approach. The last international Space Treaty proposed by COPUOS (Committee on the Peaceful Uses of Outer Space) was the Moon treaty in 1979, and since then, there has been no new international space treaty.

12.7   General Legal Conclusions

Conclusion 1: According to the Outer Space Treaty, the space elevator must be supported by an international organization or a sponsored nation state. The form the space elevator organization could develop into one of three alternatives:

- Either, an international organization, such as UN IADC
- or, it could be a state sponsored organization such as NASA
- or, it could be a corporation that has the sponsorship of a nation state

As such, the space elevator would be sponsored by a nation state, or international agency, with an international satellite designation number from the UN space registry office and approval from the ITU for a communication infrastructure at a GEO slot.

Conclusion 2: The space elevator infrastructure, with multiple systems around the globe, will satisfy the following legal regimes:

- Terrestrial: The Convention of the Sea enables the Marine Node to be "on the high seas," ensuring operational flexibility and legal "correctness."
- Aeronautical: The Chicago Convention allows the space elevator infrastructure to exist in the atmosphere if it provides sufficient warning to ensure safety of flight.
- Space: The international laws governing the objects in outer space ensures that the organization [public or private] will have state sponsorship to enable registration upon launch and frequency and GEO slot coordination.

Conclusion 3: Legal answers often induce technical challenges!

Chapter 13
Market Projection

13.1 Background
The following chapter will discuss many aspects of the market demand during the 2030 timeframe, including traditional and innovative markets.   Recently, in an article in Spaceflight, the concept of dreaming big and proposing breakout technologies was acknowledged to be daunting. It begins:

> "In the rough and tumble world of commercial marketing it is an axiom that belief in a projected profit precedes investment; nobody can prove a positive by eliminating a negative.   So it is impossible to know for sure if the profit is real until the investment provides the funds to complete development. In the world of satellite launchers that means a lot of faith is needed in the corporate framework of the new developer and, by definition, "new" means "no precedent." That in turn means "no parallel" against which to judge success or failure." (The British Interplanetary Society, 2012).

As a result of this phenomenon, the proper approach to mega-projects is to

- Dream Big,
- Sell Aggressively,
- Design to the future Market, and
- Convince investors that there are big profits for those who take early risks.

13.2   Market Projection
Establishing a market projection is a process of looking into the future and using past data to estimate future business opportunities. This process works extremely well when future business resembles past businesses. In the case of space elevators, the ability to supply routine, safe, and frequent access to GEO and beyond is not linearly extrapolated from launch vehicles with their infrequent launches, caustic propellants, violent liftoffs, potential for explosion, vast support infrastructure and extreme prices. A space elevator creates a phenomenal opportunity for new satellites to have design flexibility and cost significantly less. To look at a historical parallel, one must go all the way back to the transcontinental railroads and their creation of new and remarkable markets. The following was excerpted from Space Elevator Systems Architecture (Swan and Swan, 2007, p. 6):

> "A space elevator to support activities beyond low Earth orbit will be a watershed in human exploration. The ability to move masses, on schedule with almost no chance of loss and for $500 per kilogram, will enable a transportation industry similar to the advent of the transcontinental railroad or the autobahn/interstate highway systems. Some very interesting parallels can be developed between the infrastructures of a transcontinental railroad and the space elevator. Table 13-I relates the facts as outlined by Stephen Ambrose in his book "Nothing Like it in the World" (2000) and the projected strengths of a space elevator infrastructure sending mass "to the planets and stars." Ambrose

noted in his book "President Andrew Jackson traveled no faster than Julius Caesar," and that... "Thoughts or information could [not] be transmitted any faster than in Alexander the Great's time." (Ambrose, 2000, p. 357). By 1869, human movement had advanced to a heart stopping 90 kilometers an hour while word and ideas had leaped to light speed, telegraphed across a continent. No wonder Horace Greeley called the transcontinental railroad "The Grandest and Noblest enterprise of our age." (Ambrose, 2000, p. 82). The transcontinental railroad was described as "the road (that) would be of a size unprecedented anywhere in the world, and it would go in advance of settlements through an area whose remoteness and climate discouraged or completely precluded rapid migration." (Ambrose, 2000, p. 64).

The new capability to supply 14 metric tons to GEO routinely, safely, inexpensively, and frequently will open up markets that have not existed. This remarkable change will enable businesses to flourish and operations to be conducted on previously unknown scales. This marketing projection will look at three segments that could exist in orbit, realizing that space elevators have other strengths as well, such as interplanetary launch. These three markets are:

- Communications and Meteorological satellites
- Low Earth Orbit satellites
- Start-up businesses
  o Space Solar Power Industry
  o Other Innovative Businesses

NY to San Francisco by Railroad	Pre- Golden Spike	Railroad Operations
	Via Panama 3/14 – 8/30/1849 Via Straights Magellan 7/14 – 1/26/1849 Across the plains approx. 6 months. Multiple deaths along the way Mail costs dollars per ounce Trip cost about $ 1,000.00	Government Awarded Loans to build Right of way over public land Five alternate sections per mile awarded Trip time – approx. 7 days Trip cost - $70.00 Mail costs at pennies per ounce
Space Elevator	Traditional Launching	Space Elevator Operations
	Launch costs Commercial: $25,000/kg Government $40,000/kg Space Shuttle - $2.4 B per Launch Rate About 80 launches per year Probability of Success – 95% Launch on time rate – approx. 0%	Lift Costs $500 per kilogram for materials Human launch by rockets initially Lift Rate Seven carriers on space elevator Each carrier at 14 tons payload Week trip – estimate 7 days Probability of Success –estimate >99% Launch on time rate – estimate >99%

Table 13-I. Transcontinental Railroad vs. Space Elevator

Communications and Meteorological Satellites
The traditional GEO communications satellite business consists of $300M satellites, with 15-year lifetimes, taken to GEO with a breakout of roughly $100M for launch, $200M spacecraft construction, plus variable daily operations costs. They are usually launched in tandem as they are only about four metric tons apiece. This would fit well with the space elevator's 14 MT cargo capacity. In addition, the space elevator's departure schedule of seven times a week [50 weeks a year] would create a total of 350 opportunities per space elevator per year. If there are only approximately 45 GEO communications satellites (Teal Group, 2012) and another 22 Metsats for a total of 67 satellites per year [or 23 cargo loads], traditional GEO satellites will not be a significant space elevator market [see growth chart in Table 13-II]. An encouraging thought also exists, as lower cost to GEO leads to lower cost satellites – customers will recognize and react with more payloads to GEO for the same budget.

	2020	2023	2026	2029	2032	2035	2038	2041
Demand [Teal Group]								
GEO Sat Comm 45 + 1% per year	45	46	48	49	51	52	54	55
@ 4,000 kg each = tons / yr.	180	185	191	197	203	209	215	221
#Tether climber@12MT of cargo [3 s/c]	15	16	16	17	17	18	18	19
GEO Met-Sat half of Comm + 1% per year	22	23	23	24	25	26	26	27
@ 4,000 kg each = tons / yr.	88	91	93	96	99	102	105	108
# Tether climber@12 MT cargo [3 s/c]	8	8	8	8	9	9	9	9
Total mass = # of GEO sats x 4	268	276	284	293	302	311	320	330
Total number of tether climbers needed	23	24	24	25	26	27	27	28

Table 13-II. Communications and Metsats Projection

Low Earth Orbit Satellites
The traditional LEO satellite business consists of 40-50 satellites taken to LEO each year (Teal Group, 2012) with a breakout of roughly $40M for launch and $ 40M per spacecraft. They are often launched in groups as they are sometimes only one metric ton apiece. To go into a LEO orbit from a space elevator is quite a different prospect when compared to just "dropping off" at GEO as you must first take them off the space tether [above 24,000km altitude], which places them in a highly elliptical equatorial orbit. The next step is to change inclination and circularize towards polar with a repeating node requirement [new requirement to ensure safety with space elevator]. This rate of 50 satellites a year to LEO can be expected to continue, and even expand, as both construction and launch costs will be greatly reduced. Those with designs to maintain an orbit (station-keeping) will simply trade orbit-raising fuel for fuel applied to apogee lowering and inclination changing maneuvers. Ion thrusters are very attractive for those missions that can tolerate longer periods between launch and achieving mission orbit. Missions that do not have orbit maintenance needs

would purchase orbit placement "tug" services from a likely spin-off business. These tugs would be reusable and offer to place LEOs in their mission orbit from the space elevator enabling reduction in the complexity and mass of LEO satellites. These tugs would also serve the valuable service of removing end–of-life satellites including non-cooperative [dead] satellites. Reductions in Life Cycle Costs will make many more LEO missions possible. There will be further research on this topic as market projections are developed and they justify emerging and existing LEO markets.

LEO Demand [Teal Group]	2020	2023	2026	2029	2032	2035	2038	2041
LEO Sat 50 + 1% per year	50	52	53	55	56	58	60	61
@ 1,000 kg = tons / yr.	50	52	53	55	56	58	60	61
# Tether climber @14 MT	4	4	4	4	4	5	5	5

Table 13-III. LEO Market Projection

Traditional GEO and LEO satellite markets do not justify a fully leveraged space elevator in the sense of number of cargo loads being delivered to orbit. As a space elevator can deliver up to 4,900 MT to orbit per year, the cargo capacity far exceeds the traditional satellite demand. [A climber for 50 weeks at 14 MT per climber times seven climbers per week.] Table 13-IV shows the number of GEO satellites at four MT each and the number of LEO satellites at one MT each that could be put into orbit for a yearly traditional satellite market. If one were to divide by 12 MT [assume two MT to be used for the efficiency of mounting satellites into the cargo bay and ensuring the safety of operations], the demand for tether climbers is very small compared to the 350 cargo bays that are available each year for a full up space elevator.

	Number of GEO sats	Number of LEO sats	Mass to Orbit per year MT	Number of Tether Climbers @ 12 MT
2015	67	52	320	27
2020	69	52	328	27
2025	71	53	337	28
2030	73	55	347	29
2035	78	58	370	31
2040	82	61	389	32
	Note: GEO sats = 4 MT			
	LEO sats = 1 MT			

Table 13-IV. Projected Traditional Satellite Lift Demand

The need for development of future markets for the space elevator is shown in the traditional demand for the space transportation infrastructure. The capacity of space elevators, as illustrated in these business plans, is significantly larger than anything the space industry has accomplished to date. Traditional Earth orbiting satellites do not fill that need with current projections for GEO and LEO satellites, as shown in the last column of Tables 13-II and IV. The marketing team must find someone who has a tremendous demand for routine and safe delivery to Earth's orbit, in a range beyond 30,000 MT per year. For the price to be low, the demand must fill up the tether climber cargo bays.

Figure 1 illustrates the capacity of a single space elevator compared to the mass of GEO/LEO satellites per year.

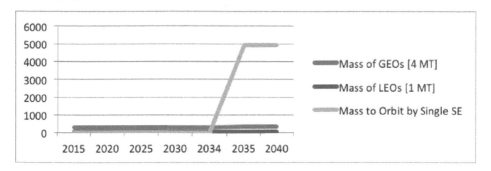

Figure 13-1. Capacity of Single SE vs. Mass of GEO/LEO Sats/yr

Start-up Businesses
When transcontinental railroads opened up the Western United States, the business community blossomed. When there is a routine, cheap and reliable ability to provide access to, and then supply businesses routinely, commerce finds a way to flourish. This parallel of a mega-project development that crossed America in 1869 is interesting in another perspective. Sidney Dillon, in his article entitled "Historic Moments: Driving the Last Spike of the Union Pacific," published in Scribner's Magazine summarized that the expectations of the builders and investors was that the continental railroad would open up trade with the East [Japan, China and India] (Dillon, 1892). As it turned out, the Suez canal opened the same year as the continental railroad completed its tracks. Dillon was quoted by Ambrose (2000, p. 371) as saying that commerce and trade with Asia "have fallen far short of fulfillment". He added "the enormous development of local business has surprised anything we could have ever dreamed of." Asian trade increased 5% while 95% of the Union Pacific business was intra-continental. This points out that future business projections in "breakout" businesses are very difficult to understand, much less predict.

Indeed, this mega-project of a transcontinental railroad opened up the United States to rapid development and was a growth stimulus for its second century. It would seem that the GEO Arc would be just such a parallel. The space elevator could enable a growth stimulus for the next century of Earth's movement beyond its gravitational boundaries. There is historic precedent showing that improved transportation brings increased prosperity, from Roman roads to jet aircraft. The inexpensive delivery of mass to GEO would be a remarkable breakthrough to enable space businesses. In business parlance, this is called a "breakout" in capability. It would be a tremendous jump in new, innovative, and creative utilization of zero-g, vacuum, and global vista environments leading to massive business ventures as well as scientific opportunities and government utilization of the operating arena. The strengths of the space elevator (routine, inexpensive, shape/size flexibility) will enable new and exciting opportunities that we can barely even dream of now.

It is conceivable that even traditional satellites will be completely redesigned as the mission environment would change significantly. Design criteria has a new paradigm; cost to orbit is trivial when compared to current launch expenses, fewer restrictions on size/shape [at least to a first level], and many concepts would change to adapt to the inexpensive aspects with even shorter expected satellite lifetimes. As the space elevator infrastructure is a breakout opportunity, it is very hard to estimate or project capacity and availability. As a result, the numbers will be estimated for one breakout business that will be enabled by space elevator success: Space Solar Power (Mankins, 2011). In addition, several futuristic missions will be discussed that have tremendous launch requirements. Each of them would demand greater cargo capacity when initiating business during the second half of the 2030 decade. But first, let us discuss one such business that could be essential to the health of the Earth.

Futuristic Case:
Space Solar Power Industry, if it develops, would demand more cargo capacity than three pairs of space elevators could provide. The global need for Space Solar Power (SSP) satellites is overwhelming when the aspects of energy demand, greenhouse gases, and global warming are projected for the next 50 years.

> "The National Space Society believes that one of the most important long-term solutions for meeting those energy needs is Space Solar Power (SSP), which gathers energy from sunlight in space and sends it to Earth. We believe that SSP can solve our energy and greenhouse gas emissions problems. Not just help, not just take a step in the right direction; solve. SSP can provide large quantities of energy to each and every person on Earth with very little environmental impact." (Mankins, 2011).

This SSP project is gaining high-level attention because of its major attributes:

- A completely "green" source of energy
- Phenomenal amount of energy to tap [more/yr than all oil available resources]
- Capable of placing energy almost anywhere on the Earth
- Cost effective if launch costs/constraints can be rationalized
- Global energy independence once accomplished.

For this global need to be realized, the economic equation for space development, deployment and operations must change. Current business assessments of the SSP project do not make financial sense when dealing with commercial return on investment. This lack of commercial closure is due primarily to the cost of launch to geosynchronous orbit. The simple answer is that rocket propulsion is inherently inefficient [5% of mass on the pad makes it to low Earth orbit, and only half of that 5% gets to GEO] and is essentially half of the cost of a space system to orbit. The existence of a space elevator transportation infrastructure will change the equation so that Space Solar Power will be enabled.

It is no longer acceptable to talk about the space elevator as an academic exercise with great plans for the future. Since Brad Edwards' seminal work (Edwards, 2003) explained how we could, in a real sense, build the space elevator in the very near future, the world has evolved into a state of clear and present danger. The last three years have established that the Earth is becoming warmer and that carbon dioxide is increasing. If this is left unchecked, the human condition will change in a negative direction. Throughout history the direction has always been to improve the human condition. Periodically there were setbacks and global catastrophes; but, the human race continued to improve their health and safety. Now, the belief that this vector of progress stays positive is in question. There are very few solutions for energy demands that have the potential to maintain the positive direction of human progress --- Space Solar Power could respond to this need if it was economically viable through inexpensive delivery of satellites to GEO. This leads to:

Conclusion:	SSP projects CAN NOT afford lifting to orbit by rockets.
Therefore:	Supplying to GEO can only be accomplished by space elevators!

The role of engineers and scientists is to CREATE ideas and concepts and then travel the difficult road toward new and, to some, intimidating changes. We, in the space community, must realize we are holding the future of humanity in our hands with the ability to conceive of, plan for, and build remarkable projects whose scope would be truly stellar. Our hypothesis is simple:

o This ability to lay energy on the surface of the Earth with little or no pollution or carbon footprint WILL Improve the Quality of Life for the HUMAN RACE.

o $500/kg transportation to GEO will ENABLE Space Solar Power generation (with transmission to almost anywhere on the surface without pollution or carbon footprint) *Initiate space elevator NOW!*

The SSP community must become an aggressive customer of the space elevator program. This would help drive the need for the new transportation infrastructure while solving "the ISSUE" for SSP programs; cheap, reliable, multiple trips per week to GEO. The real strength of a space elevator, which no one talks about, is the change in delivery technique. Low cost is definitely THE issue; but, the other strengths should excite the SSP community to a greater degree. The major strengths of a space elevator based space transportation infrastructure would be:

- Financial numbers that are enabling
- Revolutionarily inexpensive to GEO
- Commercial development similar to bridge building
- Operational strengths
- Routine
- Permanent infrastructure (no throw-aways)
- Multiple paths when infrastructure mature
- 24/7/365/50 yrs. [bridge similarities]
- Massive loads multi-times per week
- Opening up design options for space systems
- No shake-rattle-roll during launch
- Fewer volumetric restrictions for launch
- SSP satellite segments of 14 tons each
- Easy delivery to GEO location

- Slow acceleration leading to a week long trip
- Assembly plant delivered prior to SSP sections
- Co-orbiting [floating] at GEO for easy delivery and assembly

The design team could be released to design an SSP system that does not have to be folded into a launch vehicle fairing or survive lift off and thrust requirements that entail tremendous shake-rattle-roll dynamics. The ability to provide 14 ton sections, seven times a week, of these large SSP satellite systems on a smooth riding space elevator for a week trip to GEO from the middle of the Pacific Ocean cinches the deal – go for manufacturing on Earth and assembly through the space elevator for Space Solar Power System Development.

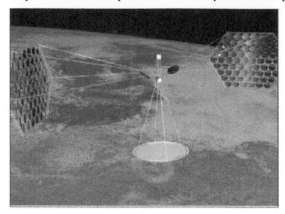

Figure 13-2. Conceptual Illustration (Mankins, 2011. p. 208)
Credit: Concept by John Mankins; Art by Kris Holland/Mafic Studios 1007.

Figure 13-2 shows the concept of a SSP system in orbit. Solar array collectors are very large and the total satellite will have mass between 3,000 to 20,000 MT. "A single Space Solar Power Satellite is expected to be above 3,000 MT, several kilometers across, and most likely be located in GEO, at 36,850km altitude, likely delivering between 1 to 10 GWe." (Mankins, 2011. p. 31). In addition, Dr. Chapman predicts that the mass of a SSP satellite, called "SunSat," will be 19,914 MT (Chapman, 2010. p. 2). A single SSP satellite could be over 500 cargo loads [remember no fuel needed].

The SSP launch demand numbers have been summarized in the left hand side of Figure 13-3. To have the SSP solution that SunSat has proposed, there would have to be 42,000 MT/year capability delivered in 2020 with a growth to 160,000 MT/year by 2050. As the first year of operations for the space elevator current laydown is 2035 with a capability of 4,900 MT for a single space elevator, the demand is not being met. However, the right side of Figure 13-3 shows the demand of SSP with the top curve satisfied by rockets and the middle curve to be satisfied by space elevators. The demand on the space elevator line is cut down by a factor of two. Therefore the second chart shows the lower demand vs. the capacity of the space elevator development because it raises spacecraft to orbit without major fuel amounts. In addition, the other two lines show a single space elevator as a baseline, and then three pairs to show the capability of the operational bridges to space. When three pairs of operational space elevators begin payload lifting, the capacity quickly goes up to 29,400 MT per year. [7x14MTx50x6 by 2035] The current layout in business plans shows the demand far outstrips the capacity of space elevators going operational in 2033; however, if there is tremendous demand, the commercial mandate will push more capacity.

Just recently, the need for inexpensive energy was addressed by the UN's Secretary-General Ban Ki-moon in the program called "Energy for All." He was quoted as saying:

"Widespread energy poverty condemns billions of people to darkness, to ill health and to missed opportunities." (Harris, 2012).

Richard Harris also reported the following from the Rio 20+ meeting:

"Three of the world's biggest problems are completely intertwined: Poor people need sources of energy to raise their standard of living; cheap energy from fossil fuels produces large amounts of carbon dioxide; and carbon dioxide is changing the climate in ways that are hardest on poor people. So at the U.N. meeting in Rio, Ban is hoping to kick-start a big initiative to end energy poverty by 2030. The plan is called Sustainable Energy For All. The idea is to make sure everyone on the planet has power, to cut in half the amount of energy that's simply wasted, and to double the share of renewable energy worldwide." (Harris, 2012).

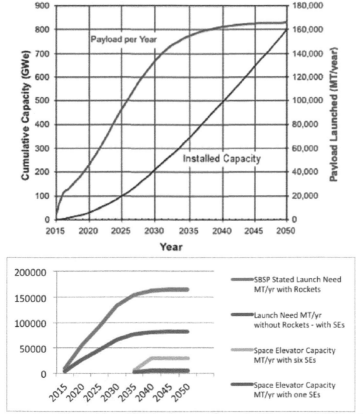

Figure 13-3. SSP Deployment Scenario (Chapman, 2010. p. 3)

Other Innovative Missions

The future is always difficult to predict, so the following ideas come out of various sources. However, they all have the common denominator that they would be enhanced with inexpensive, routine and safe transportation to GEO orbit and beyond. As we know, some of the toughest challenges facing us [excluding financial crises] include: energy, climate, population growth, food, health, fresh water, natural disasters and conflicts. Space assets have historically assisted in the mitigation of terrestrial problems, such as: weather prediction, hurricane warning, disaster support communications and observations, scientific inputs, and presenting a global view to place our problems in perspective. Some future missions that could leverage the characteristics of a space elevator might be:

Asteroid mining: Recently, commercial mining of asteroids has been announced with the first stage being development and launch of observation telescopes to search for sources of platinum. Significant investment will be required to find, approach, investigate, confirm mineral content, attachment, mining, and return of materials to a collection location. To ensure that it could actually become a viable business, launch costs must be reduced. The space elevator, with its inexpensive fees, will make a perfect partner for this financial undertaking. In addition, the return of materials from space could be accomplished cheaply and in a manner where the customer does not have to experience deceleration from 25,000 mph and recovery from the ocean or national territories. The space elevator would be perfect for this business venture.

Interplanetary flights: Scientific missions to the planets and other bodies in our solar system requires an extreme amount of fuel to escape the gravity well and initiate flight towards their mission goals. The space elevator can set up the proper delta velocity of the appropriate radius from the center of the Earth creating a high velocity toward their target. This safe and routine approach to launch at high velocity without rocket fuel can only enhance scientific knowledge.

Innovative missions at GEO: The beauty of geosynchronous orbits resides in the fact that it matches the rotation rate of the Earth. As such, the slots around the GEO arc are allocated according to frequency conflicts and requests from various nations. Once the ability to release from the space elevator at GEO altitude has fully refined, many new businesses will be developed. The ability to get to valuable nodes cheaply and safely will lend itself to commercial utilization.

Colonization of the Solar System: The National Space Society [originally the L-5 Society] was founded on the belief that humanity's future resides in the solar system and the stars. The stated goal was to move humans off-Earth and towards colonization of planets as well as large space ships that house one million people using rotation as gravity inside our solar system. In addition, The British Interplanetary Society has published many papers that have dealt with World Ships that are on the order of 25 miles long and 5 miles in diameter. These ships are to explore the solar system and go beyond to the next star. It is inconceivable to this team that the dream of colonization can occur with current launch system limitations. The space elevator transportation infrastructure to GEO and beyond is perfect for the dreamers of colonies beyond Earth orbit.

Marketing, advertising, television, social media: The 21st century broke on a changing world where global aspects were dominating the financial health of countries and tying together the economies of major states around the world. Currently, the business of marketing, advertising, and television is huge and growing. Who knows how the ability to place people and equipment in space, inexpensively and safely, will impact this tremendously evolving market. When will we have people voting television stars "off the island" of a space station at GEO? In addition, the social media arena has exploded and there is no telling where that will take us in the future with respect to "flying to the Moon." The key element in this discussion is that for the first time, those markets will have inexpensive and routine access to Space.

Earth Sun shade: Scientists have come up with new strategies to tackle the problem, one of which is an ambitious idea to contain global warming by putting sunshades in space. University of Arizona astronomer Roger Angel has suggested putting sunshades in space and has detailed his idea in a paper "Feasibility of cooling the Earth with a cloud of small spacecraft near L1" (Angel, 2006). His plan involves launching a constellation of trillions of small free-flying spacecraft a million miles above Earth into an orbit aligned with the sun, called the L-1 orbit. Angel proposes to design lightweight flyers made of transparent film pierced with small holes, two feet in diameter, 1/5000 of an inch thick, and weigh about a gram, the same as a large butterfly. The weight of all flyers would be 20 millions tons (Purang, n.d.). This would require 400 space elevators working for five years

Nuclear waste disposal: Current plans for disposal of massive amounts of residual radioactive material across the world are being argued from many perspectives, but the predominate view is "not in my backyard." Current "solutions" focus upon burial in a mountain or cavern and have tremendous local pushback and concern about future impacts on people's lives and their children's lives. The most significant issue is the high-level radiation waste produced by nuclear reactors. As it contains fission products and transuranic elements generated in the reactor core, it is highly radioactive and often thermally hot. High-level waste accounts for over 95% of the total radioactivity produced in the process of nuclear electricity generation. The amount of high-level waste worldwide is currently increasing by about 12,000 metric tons every year (Wikipedia, 2013). This is only one component of the vast nuclear disposal problem; but, those 12,000 MT would require 2.5 space elevators working continuously each year to just keep up. As such, a method of launching nuclear material into the sun would solve many of Earth's current and future radiation problems. Massive movements of nuclear material to the space elevator and release at the outer reaches of the 100,000km long tether would ensure that the material would escape the Earth's gravity and be released towards the Sun for final consumption, safely.

13.3 Future demand
After much research into these various innovative missions of the future, the estimate of future demand was created. The breakdown is given in Table 13-V:

Demand in Metric Tons	2031	2035	2040	2045
Space Solar Power	40,000	70,000	100,000	130,000
Nuclear Materials Disposal	12,000	18,000	24,000	30,000
Asteroid Mining	1,000	2,000	3,000	5,000
Interplanetary Flights	100	200	300	350
Innovative Missions to GEO	347	365	389	400
Colonization of Solar System	50	200	1,000	5,000
Marketing & Advertising	15	30	50	100
Sun Shades at L-1	5,000	10,000	5,000	3,000
Current GEO satellites + LEOs	347	365	389	400
Total Metric Tons per Year	58,859	101,160	134,128	174,250

Table 13-V. Projected Demand [MT/yr]

This leads to a chart comparing the total demand for access to GEO beyond 2031 and the supply of space elevator cargo tether climbers (Figure 13-4). This indicates options of one space elevator with a capability of 4,900 MT per year or an aggressive approach with three pairs of space elevators owned by three separate organizations providing 29,400 MT per year.

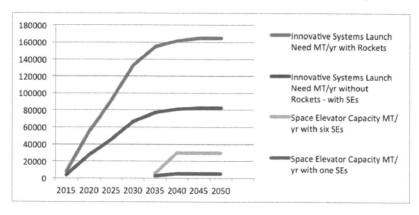

Figure 13-4. Total Demand beyond 2030 [Estimate by Swan from research]

13.4 Findings
Based on the above, the findings are:

Finding 13-1: Market projections show robust customers demand for multiple space elevators as soon as they are available. This is not surprising as the expected fee is $500 per kg or three orders of magnitude less than today's fees.

Finding 13-2: The traditional GEO and LEO markets could be satisfied with a fraction of a space elevator capacity.

Finding 13-3: Space Solar Power will drive the demand for space elevator infrastructure for safe, reliable, inexpensive and routine delivery of mass to GEO. One pair, and even three pairs, of space elevators will only minimally satisfy the needs of the SunSat Corporation.

Finding 13-4: The future demand from innovative businesses will exceed the initial supply.

Chapter 14
Financial Perspective

14.1 Background
Let us start this chapter with couple of pertinent quotes:

> "Champions know that success is inevitable; that there is no such thing as failure, only feedback. They know that the best way to forecast the future is to create it." (Gelb, 2012).

> "Good business leaders create a vision, articulate the vision, passionately own the vision, and relentlessly drive it to completion." (Welch, 2012)

This chapter is laid out to create a vision of what can be accomplished within a framework of financial estimates. Development of a space elevator needs to be initiated, fought for, struggled with, and accomplished within a projected budget. This effort will need a champion to lead with a vision that others can enthusiastically join and help bring to fruition. A space elevator will change the way mankind explores the universe and will enable commercial ventures previously only dreamed of. The authors believe the demand for space elevator cargo capacity will expand rapidly and will quickly build beyond the cargo capacity of a single space elevator. Even the projected six space elevators operating 50 weeks a year with seven tether climbers per week at 14 metric tons per cargo load may not be enough. This market pull was explained in the last chapter to include the traditional GEO/LEO satellite market as well as many innovative future markets. However, it will take a champion and a support team to show the vision, explain the path, and encourage success. The human race needs the ability to move off planet in a routine and easy manner. This infrastructure financial proposal will show the way. The space elevator offers so much to the human condition, with its opening up of the solar system, that the risk is eminently acceptable.

This chapter addresses the future with two supportive business plans:

Business Plan #1: Traditional Single Space Elevator with a Spare – the authors will show the financial numbers for a single space elevator [with backup spare] that is commercially viable, but limited in vision and scope.

Business Plan #2: Aggressive Development of Future Market for Three Pairs of Space Elevators – this projection has six operational space elevators in three pairs with three separate owners/operators. The future markets were projected in the last chapter, which leverages the huge demand for mass to orbit.

This chapter will further address many parts of the puzzle, based upon the market projection from the last chapter. These business plans describe how a small group of innovators can create a company while relying upon grants to initiate the space elevator project. After about four years, they would either be bought out by modest-risk investors looking for major profits, or they would develop by themselves with similar investments. After a few years establishing a good marketing plan and a solid development schedule [with risk reduction programs and government relations teams], this small company would be purchased by a large firm that would then develop and build space elevators.

For Business Plan #1, the first space elevator is initiated with action soon afterwards to build a second tether to be used as a backup and replacement. For Business Plan #2, the initial stages are the same; but the first space elevator built [with backup spare] has as its highest priority to build more space elevators and so ensure a permanent break out of Earth's gravity well. In each business case, the space elevator pairs are sold to separate firms to own and operate. Each of the developmental phases has a key significant profit estimate for the various owners. Risk is inherent in mega-projects such as the initiation of gateways to the solar system; however, this risk is well worth the investment, time and stress. This mega-project will be huge and stressful; but, the rewards for humanity and individual investors will be great.

During the cost vs. income portion of this chapter, the number $500/kg surfaces as the standard for this study report. This is an estimate within a 25 year projection. However, to put the whole space elevator infrastructure development into perspective, this estimate is applied across the study. This estimate reflects the growth of business and resulting costs and is derived in table 14-XIII.

14.2   Commercial Approach
This chapter will discuss multiple facets of financial growth from innovation to operations and consists of three major segments:
- Business Approach
- Financial Layout
- Major Assumptions for Financial Projection

To visualize the future and then plan for a mega-project requires experience in lifecycles of projects that cost more than one billion dollars and take more than ten years to complete. This usually requires big dreams, as the timelines are long and focus can be lost unless the vision turns into goals and objectives tied to timelines and funding profiles. As this mega-project goes forward, there are three alternative approaches: an individual government organization [such as NASA or JAXA], a consortium of governments that sponsor a semi-governmental organization [such as COMSAT or INMARSAT], or the basic builder and owner relationships inherent in the commercial arena [Mercedes Trucks & Mayflower Moving Corporation]. This business plan looks at all three choices, but focuses on the last.

Government agency: This first alternative has a historic place in space infrastructures with a government run, contractor accomplished, program such as Apollo or meteorological satellites.   There are many advantages to this approach, as once the government has committed, the funding profile is almost guaranteed. The difficulties arise when considering current variability in funding environments and limited public access.   In addition, the approach of government development and operations is costly.

Government Consortium: This is accomplished by grouping several government organizations together with funding and support. A new organization is created such as the original COMSAT, which was established to initiate GEO communications satellites. The initiation of this type of global reach organization has strength, once it is established and funded. However, in today's financial environment within most of Earth's governments, this approach would require a tremendous champion who could "push" through the concept. The logical place for this type of organization to reside would be within the United Nations in a newly created organization. To gain approval inside the current bureaucracy of the UN for a new office to be funded at the $15 billion level seems improbable. However, if it was successful, access would be assured.

Commercial: The beauty of this approach is that once the project is "bought into" by a corporate board of directors, or individual investors, the project proceeds rapidly. Historically, the profit motive has proven to lead to success, even in the most challenging of projects. The disadvantage is that commercial entities must gain approval from their own government and cooperation from many other governments from around the world.

Chosen Option: The commercial approach is chosen for this Cosmic Study, as it can be laid out and described in quantitative steps leading to a set of goals. This approach could be successful in most countries with the proper financing and governmental support. There are many other approaches that would work; however, to provide a structure inside this chapter's financial projections, the commercial sector will be utilized. Translating the rest of the chapter to one of the other two alternatives would not be difficult as the numbers to develop a space elevator and then operate it for 15 years will be consistent with the chosen option. The model selected for this approach uses large construction efforts as its basis, with bridge building as the specific example. The phases are set out in Table 14-I. Builders are authorized to build the bridge by governments and the owners pay for the completion of the structure. The owners are then the operators and charge for utilization of the infrastructure. The dreamers and the speculators use grants to start the activity and then the high risk "angels" invest to develop two major items; a complete business plan, a market projection, and a development plan with schedule and funding estimates. The third phase has to do with the efforts needed to design, develop and deploy multiple bridges to space. This effort is a massive activity requiring investment and time. Once the ability to build space elevators is demonstrated, commercial ventures will need to build at least two space elevators to ensure a profit [including costs for operations and maintenance with replacement tethers]. The goal of moving to the operational phase will be fulfilled when new owners buy a pair of space elevators or multiple owners buy many pairs of space elevators operating for profit. The concept of pairs is to ensure a robust business and to have the ability to go up continuously on the first space elevator and then up and down on the second while adjudicating scheduling conflicts. In addition, having the back-up second elevator ensures that business will continue in case of equipment problems on one of the space elevators.

Phase	Name and Mission	Company	Years	Objectives	Product
I	Grants and Endowments Invest in Risk Reduction & Market	Int. Space Elevator Creators, Inc.	2013-19	Create business plan & lay out development	Intellectual property
II	Founding Partners Establish Development Plan Confirm Market	Carbon Space-Way, Inc.	2019-23	Risk reduction & prototypes	Schedules, business plan, legal approach
III	Strategic Investors Lower Risk and Build Space Elevators	Carbon Space-Way, Inc.	2024-36	Build 1st SE & set up production	Space elevator 1st operations
IV	Owners/Operators Buy, Establish and Run Business	Clarke Space-Way, Inc.	2035 ++	Operations	Profit and customer satisfaction

Table 14-I. Phased Approach to Development

14.3 Business Strategic Approach

The Goal: To show how a space elevator can pay for itself as a commercial operation. The assumption is that using a space elevator to carry cargo out of Earth's gravity well is more scalable, and significantly less expensive, than using rockets. The result is a remarkable price per kilogram of cargo going into Earth's orbit and beyond.

Why: No one will build a space elevator because 'it's cool' – it's far too expensive for that. A compelling case to build and operate a space elevator infrastructure, as opposed to using conventional rockets, must be made. There are only three reasons to build a space elevator:

- It is deemed a matter of national security or national pride. In this case, money is essentially not an issue. An example is the early American attitude towards the space race and the sprint to the moon. Money was not an issue – NASA was given whatever it needed to accomplish the goal. Similar activities are presently taking place in China, India and Brazil.
- It can be a 'paying proposition' – it must be the best/cheapest way to accomplish some commercial activity. There will be a tremendous profit from routine and safe delivery to GEO and beyond.
- Improvement in the global environment is required [stop launching chemical rockets and reducing debris sources, enable space solar power, send radioactive material to the sun, etc.].

There seems to be no push at the moment [or in the foreseeable future] to build a space elevator because of national security or pride. Therefore, if we want to convince someone to build a space elevator, we have to show them how they can make money or "save the planet's environment." One concept that has worked well in the past has been to gather "anchor tenants" who would provide long term financing.

Business Vision: To develop a workhorse transportation infrastructure that moves cargo routinely and safely to Earth orbit and beyond with a return on investment concomitant with the risks.

14.3.1 Business Assumptions

[1] Breaking out of the gravity well will be a profitable business – inexpensive and non-destructive compared to rockets.
[2] Multiple international consortia will own and operate space elevator pairs
[3] A large construction company will build the space elevators
[4] The initial funding for development will be grant based
[5] R&D will be aggressively pursued with tremendous leverage of university and corporate IR&D
[6] Major funding for development and production will be from loans to the construction company
[7] The construction company will be profitable upon sale of space elevator pairs, especially the second and third pair
[8] Material development will match the projected schedule for full operations in 2035 [otherwise, the space elevator schedule will slip year-to-year to the right]
[9] The development of support equipment, such as the base station and tether climbers, will be completed prior to operations, and sufficient equipment will be available to initiate profitable businesses immediately.

14.3.2 Business Plans

In this section, two business plans will be presented after the description of the phased approach to accomplish the financing. The total financing will occur in a similar manner whether the first or second business plan is chosen. The difference occurs when owners buy a space elevator pair. The capacity of the space elevator infrastructure is then dependent upon the type of business plan chosen. Each of the two business plans leads to profitable companies operating space elevators.

Business Plan #1: Traditional Single Space Elevator with Spare

This business plan is a scenario for the next 25 years, with an initial construction company specializing in space elevator creation and an operations company buying the space elevator and a spare. The space elevator construction company [suggested name: Carbon Space-Way Inc. CSWI] specializes in building space elevators starting with the traditional approach from GEO and then building the backup from the ground called the replicator space elevator. The first space elevator is used to develop a commercial business, while the second one is for backup and to replace the tether after 7.5 years [assumption on tether lifetime]. We must never get caught inside the gravity well again. Once the first one is accomplished, the second one is built in a shorter time period as there is the ability to run an elevator in parallel with an existing one. The buildup to the complete tether is accomplished by the construction company that owns the starter tether. The initial goal will be to focus all efforts into increasing the tether from a 'seed tether' to one able to carry 30 metric tons. It is desirable to do this within two years. For this business plan, the second tether [backup space elevator] is constructed during the first one's commercial activities. The traditional demand of GEO/MEO/LEO space systems has previously been strong enough to kick off commercial ventures. The follow-on market is expected to develop and fill cargo capacity.

Business Plan #2: Aggressive Development of Future Market for Three Pairs of Space Elevators

This business plan is a scenario for the next 30 years, with an initial construction company specializing in space elevator creation and an operations company for each pair of space elevators. The space elevator construction company [suggested name: Carbon Space-Way Inc. CSWI] specializes in building the space elevator starting with the traditional approach from GEO and then building multiple elevators and selling them in pairs. The remaining 25 years of this scenario will be for-pay cargo and maintenance of the space elevators. Replacement is a key operational task. If we continue to use this approach, we can roll one up from the ground to the Apex Anchor as needed. This ensures that the tether is replaced as needed [assume 7.5 year replacement cycle]. This would be a task that the operations company would ask the construction company [as the experts on the Apex Anchor] to orchestrate. They will have to plan for this activity after selling each pair of elevators to a company.

As shown earlier, there is a demand that will "push" for multiple space elevators. This anchor tenant customer, space solar power (SSP), is a new and very demanding business delivering inexpensive energy to any location on the surface of the Earth with a small carbon footprint. The demand matches the delivery of our first elevators because SSP satellites will be waiting for us, as they CANNOT proceed at the current cost of launching massive spacecraft to GEO. The numbers in the third part of this chapter show that after the initial space elevator goes operational in 2035, there will be sufficient space elevator cargo demand to justify full capacity of seven tether climbers per week at 14 MT each, for six operational space elevators. The demand is there! In addition, the previous marketing chapter showed that there were several innovative future markets that could also require major proportions of space access infrastructures. As such, the predominant conclusions about demand for space elevator cargo climbers are:

- SSP will drive the demand for space elevator infrastructure for safe, reliable, inexpensive and routine delivery of mass to GEO.
- Multiple pairs of space elevators are needed to minimally satisfy the needs of the SunSat Corporation.
- The space elevator will significantly benefit the human condition by orbiting GEO SSP satellites, which will supply inexpensive energy to any location on the surface of the Earth.

14.4 Financial Layout

Now that the concept has been laid out, a multi-phase approach must be presented to explain the financial demands for the development of a mega-project. Each phase has a commercial entity and a specified mission timeframe. This chapter will then describe each of the following phases in detail (Table 14-II).

Phase	Name and Mission	Company Name	Source of Funding	Total Amount Invested [$Million]	Projected Profit Amount [$Million]
I 2013-2019	Grants and Endowments Invest in Risk Reduction & Market	Int. Space Elevator Creators, Inc.	"free grants"	64	15
II 2019-2023	Founding Partners Establish Development Plan Confirm Market	Carbon Space-Way, Inc.	Partner Investments	924	200
III 2024-2036	Strategic Investors Lower Risk and Build Space Elevators	Carbon Space-Way, Inc.	Major Investors	9,117 + 1,124 purchase of CSWI	4,000
IV 2035 ++	Owners/Operators Buy, Establish and Run Business	Clarke Space-Way, Inc.	Owners	13,500 including purchase CSWI	3,000 + +

Table 14-II. Developmental Phases

14.4.1 Phase I

Market Analysis and Construction Plan

Early space elevator developers must create a company and raise money to move from academic studies to refinement of the initial development and construction plans. This company could be called the International Space-Way© Creators, Inc. or ISWC-I (Figure 14-1). The process of developing a space elevator program will take some "seed" money that should be acquired in the form of grants (Table 14-III). These funds could come from government R&D grants, private donations - endowments, or stimulus funding from governments [local, state or federal]. The profile would be:

	2013	2014	2015	2016	2017	2018	2019
	Foundation Start	Cosmic Study Endorsed	Material Research Focused	Material Research & System Design	Material Research & System Design	Material Research & System Design	Material Research & System Design
Research Grants [$M]	3	3	5	11	11	11	20

Table 14-III. Initial Grant funding for ISWC-I

At this point, there will be some basic questions answered and research completed on business competitors and material development, including more detailed research on new market opportunities. In addition, there would be a preliminary plan for space elevator research and development, prototyping, construction and transition to operations. The developmental cost profiles would be established, the technology risks identified, and legal and regulatory activities initiated. One product of this seven-year activity would be the initiation and maintenance of detailed market analyses.

Foundation -- International Space-Way© Creators, Inc. ISWC-I

Space elevator creators must form a company and raise money to move from academic studies to initial development and construction. The ISWC-I searches for granting organizations who would want to support the concept of a space elevator infrastructure going to GEO and beyond while breaking the gravity well restrictions for the human race. The concept is seven years of grants followed by the sale of the company to CSWI.

Figure 1. Foundation of ISWC-I

14.4.2 Phase II
Founding Partners
Once the market analysis has been presented and risk analysis identified, the search begins for funding partners for the next stage of the development (Figure 14-2). This stage consists of financial investors who work in the high risk/high payoff arena. The ISWC-I searches for investors who would want to support the concept of a space elevator infrastructure going to GEO and beyond while breaking the gravity well restrictions for the human race. This would have of a time period of from three to five years with money reflecting the status of the technology. The layout below shows the process in a simple four year Phase II timeframe. The founding partners create Carbon Space-Way, Inc. [CSWI] and purchase ISWC-I for its intellectual property and proprietary plans. Their expectations are high risk with commensurate return on investment (Table 14-V). Their profit arises when they sell CSWI to Strategic Investors after three years of developing the system and further reducing risk.

Founding Partners
Carbon Space-Way©, Inc.

The entity to actually transition from research to initiating development of space elevators. The Founding Partners will be owners of the new company, Carbon Space-Way©, Inc., which will create a realizable plan towards operations. This will include all the lowering of risk, coordinating with legal and regulatory agencies, identifying real customers, and a layout for entering production.

Figure 14-2. Founding Partners – CSW-I

US $M	2020	2021	2022	2023
	Purchase IP & Patents + Material Research Focused	Material Research & System Design	Material Research & System Design	Material Research & System Design
Purchase	79			
Founding Partners	82	91	262	489

Table 14-VI. Summary of Expenses for Founding Fathers

14.4.3 Phase III
Strategic Investors

At this point, strategic investors must show up with a major share of the initial investment to take the space elevator from concept with research/development activities to actual construction while transitioning to operations (Figure 14-3). Development of the first operational space elevator pairs is shown within the financial roadmap stretching from 2013 to 2037 in Table 14-VII.

Strategic Investors

Strategic Investors will purchase the company, Carbon Space-Way©, Inc., and turn it into a production program. They will be collecting investments to finance major milestones, similar to bridge building. They will take the design from concept to deployed hardware. Upon successful completion of the first space elevator, the investors will own the resulting technology and will create a backup space elevator to ensure the gravity well is no longer a threat. They

Figure 14-3. Strategic Investors

The cycle of development will parallel most traditional space programs with refinement of materials, lowering of risks, prototyping of major elements and then launching of the first satellite. The space elevator is unique in that it then has a major activity related to going from a GEO satellite in an allocated slot to a satellite that is 100,000km long with an attachment to the base station and an Apex Anchor stabilizing a long dynamic tether. During the initial phase, while grants are being provided, the focus will be on this cycle of development. Along with the first elevator being developed, plans must be solidified for the rapid replication of the space elevator to ensure that full advantage is taken of escaping from the gravity well. During the first few years, many intriguing questions will surface that should stimulate creative solutions. The development of a space elevator will push the minds of its developers;

however, the rewards of having a true transportation infrastructure to the solar system will be remarkable.

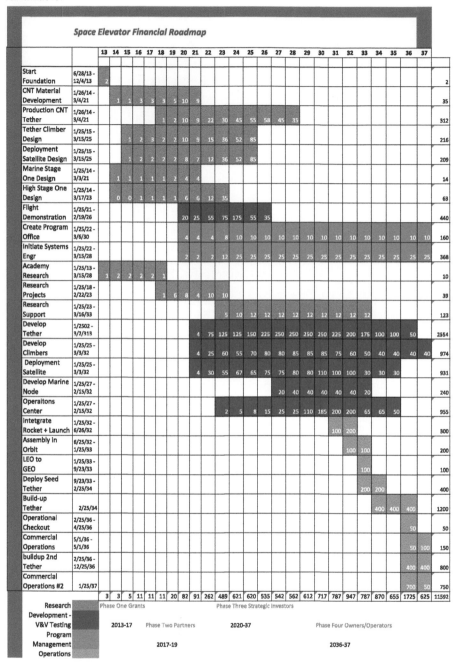

Table 14-VII. Strategic Investment Layout

Strategic Investors must understand where there is still some risk and realize that the payback is extraordinary. They will purchase the R&D company, Carbon Space-Way, Inc. from the founding partners. The concept is simple: big investment into hardware and operational facilities will yield massive profits at marginal risks. The construction company will only be paid for product and will not be large risk takers, only the producers of space elevator pairs. They will own the products of the CSWI. The first product will be the first space elevator for commercial use as well as its replicator. In addition, they could develop production lines of other essential items such as tether climbers and stations after the space elevator pair is presented to the new owners/operators. A vital role of the CSWI will be to nurture and maintain the skills needed to continue producing space elevator systems. The backup for the business is essential, but the reality of not being forced back into the gravity well is paramount. This would probably require the company to have a spare tether in a GEO seed sphere or develop a second space elevator deployed as a backup. All these aspects of a new business must be evaluated and planned for by the Carbon Space-Way Inc. as they develop their new businesses delivering cargo to Earth's many orbital regimes and even send some spacecraft towards other bodies in our solar system and beyond. The current strategy would be to provide the owner-operator a replacement space elevator tether every 7.5 years to ensure that wear and tear on the system is accounted for and the tether's structural integrity is assured during operations. In addition, the CSWI would have the business of supplying products to the owner/operators from such items as: tether climbers, base stations, GEO stations, apex anchors and other equipment. The Strategic Partners funding profile is shown in Table 14-VIII.

In Million $US	2020-23	2024-26	2027-32	2033-36
Phase III	Kickoff Development of Space Elevator	Flight Demo and Initiate Build	Focus on Construction	Launch, Operations, and Tether Build-up
Design	290	432	80	0
Flight Demo	175	265	0	0
Program Office	38	105	210	140
Research	37	34	84	12
Build	382	912	2660	705
Launch	0	0	300	0
Operate	2	28	845	2030
Totals	924	1776	4179	2887
9,766				

Table 14-VIII. Strategic Partners Funding Profile

14.4.4 Phase IV
Owner Purchase
The business scenario changes during this last phase when the owner purchases the space elevators and conducts business. At this point, the chapter will diverge into two separate business plans with several parallels; however, the approach is different with a market demand that is significantly varied. The chart below (Table 14-IX) summarizes funding from the new owner/operator over the phases for a single pair of satellites, a commercial one and a backup.

		Clarke Pair Payments (B$US)
2032	Launch # 1 Space Elevator	
2033	Ribbon Buildup and testing	
2034	Ribbon Buildup and testing	
2035	First Tether Completed	
2036	Commercial Operations Start	13.5
2037	Second Tether Completed – Commercial Operations	
	Total Sale Price for two Space Elevators	13.5

Table 14-IX. Owner/Operator Investment Layout

Business Plan #1:   Traditional Single Space Elevator with Spare
This special case is one that is used as a baseline for understanding of the "Traditional Satellite Case." The idea is to understand what the market seems to be with only the traditional GEO/LEO satellites filling up tether climber cargo bays (Table 14-X). Once the capability to escape the gravity well has been accomplished, it must never again be lost. The key element here is multiple space elevators. This "Traditional" case looks at one space elevator with revenue being created with sufficient tether climbers per month to satisfy the current needs of the GEO/LEO community. The numbers show a requirement for only 2.5 tether climbers per month for this traditional market. The price will be determined by estimating the cost of a space elevator and then dividing by the loads to orbit during the year. The other assumption is that cargo loads are 85% of the 14 MT capacity.

	number of GEO sats	number of LEO sats	Mass to Orbit per year MT	Number of Tether Climbers per year @12MT
2015	67	52	320	27
2020	69	52	328	28
2025	71	53	337	29
2030	73	55	347	29
2035	78	58	370	31
2040	82	61	389	32
	Note: GEO sats = 4 MT,			Loads
	LEO sats = 1 MT		12 MT for	accounting mismatching

Table 14-X. GEO/LEO Market

The need to keep the price-to-orbit down is one that has to be a criterion for any development program. This will encourage investors to pursue space businesses as transportation costs become more affordable. The chart and table below reflect a single business space elevator where the investor is the operator and has a very long time for repayment of debt. The first significant investment is in 2036 [purchase] and the first positive profit is in 2048 or 11 years of continuous investment. The assumptions are that the owner buys the two space elevators for $13.5 Billion with the traditional market as his income and a need for a replacement tether at the 7.5 year point for an additional $2 Billion. If the GEO/LEO traditional set of satellites were the total market, we would have a ready backlog, although limited, for the first year or two [2036 timeframe]. This would mean 31 cargo loads in one year on a single space elevator. This would be 31 x 14 metric tons [MT] capability, but only 434 MT of customer satellites. To make profits in a timely manner, the price would be about $6,000 per kg. or $2.6 Billon per year. The numbers would be as shown below (Table 14-XI, Figure 14-4):

	Expense tether & operations	Cost of Money[5%]	Mass of Traditional S/C [MT]	Income @ $ 6k / kg	Profit	Cumulative Profit
2036	-13500					-13500
2037	-360	-675	340	2040	1005	-12495
2038	-360	-625	343	2058	1073	-11422
2039	-360	-571	347	2082	1151	-10271
2040	-360	-514	351	2106	1232	-9038
2041	-360	-452	355	2130	1318	-7720
2042	-360	-386	360	2160	1414	-6306
2043	-2360	-315	365	2190	-485	-6792
2044	-360	-340	370	2220	1520	-5271
2045	-360	-264	374	2244	1620	-3651
2046	-360	-183	378	2268	1725	-1925
2047	-360	-96	382	2292	1836	-90
2048	-360	-4	385	2310	1946	1856
2049	-360	93	389	2334	2067	3923
2050	-2360	196	394	2364	200	4123

Table 14-XI. One Space Elevator Cost vs. Profit Tradeoff
Traditional GEO/LEO @ $6,000 / kg

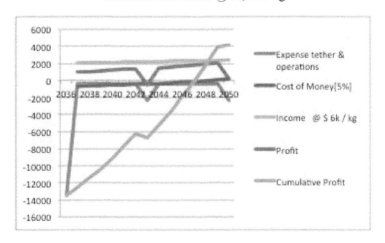

Figure 14-4. Profit shown for Single Space Elevator at $6,000/kg

Finding BP1 #1: The authors' conclusion is that: yes – a single space elevator pair could be developed without the follow-on pairs of systems; but the overall risk to investment and the lack of development of future markets increases the monetary risk as perceived by serious investors. There must be large payoffs for high-risk investments. In addition, robust markets must be developed to continue into the future. The authors feel that a single space elevator development pair is not the appropriate approach. One pair of space elevators [one operational and one spare] will need to charge $6,000 per kg for the first eleven years to return sufficient funds to entice investors for the traditional satellite market. This is essentially what innovative rocket designers are talking about with respect to the future of CNT materials applied to launch vehicles and spacecraft.

Special Case: Single Space Elevators with Growth Market
As shown in the market chapter (13), the marketing team must find a tremendous demand for routine and safe delivery to Earth's orbit and beyond, in the range of 30,000 MT per year. For the cost to be low, the demand must fill up the tether climber cargo bays. This special case is one that projects a simple growth of the demand market over the time period shown. The cost varies as the customer mass increases with a constant yearly income goal of $2.5 Billion. The range goes from traditional market (340 MT) to the maximum capability of a space elevator as explained earlier (4,900 MT). The resulting cost varies from $6,000/kg to $429/kg when cargo bays fill up all year long. If one were to show the growth of mass to orbit vs. cost chart, one would see the relationship, as shown in the chart (Table 14-X11) and graph (Figure 14-5) below:

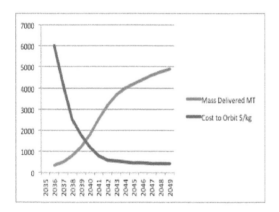

Figure 14-5. Cost vs. Mass Growth

	Mass Delivered MT	Cost to Orbit $/kg
2035		
2036	340	6000.00
2037	500	4100.00
2038	800	2520.00
2039	1200	1800.00
2040	1800	1200.00
2041	2550	800.00
2042	3200	600.00
2043	3700	550.00
2044	4000	500.00
2045	4200	480.00
2046	4400	450.00
2047	4600	440.00
2048	4750	429.00
2049	4900	429.00

Table 14-XII. Cost vs. Mass Growth

When this is put into a spreadsheet for the actual profit of the space elevator vs. costs and operations, the following table (Table 14-XIII) emerges.

	Expense tether & operations	Cost of Money[5%]	Mass of S/C [MT]	price $k/MT	Income $US M	Profit $US M	Cumulative Profit $US M
2036	-13500						-13500
2037	-360	-675	340	6.00	2040	1005	-12495
2038	-360	-625	500	4.10	2050	1065	-11430
2039	-360	-571	800	2.52	2016	1085	-10345
2040	-360	-517	1200	1.80	2160	1283	-9062
2041	-360	-453	1800	1.20	2160	1347	-7716
2042	-2360	-386	2550	0.80	2040	-706	-8421
2043	-360	-421	3200	0.60	1920	1139	-7282
2044	-360	-364	3700	0.55	2035	1311	-5972
2045	-360	-299	4000	0.50	2000	1341	-4630
2046	-360	-232	4200	0.48	2016	1424	-3206
2047	-360	-160	4400	0.45	1980	1460	-1746
2048	-360	-87	4600	0.44	2024	1577	-169
2049	-360	-8	4750	0.43	2038	1669	1500
2050	-360	75	4900	0.43	2102	1817	3317

Table 14-XIII. Profit Table with Varying Mass and Price
[red line is baseline used in study report - $500/kg]

Finding BP1 #2:   The authors' conclusion is that: yes – a single space elevator pair could be developed if the market grows rapidly.   Indeed, if the price started out at the highest levels, the $2 billion income could be realized over ten years with the price matching demand curves. The authors feel that single space elevator development is not the appropriate approach. Once again, the market has to be developed and one pair of space elevators [one operational and one spare] will need to charge $6,000 per kg to return sufficient funds at the beginning of the cycle. The market has to be brought onboard by potential customers with the belief that the space elevator infrastructure will be robust and able to handle future markets. With one elevator, the robustness is in question and customers' belief in the future would be doubtful.

Business Plan #2:   Aggressive Development of Future Markets for Three Pairs of Space Elevators
This business plan is a scenario for the next 30 years, with an initial construction company specializing in space elevator creation and an operations company for each pair of space elevators. Carbon Space-Way Inc. (CSWI) will specialize in building space elevators starting with the traditional approach from GEO and then building multiples from the ground using the replicator space elevator. Figure 14-6 and Table 14-XIV shows the growth of the cargo capacity of space elevators as the project goes forward. Hopefully, by the time readers finish this chapter, they will understand the flow of demand from current to future and the financial investments needed relative to phases of the project. Traditional Earth orbiting satellites do not fill that need with current projections for GEO and LEO satellites as shown in the last column of the Table.   This table shows the capacity of each pair of space elevators as they come online with the total cargo capacity of all six space elevators by 2042.

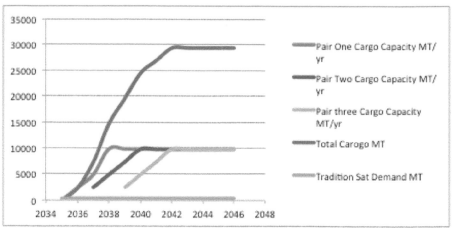

Figure 14-6. Demand vs. Capability

	Pair One Cargo Capacity MT/yr	Pair Two Cargo Capacity MT/yr	Pair three Cargo Capacity MT/yr	Total Cargo MT	Tradition Sat Demand MT
2035	0	0	0	0	330
2036	2450			2450	336
2037	4900	2450		7350	340
2038	9800	4900		14700	345
2039	9800	7350	2450	19600	350
2040	9800	9800	4900	24500	355
2041	9800	9800	7350	26950	360
2042	9800	9800	9800	29400	365
2043	9800	9800	9800	29400	370
2044	9800	9800	9800	29400	375
2045	9800	9800	9800	29400	380
2046	9800	9800	9800	29400	385

Table 14-XIV. Demand vs. Capability

Three pairs will be sold to owner/operators to ensure competition to GEO and beyond and to guarantee that mankind can escape the gravity well in the future. This business plan is based on a 29 MT space elevator. It shows the potential for two large business opportunities. The first is the construction corporation that builds the infrastructure and the second [and follow-ons] is the operational business of the transportation infrastructure to Earth orbit and beyond.

The second business would stay where constructed, near the Replicator Space Elevator owned by CSWI. The third and follow-on businesses would be located closer to owners' territories, east or west of the original location. Each would be in competition with the others with separate infrastructures, businesses, and strategies for success. These owners could be commercial companies, national organizations or international agencies. Figure 14-7 shows the Pacific Ocean location where the Replicator Space Elevator has handed over two elevators to the first operational corporation.

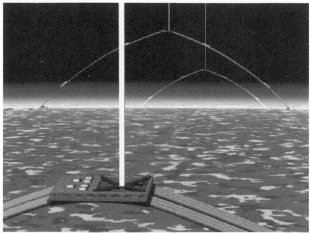

Figure 14-7. Space Elevators in the Pacific (Knapman, 2012)

At this point, the space elevator tethers are being produced and anchored in the oceans. Each pair is then sold to an owner/operator in the sequence shown. The first pair goes for $13.5 Billion, paid in the first year at delivery, with the other two pairs going for $10 Billion. It would look something like Table 14-XV.

Phase V – Owner Operations
Each pair is operated by a separate organization of similar design. The operation of a space elevator is estimated to be $360 million per year per pair.

	US $Billions	Pair #1 Payments	Pair #2 Payments	Pair #3 Payments
2035	Launch # 1 Space Elevator	0.5		
2036	Ribbon Buildup and testing	1		
2037	First Ribbon Completed - Replicant starts Op's	4.5	0.5	
2038	Second Ribbon completed	6	1	0.5
2039	third Ribbon completed [Artsutonov Pair complete]	1.5	4	1
2040			4.5	4
2041	Fourth/Fifth completed [Pearson Pair complete]			4.5
2042	Sixth/Seventh completed [Clarke Pair completed]			
		13.5	10	10

Table 14-XV. Payment for Pair of Space Elevators

Inside the owner's expenses are the normal charges such as cost of money, insurance of the system of systems, replacement costs [assumed to be $2B every 7.5 years for tether replacement], maintenance of tether climbers and expenses for personnel. It is now necessary to estimate income for the owners. It would be as shown in Table 14-XVI and Figure 14-8 for one pair of space elevators.

year	Purchase	Operations Expenses	Income	Profit	Cum Profit
2034		50		-50	-50
2035	500.0	500		-1000	-1050
2036	1,000.0	360	750	-610	-1660
2037	4,500.0	360	1,960.00	-2900	-4560
2038	6,000.0	360	1,960.00	-4400	-8960
2039	1,500.0	360	1,960.00	100	-8860
2040		360	1,960.00	1600	-7260
2041		360	1,960.00	1600	-5660
2042		360	1,960.00	1600	-4060
2043		360	1,960.00	1600	-2460
2044		360	1,960.00	1600	-860
2045		360	1,960.00	1600	740
2046		2360	1,960.00	-400	340
2047		360	1,960.00	1600	1940
2048		360	1,960.00	1600	3540
2049		360	1,960.00	1600	5140
2050		360	1,960.00	1600	6740
2051		2360	1,960.00	-400	6340
2052		360	1,960.00	1600	7940

Table 14-XVI. Expense vs. Profit

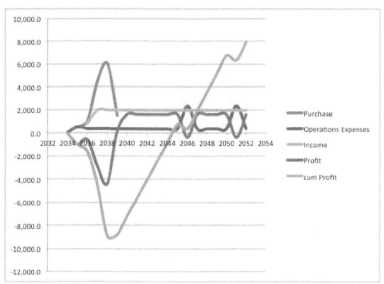

Figure 14-8. Owners' Investment and Return [break even +10 years]
Note: this is at $500/kg to GEO for one pair of space elevators

Findings of Business Plan 2

- **Finding BP2 #1:** In addition, "strategic investors" leverage $9.8 billion prior to the first space elevator and another $5 billion replicating the first three pairs – which they then sell for $33.5 billion.
- **Finding BP2 #2:** The owners each spend multiple billions of dollars to purchase a space elevator pair. The authors have shown they can sell their payload capacity and have a positive cash flow within a reasonable period of time with a huge backlog of business.
- **Finding BP2 #3:** The driving force for space elevator funding is recognition that the demand for 14 MT cargo loads is robust; however, customers with that demand are still only in the planning stages.

14.4   Financial Assumptions

- People putting up the money to build and operate a space elevator will be a commercial enterprise. The money must support all phases: research, development, prototypes, construction and operations.

- Carbon Space-Way, Inc. [CSWI] makes a deal with its 'supporting government' that goes something like this: "We will take all of the technical and financial risk associated with building a space elevator; however, we want you to authorize the launch, support a GEO slot allocation, defend it and indemnify it. In return for your support, CSWI will guarantee the ability to purchase 10% of launch capacity each year for whatever purpose you want."

- Space elevator pairs need to have two-way capability, so the proposal is simple... each operational business has two tethers. The first is ALL up for the mainline business activity and the second is for specialized activities such as the down direction, research for science, understanding the dynamics of tethers, work on the next generation, etc. But most importantly, the second tether will have business going up and some [definitely not as much] coming down the tether. This second tether is, most importantly, the corporation's insurance approach.

- For planning purposes, ten years after the first commercial space elevator ride, there would be a human rated version. Perhaps this is the purpose of the second tether. It is important we have this in the future. We need to either protect to a certain level or dump the radiation in the belts [can be accomplished for short periods of time]. For the pricing model, we need to set a goal and plan.

14.5   Conclusion

The authors conclude that three pairs of space elevators with a separate replicator seems to match the needs of future space endeavors as well as give appropriate, and timely, profits to investors. The identified price of $500 per kg will not only make sufficient profits for the four major contractors [a builder and three operators], but will stimulate the industry towards innovative missions and enable the spread of humanity off planet. New missions will be ready and waiting for this space elevator infrastructure because multiple space elevator planning would be advertised and progress would be identified publicly on tether risk reduction. In addition, the incentive of $500/kg will motivate big thinkers into believing space elevators enable their missions at an appropriate price point. A price of $500 per kg to orbit will enable history-making missions to be accomplished through an innovative transportation infrastructure called the space elevator. New customers will see that there is a robust, dependable, and large capacity to GEO and beyond. This will lead to innovative missions being ready for orbit as space elevators mature. They are shown once again below (Table 14-XVII):

	Demand MT/yr			
	2031	2035	2040	2045
Space Solar Power	40000	70000	100000	130000
Nuclear Materials Disposal	12000	18000	24000	30000
Asteroid Mining	1000	2000	3000	5000
Interplanetary Flights	100	200	300	350
Innovative Missions to GEO	347	365	389	400
Colonization of Solar System	50	200	1000	5000
Marketing & Advertising	15	30	50	100
Sun Shades at L-1	5000	10000	5000	3000
Current GEO satellites + LEOs	347	365	389	400
Total MT	58859	101160	134128	174250

Table 14-XVII. Projected Future Demands

This is the type of mission growth that space elevators enable. Once again, the space elevator must assist its future customers to:

o Dream big,
o Sell aggressively,
o Design to the future market, and
o Convince investors that there are big profits for those who take the early risk.

Finding 14-1: Space elevators will make major profits in the long run. As in most transportation infrastructures, the initial investments are massive and will require flexibility and creative funding; however, as the profit potential is so great, there will be money to be invested.

Chapter 15
Conclusions and Recommendations

This chapter will look at the key steps to the future for the space elevator. The conclusions and recommendations follow to ensure that the readers of this cosmic study report know where to proceed.

15.1 Next Steps

The authors and editors believe that global industry is progressing in many of the areas of interest to space elevator development; however, emphasis must be placed on some critical activities to ensure progress towards the critical developments. As such, the first recommendation and the first series of activities should be:

Step ONE: Create a foundation – This would develop a dedicated core of professionals who would solicit donations or grants from governments, individuals, or other foundations to then distribute in a manner supporting development of critical research. There are three organizations today that are doing something similar, but smaller. The Japanese Space Elevator Association is actively working with its academia and industry to further the concept of space elevators for Japan. The European Spaceward Foundation is supporting European space elevator games with the idea of stimulating the academic and industrial base of Europe. The International Space Elevator Consortium has run conferences for the last few years with sponsorship of games and studies. All three of these organizations could be a "core" for the larger and more active Space Elevator Foundation that would gather and disperse money. The financial roadmap shown in chapter 13 shows the level of investment at somewhere around three to ten million dollars [US] per year during the first six years.

Step TWO: Initiate research with hardware prototypes as objectives. This step has multiple paths for dispersal of funds at the best locations around the globe to accomplish the goals. As shown earlier, the major hardware prototypes would fall into the research categories of:

1. CNT Specific Strength Demonstration
2. Tether Climber Design
3. Deployment Satellite Design
4. Marine Stage One Prototype
5. High Stage One Prototype
6. Dynamics and Deployment Simulations
7. Flight Prototype Demonstration

All the investment of the first six prototypes would lead to the significant step of a technology flight experiment prototype test of an "almost full up" space elevator which would include the following components:

- 1,000km of tether representing operational 1-meter wide design
- Deployment satellite prototype launched into LEO and moved to test altitude
- Reel-out/in procedures checked and practiced
- Apex Anchor characteristics represented at the top end
- Mass at the lower end representing Marine Node with characteristics such as reel-in/out tether.
- Tether climber prototype with climbing gripper and motor

- Solar arrays producing needed energy supply for a full up climber
- Communications architecture tested with location of climber and tether segments routinely available to Operations Center
- Operations Center testing software to include dynamic control of tether motion.

An experiment should be established to "proof-test" the concepts and prototype equipment, with their methodology, for full up operations of a space elevator baseline. This would include these key characteristics:
- The initial set of parameters could be structured around the future space elevator concept described in this Cosmic Study.
- The in-flight hardware would enable design and testing for the space elevator baseline.
- The flight components would model all the major system of systems with the hardware, software, and operational procedures needed to implement the full up space elevator.
- The prototype hardware would be built for flight experimentation and would also be "proof-testing" of concepts, designs and procedures.
- The components would be flight-ready hardware and exercised in an environment similar to GEO but easier to get to and less hazardous to operate.
- This in-flight testing program would enable the space elevator designers to have confidence in the equipment, processes and team.

Step TWO requires a large portion of funds to be dispersed by the Space Elevator Foundation. The financial roadmap showed the numbers per year in Chapter 13.

Step THREE: Initiate a "Program Office". This activity would be in parallel with prototype developments inside the Space Elevator Foundation. The purpose of this activity would be to pursue the issues that require long preparation and will ensure a smoother development of this mega-project. These would include, but not be limited to, the following list of activities:

- Research and recommendations about the legal situation.
- Recommendation of specific location for first pair of space elevators.
- Research and recommendations about the regulations and government policies towards a space elevator implementation.
- Development of a preliminary set of requirements for the start of a program office supporting the development of the space elevator. This would lead to the initial Systems Requirements Document.
- Development of a preliminary Concept of Operations.
- Development of a preliminary budget for pre-development and the full up space elevator infrastructure construction.

This step requires modest funding in that the team has to be created and current on all the space elevator activities.

15.2 Potential Role for the International Academy of Astronautics
The authors believe that the IAA will have a significant role in future space development with their global reach inside National Space Agencies. As such, the suggestion is that:

- The Academy establish a Space Elevator Permanent Committee to coordinate efforts in space elevator research and development projects within National Space Agencies. Initially, the efforts would be centered around follow-up activities resulting from the distribution of this report to 300 locations inside the global space arena. This focus would ensure a global enterprise.

- The Academy assists Space Elevator activities in understanding the developing space markets, such as the Space Solar Power or Asteroid Mining ventures.

15.3 Conclusions
The conclusions from this study fall into a few distinct categories:

- **Legal:** The space elevator can be accomplished within today's arena!
- **Technology:** Its inherent strengths will improve the environment and reduce space debris in LEO and beyond. It can be accomplished with today's projections of where materials science and solar array efficiencies are headed. The critical capability improvement is in the space elevator tether materials growth, currently projected to achieve the necessary strength to weight ratio in the next 20 years. Space Elevators will open up human spaceflight and decrease space debris and environmental impacts.
- **Business:** This mega-project will be successful for the investors
- **Culturally:** This project will drive a renaissance on the surface of the Earth with its solution to key problems, stimulation of travel throughout the solar system, and inexpensive and routine access to GEO and beyond.

15.4 Recommendations
The authors and editors of this study believe that the global community should:

- Publish and distribute this International Academy of Astronautics Study Report.
- Establish a Space Elevator Foundation during 2013.
- Assist in funding the Space Elevator Foundation to the level required to conduct the early activities and then transition to the technological prototype developments.
- Support the "Next Steps" shown earlier in this chapter.
  - Step ONE: Create a foundation
  - Step TWO: Initiate research with hardware prototypes as objectives
  - Step THREE: Initiate a "Program Office".

15.5 Cosmic Study Result
The authors have come to believe that the operation of a space elevator infrastructure will lead to a "game changing" experience in the space world. Each of the authors considers that the space elevator can be developed when the tether material is mature enough for the demands of the space elevator. Our final assessments are:

**A Space Elevator Appears Feasible, with the realization
that risks must be mitigated through technological progress.
&
A Space Elevator Infrastructure will be achievable
through a major global enterprise.**

References

AIAA/INCOSE. (1997) "SE Primer - Systems Engineering, A briefing", August 1997.

Ambrose, S. (2000), "Nothing like it in the World". Simon & Schuster, New York, 2000.

Angel, R. (2006), "Feasibility of Cooling the Earth with a Cloud of Small Spacecraft near L1," Proceedings of the National Academy of Sciences, v 103, n46, 2006 November 14, 2006. Pp. 17184–17189. Available at:
http://www.ncbi.nlm.nih.gov/pmc/articles/PMC1859907

Artsutanov, Y. (1960), "Into the Cosmos by Electric Rocket," Komsomolskaya Pravda, 31 July 1960. (Contents described in English, Lvov in Science, 158, 946-947, 1967.)

Barber, A.H. et al. (2005), "Stochastic strength of nanotubes: An appraisal of available data", *Compos. Sci. Technol.*, Vol 65 No 15-16, pp. 2380–2384.

Barnds, J., et al. (1998). TiPS: Results of a Tethered Satellite System. Tether technology Interchange Meeting, NASA/CP-1998-206900, NASA Marshall. January 1998.

Barry, R.G., Chorley, R.J. (1998), *Atmosphere, Weather & Climate, (Seventh Edition),* Routledge, London, Section 6-3

Behabtu, N. et al (2013), "Strong, Light, Multifunctional Fibers of Carbon Nanotubes with Ultrahigh Conductivity", *Science*, Vol. 339, pp. 182-186.

Belytschko, T. et al (2002), "Atomistic simulations of nanotube fracture", *Phys. Rev. B*, Vol 65 no 23, 235430.

Brambilla, G. & Payne, D.N. (2009) "The ultimate strength of glass silica nanowires", *Nano Lett.*, Vol 9 No 2, pp. 831-835.

Carroll, J.A. (1993). SEDS Deployer Design and Flight performance. AIAA Space Programs and Technologies Conference and Exhibit, Huntsville, AIAA-93-4764. September 1993.

Carroll, J.A. and Oldson, J.C. (1995). SEDS characteristics and capabilities. In Proceedings of the 4th International Conference on Tethers in Space, pp. 1079-1090.

Chapman, P. K. (2010), "Deploying Sunsats", Online Journal of Space Communications, Issue 16, Winter 2010: Solar Power Satellites. Available at:
http://spacejournal.ohio.edu/issue16/chapman.html

Chobotov, V.A. and Mains, D.L. (1999). Tether Satellite System Collision Study, , Acta Astronautica, Vol 44, Nos. 7 – 12, pp 543 – 551, 1999.

Clarke, A. C. (2003), "Discussion by GEO satellite relay from Sra Lanka, 2nd Annual International Space Elevator Conference, 2003, Sante Fe, NM.

Clarke, A. C. (1979), "The Fountains of Paradise", Harcourt Brace Jovanovich, New York, 1979.

Cohen, S. S., Dynamics of a Space Elevator, Master of Engineering Thesis, McGill University, Montreal, Quebec, 2006.

Cohen, S. S. and Misra, A. K., "Elastic Oscillations of the Space Elevator Ribbon," Journal of Guidance Control and Dynamics, Vol. 30, No. 6, pp. 1711-1717, 2007.

Cohen, S. S. and Misra, A. K., "The Effect of Climber Transit on the Space Elevator Dynamics," Acta Astronautica, Vol. 64, pp. 538-553, 2009.

Cohen, S. and Misra, A. K., "Satellite Placement Using the Space Elevator," Climb, Vol. 2, No. 1, 2013.

Cornwell, C.F. et al. (2011) "Very-high-strength (60-GPa) carbon nanotube fiber design based on molecular dynamics simulations", *J. Chem. Phys.*, Vol. 134, 204708.

Cosmo, M.L., and Lorenzini, C.E., Tethers In Space Handbook, prepared for NASA Marshall Space Flight Center by Smithsonian Astrophysics Observatory, Cambridge, MA, December 1977.

Cronin, S.B. et al (2005), "Resonant Raman spectroscopy of individual metallic and semiconducting single-wall carbon nanotubes under uniaxial strain", *Phys. Rev. B*, Vol 72 No 3, 035425.

Demczyk, B.G. et al (2002), "Direct mechanical measurement of the tensile strength and elastic modulus of multiwalled carbon nanotubes", *Materials Science and Engineering*, vol A334, pp. 173–178.

Dillon, S. (1892), *"Historic moments: Driving the last spike of the Union Pacific".* *Scribner's Magazine, August, 1892. pp. 25-259. Available at:* *http://www.unz.org/Pub/Scribners-1892aug-00253*

Dobrowolny, M. and Stone, N.H. (1994). A Technical Overview of TSS-1: the First Tethered Satellite System Mission, Il Nuovo Cimento, Vol. 17C, N.1, pp. 1-12.

Dwyer, J. R. and Smith, D. M. (2012), "Deadly Rays from Clouds," Scientific American, 307, August 2012. pp. 54-59.

Ebbesen, T.W. & Ajayan, P.M. (1992) "Large-scale synthesis of carbon nanotubes" *Nature*, Vol. 358, pp. 220-222.

Edwards, B. and Laine, M. (2003), "The Space Elevator". Available at: http://www.mill-creek-systems.com/HighLift/chapter3.html

Edwards, B. and Ragan, P. (2006), *Leaving the Planet by Space Elevator*, Lulu.com

Edwards, B. C., and Westling, E. A., "The Space Elevator: A Revolutionary Earth-to-Space Transportation System", BC Edwards, 2003

Edwards, B, et.al., The Space Elevator, NIAC Study – the NASA Institute for Advanced Concepts Phase I, Oct. 2000. http://www.niac.usra.edu/studies/472Edwards.html

Edwards, B., et.al., The Space Elevator, Phase II Jan. 2003. http://www.niac.usra.edu/studies/521Edwards.html.)

Edwards, B. (2004), "Personal communications", 1 Aug 2004.

EUSPEC (2011), "Evaluation", Available at: http://euspec.warr.de/handbook
Highlift at: http://www.mill-creek-systems.com/HighLift/chapter3.html

Filleter, T. & Espinosa, H.D. (2012) "Multi-scale mechanical improvement produced in carbon nanotube fibers by irradiation cross-linking", *Carbon*, in press (2013)

Flyvbjerg, B. (2003), "Megaprojects and Risk: An Anatomy of Ambition". Cambridge University Press, 2003.

Fujii, H.A., Watanabe, T., Kusagaya, T. and Sato, D., "Dynamics of Flexible Space Tether Equipped with a Crawler Mass," Journal of Guidance, Control, and Dynamics, Vol. 31, No.2, pp.436-440, March/April 2008.

Fujii, H.A. et al. (2009). Sounding rocket experiment of bare electrodynamic tether system. Acta Astronautica, vol. 64, p.313-324.

Gale, S. F. (2011), "Biggest isn't always better," *PM Network*, March 2011. Available at: http://www.pegasus-global.com/newsletters/201104/Patricia_D_Galloway_Columbia_River_Crossing_Leadership_On_Megaprojects.pdf

Gao, P. et al (2010), "Self-Built Tensile Strain in Large Single-Walled Carbon Nanotubes", *ACS Nano*, Vol 4 No 2, pp. 992-998.

Gardner, J. (2003), "Where on Earth? Choosing an Anchor Point," *2nd Annual International Space Elevator Conference*, Sante Fe, NM. Oct 2003

Gassend, B. (2004), "Non-Equatorial Uniform-Stress Space Elevator," *3rd Annual International Space Elevator Conference*, Washington DC, 20 June 2004.

Gassend, B. (2004), "Exponential tethers for accelerated space elevator deployment". In Proc. of 3rd International Space Elevator Conference, June 2004.

Gelb, M. J. (2012), http://thinkexist.com/quotes/michael_j._gelb, June 2012.

Gilchrist, B. et. al. (1998). Enhanced electrodynamic tether currents due to electron emission from a neutral gas discharge: Results from the TSS⊔1R mission. Geophysical Research Letters, Vol. 25, No. 4, pp. 437-440, February 15, 1998.

Harris, R. (2012), "Rio Environment Meeting Focuses On 'Energy For All'" 19 June 2012. Available at: http://www.wbur.org/npr/155294726/rio-environment-meeting-focuses-on-energy-for-all

Hata, K. et al. (2004) "Water-Assisted Highly Efficient Synthesis of Impurity-Free Single-Walled Carbon Nanotubes" *Science*, Vol. 306 no 5700, pp. 1362-1364.

Hoyt R. and Twiggs, R. (2003). The Multi-Application Survivable Tether (MAST) Experiment. AIAA Paper 2003-5219.

Huang, S. et al (2004) "Growth Mechanism of Oriented Long Single Walled Carbon Nanotubes Using "Fast-Heating" Chemical Vapor Deposition Process", *Nano Lett.*, Vol 4 No 6, pp. 1025-1028.

Hong, B. et al. (2005) "Quasi-Continuous Growth of Ultralong Carbon Nanotube Arrays", *J. Am. Chem. Soc.*, Vol. 127 No 44, pp. 15336-15337.

Iijima, S. (1991) "Helical microtubules of graphitic carbon" *Nature*, Vol. 354, pp. 56-58.

INCOSE. (2006), "Systems Engineering Handbook", v3, June 2006

International Academy of Astronautics. (2000), "2001 Position Paper On Orbital Debris", International Academy of Astronautics, 24.11.2000.

International Academy of Astronautics (2005), "2006 Position Paper On Space Debris Mitigation", International Academy of Astronautics, 10.15.2005.

Isaacs, J., Vine, A. C., Bradner, H. and Bachus, G. E. (1966), "Satellite Elongation into a true Sky-Hook," Science, 151, 682-683, 1966.

Iwanaga, H. & Kawai, C. (2005) " Tensile Strength of Silicon Nitride Whiskers Synthesized by Reacting Amorphous Silicon Nitride and Titanium Dioxide", *J. Am. Ceram. Soc.*, Vol 81 No 3, pp. 773-776.

Jiang, J.H. et al. (2004), "Geographical distribution and interseasonal variability of tropical deep convection: UARS MLS observations and analyses," *Journal of Geophysical Research,* Vol. 109, D03111.

Johnson, L. et al (2003). Propulsive Small Expendable Deployer System (ProSEDS) Experiment Mission Overview and Status. In 39th AIAA ASME SAE ASEE Joint Propulsion Conference.

Jorgensen, A., B. Gassend, R. H. W. Friedel, T. Cayton, S. E. Patamia, "Space Elevator Radiation Hazards and How to Mitigate Them," 3rd Space Elevator Conference, Washington, DC, June 29, 2004.

 Jorgensen, A. M., S. E. Patamia, and B. Gassend. "Passive radiation shielding considerations for the proposed space elevator." Acta Astronautica 60.3 (2006): 198-209.

JSETEC (2011), "Results". Available at: http://www.jsea.jp/ja/jsetec2011_result

JSTM (2010), "Strategic Technology Road Map 2010", Ministry of Economy, Trade and Industry of Japan. Available at:

http://www.meti.go.jp/policy/economy/gijutsu_kakushin/kenkyu_kaihatu/str2010.html (In Japanese only)

Kare, J. (2011), personal communication.

Keshmiri, M. and Misra, A.K., "On the deployment of a subsatellite in a space elevator system", 63rd International Astronautical Congress, Naples, Italy, October 2012, Paper No. IAC-12.D.4.3.8.

Knapman, J. (2005), "Dynamically Supported Launcher," *Journal of the British Interplanetary Society*, Vol. 58, No. 3/4, pp. 90-102

Knapman, J. (2009), "The Space Cable: Capability and Stability," *Journal of the British Interplanetary Society*, Vol. 62, No.6, pp. 202-210

Knapman, J. (2010), "Diverse Configurations of the Space Cable," *61st International Astronautical Congress*, Prague, Czech Republic, 27 September 27- 1 October 2010

Knapman, J. (2011), "Space Elevator Stage I," *62nd International Astronautical Congress*, Cape Town, South Africa, 3-7 October 2011

Knapman, J. and Lofstrom, K. (2011), "Space Elevator Stage I: Through the Stratosphere," *2011 Space Elevator Conference*, Redmond, Wa, 12-14 August 2011

Knapman, J. (2012), "Benefits and Development of a High Stage One," *63rd International Astronautical Congress*, Naples Italy, 1-5 October 2012.

Kong, J. et al. (1998) "Synthesis of individual single-walled carbon nanotubes on patterned silicon wafers" *Nature*, Vol. 395, pp. 878-881.

Koziol, K. et al (2007) "High-Performance Carbon Nanotube Fiber", *Science*, Vol 318 No 5858, pp. 1892-1895

Kruijff, M., Gijsman, P., Heide, E.J. van der. (1999). Opening the Way for Large, Light and Non□Hazardous Space Structures: Report of a search for a UV□degradable material, IAC-99-I.3.05, Amsterdam, 1999.

Kruijff, M. and Heide, E. J. van der. (2009). Qualification and In-flight Demonstration of a European Tether Deployment System on YES2. In Acta Astronautica, vol. 64, p.882-905.

Kruijff M., Heide E.J. van der, Ockels W.J. (2009). Data Analysis of a Tethered SpaceMail Experiment. In Journal of Spacecraft and Rockets, Vol. 46, No. 6, pp. 1272-1287. (presented as AIAA-2008-7385).

Laine, Michael, Chapter 3: Spacecraft at: http://www.mill-creek-systems.com/HighLift/chapter3.html

Laine, M. (2006), "LiftPort Group Space Elevator Road Map." LiftPort, 2006

Lang, D. D., "Approximating Aerodynamic Response of the Space Elevator to Lower Atmospheric Wind," Space Exploration 2005, SESI Conference Series, Vol. 1, 2005.

Lang, D. D., "Space Elevator Dynamic Response to In-Transit Climbers," 1st International Conference on Science, Engineering, and Habitation in Space, Albuquerque, NM, Space Engineering and Science Inst., Paper 10152148, 2006.

Lang, D. D., "Space elevator initial construction mission overview", URL: /http://home.comcast.net/~GTOSS/S (cited 1 Feb. 2010)

Larson, Wiley., Space Mission Analysis and Design, Space Technology Library, Microcosm Press, 1999.

Larson, W. et al. (2009) "Applied Space Systems Engineering", McGraw Hill, 2009.

Larson, W. et al (2009), "Applied Space Systems Engineering", McGraw Hill, Boston, 2009. Pg. 304.

Levin, E.M. (2007). Dynamic Analysis of Space Tether Missions. Advances in the Astronautical Sciences, vol. 126.

Li, W.Z. et al. (1996) "Large-Scale Synthesis of Aligned Carbon Nanotubes" Science, Vol. 274 no 5293, pp. 1701-1703.

Li, Y-L et al (2004) "Direct Spinning of Carbon Nanotube Fibers from Chemical Vapor Deposition Synthesis", Science, Vol 304 no 5668, pp 276-278.

Lin, W. et al (2010) "Microwave Makes Carbon Nanotubes Less Defective", ACS Nano, Vol 4 No 3, pp. 1716-1722.

Liu, K. et al (2010) "Carbon nanotube yarns with high tensile strength made by a twisting and shrinking method", Nanotech., Vol 21 No 4, 045708.

Lofstrom, K. (1985), "The Launch Loop," AIAA Paper 85-1368, July 1985.

Loftus, J. P. and Stansbery, E. G. (1993), "Protection of Space Assets by Collision Avoidance.", 44th Congress of the International Astronautical Federation, Austria. IAA 6.4-93-752

Lorenzini, C. and Cosmo, M., "Wave Propagation in the Tether Elevator/Crawler System," Acta Astronautica, Vol. 21, No. 8, pp. 545-552, 1990.

Ma, W.J. et al (2007) "Directly Synthesized Strong, Highly Conducting, Transparent Single-Walled Carbon Nanotube Films", Nano Lett., Vol 7 No 8, pp. 2307-2311.

Ma, W.J. et al (2009) "Monitoring a Micromechanical Process in Macroscale Carbon Nanotube Films and Fibers", Adv. Mat., Vol 21 No 5, 603-608.
O'Brien, N.P. et al. (2012) "A theoretical quantification of the possible improvement in the mechanical properties of carbon nanotube bundles by carbon ion irradiation", Carbon, Vol. 53, pp. 346-356.

Mankins, J. (2011), "Space Solar Power, The First International Assessment Of Space Solar Power: Opportunities, Issues And Potential Pathways Forward", IAA, October 2011.

McCoy, J.E. et al. (1995). Plasma Motor-Generator (PMG) Flight Experiment Results. In the fourth Conference On Tethers in Space, pp. 57-82.

Merrow, E. (2011), "Industrial Megaprojects, Concepts, Strategies, and Practices for Success". John Wiley & Sons, 2011

METI. (2010). "Strategic Technology Roadmap". Ministry of Economy, Trade & Industry of Japan, 2010. Available (in Japanese only) at: http://www.meti.go.jp/policy/economy/gijutsu_kakushin/kenkyu_kaihatu/str2010.html

METI. (2010) "Technology Strategy Map", Ministry of Economy, Trade and Industry of Japan, 2010. Available at: http://www.meti.go.jp/policy/economy/gijutsu_kakushin/kenkyu_kaihatu/str2010.html

Modi, V. J., Bachman, S., and Misra, A. K., "Dynamics and Control of a Space Station Based Tethered Elevator System," Acta Astronautica, Vol. 29, No. 6, pp. 429-449, 1993.

National Space Society. (2007),"Space Solar Power: An Investment for Today – An Energy Solution for Tomorrow," National Space Society, Oct. 2007

NASA. (2010), "Debris density charts from NASA Orbital Debris Program Office", May 2010.

NASA Tech Briefs, Nov 2012.

NASA (1967). Gemini XII Program Mission Report, Manned Spacecraft Center, Houston, USA, January 1967.

NTRM (2012), "NASA Space Technology Roadmaps and Priorities: Restoring NASA's Technological Edge and Paving the Way for a New Era in Space," National Academy of Science Report, Washington D.C., 2012.

Ohkawa, R., Uchiyama, K., and Fujii, H. A., "The Effect of Disturbance on Space Elevator Dynamics with Flexibility," 61th International Astronautical Congress, Prague, IAC-10-D4. 4. 5, 27 Sep. -1 Oct. 2010.

Pan, Z. W. et al. (1998) "Very long carbon nanotubes". Nature, Vol. 394 pp 631-632.

Pearson, J., "The Orbital Tower: A Spacecraft Launcher Using the Earth's Rotational Energy," Acta Astronautica, Vol. 2, pp. 785-799, Sep/Oct 1975.

Peng, B. et al. (2008) "Measurements of near-ultimate strength for multiwalled carbon nanotubes and irradiation-induced crosslinking improvements", Nat. Nanotechol., Vol. 3 No 10, pp. 626-631.

Penny, R. and Jones, R. (1983), "A Model for Evaluation of Satellite Population Management Alternatives", AFIT Master's Thesis, 1983.

Penny, R., Swan, C. and Swan, P. (2011), "Space Elevator Survivability; Space Debris Mitigation". ISEC Position Paper #2010-1, International Space Elevator Consortium, Lulu, 2011.

Penny, Robert. Swan, Peter, & Cathy Swan, "Space Elevator Concept of Operations," ISEC Position Paper #2012-1, International Space Elevator Consortium, Fall, 2013.

Phelan, R. M. (1970), "Fundamentals of Mechanical Design", 3rd Edition, McGraw-Hill, NY, 1970, pp 145-7

Pugno, N.M. & Ruoff, R.S. (2004) "Quantized fracture mechanics", *Philosophical Mag.*, Vol 84 No 27, pp. 2829-2845.

Pugno, N. et al (2009) "Size effects on the strength of nanotube bundles", *Meas. Sci. Technol.*, Vol 20 No 8, 084028.

Pugno, N. M. (2013),Towards the Artsutanov's dream of the space elevator: The ultimate design of a 35 GPa strong tether thanks to graphene. *Acta Astronautica,* Volume 82, Issue 2, p. 221-224.

Purang, Deepak (n.d.), "Space sunshade may one day reduce global warming." Editorial. Available at:
http://www.streetdirectory.com/travel_guide/14921/gadgets/space_sunshade_may_one_day_r educe_global_warming.html

Raitt, D. (2005), "The Space Elevator: its Place in History, Literature and the Arts. In: Proceedings of 56th International Astronautics Congress, 17-21 October 2005, Fukuoka, Japan. IAC, 2005. IAC-05-D4.3.02

Raitt, D. and Edwards, B. (2004), "The Space Elevator: Economics and Applications." In: Proceedings of 55th IAC, 4-8 October 2004, Vancouver, Canada. IAC, 2004. IAC-04-IAA.3.8.3

Roundy, D., and Cohen, M.L. (2001), "Ideal strength of diamond, Si, and Ge", *Phys. Rev. B,* vol. 64, 212103.

Ruoff, R.S, Qian, D. & Liu, W.K. (2003) "Mechanical properties of carbon nanotubes: theoretical predictions and experimental measurements", *Comptes Rendus Physique*, Vol 4 No 9, pp. 993-1008

Sasaki, S. et al (1987). Results from a Series of Tethered Rocket Experiments. AIAA, USA.

Sasaki, S. and Oyama, K.I. (1994). Space Tether Experiments in Japan. 2nd International Workshop on the Application of Tethered Systems in Space, Kanagawa, Japan, ISAS, May 1994.

Shelef, B. (2004), "Segment Based Ribbon Architecture"., In Proc. of 3rd International Space Elevator Conference, June 2004.

Shelef, B. (2011), "The Space Elevator Feasibility Condition", Climb Journal, Volume 1, Number 1, p. 87.

Shelef, B. (2008a), "Space Elevator Power System Analysis and Optimization, Spaceward Foundation, 2008. Available at: http://www.spaceward.org/elevator-library#SW

Shelef, B. (2008b), "The Space Elevator Feasibility Condition", Spaceward Foundation, 2008. Available at: http://www.spaceward.org/elevator-library#SW

Shelef, B. (2008c), "A Solar-Based Space Elevator Architecture," Spaceward Foundation, 2008. Available at: http://www.spaceward.org/elevator-library#SW

Shinobu Doi (2011), "JEM Extended Utilization for Exposed Experiments using JEM Airlock and Robotics", 15th Annual ISU International Symposium, Strasbourg, France, Feb 16, 2011

Sidi, M., Spacecraft Dynamics and Control: A Practical Engineering Approach, Cambridge University Press, pp. 28-62, 1997.

Smith, C. M. (2013), "Starship Humanity," Scientific American, Jan 2013, pg. 39-43.

Smitherman, D. (2006), "Space Elevators: An Advanced Earth-Space Infrastructure for the New Millennium", University Press of the Pacific, 2006

Squibb, G., Boden, D. and Larson, W. (1996), "Cost Effective Space Mission Operations", McGraw Hill, 1996.

Stano, K.L. et al (2008) "Direct spinning of carbon nanotube fibres from liquid feedstock", *Int. J. Mat. Forming*, Vol 1 No 2, pp. 59-62

Suemori, K. (2012), "Film-shaped thermoelectric conversion elements can be produced in print" Available at: http://www.aist.go.jp/aist_j/aistinfo/aist_today/vol12_04/p17.html

Swan, Peter and Cathy Swan, *Space Elevator Systems Architecture*, www.lulu.com, 2007.

Swan, Peter, Robert Penny & Cathy Swan, "Space Elevator Survivability: Space Debris Mitigation," ISEC Position Paper #2010-1, International Space Elevator Consortium, Fall, 2010.

Takeichi, N. , "Geostationary stationkeeping control of a space elevator during initial cable deployment", 61st International Astronautical Congress, Prague, Czech Republic, October 2010, paper No. IAC-10-D.4.4.7.

Takeichi, N., "Geostationary station keeping control of a space elevator during initial cable deployment", Acta Astronautica, Vol. 70, pp. 85-94, 2012.

Tang, G. et al (2010) "New Confinement Method for the Formation of Highly Aligned and Densely Packed Single-Walled Carbon Nanotube Monolayers", *Small*, Vol 6 No 14, pp. 1488-1491.

Teal Group (2012), "World Space Systems Briefing". Teal Group, 2012.
The British Interplanetary Society. (2012), "Is space commercialization a myth?," Spaceflight Magazine, v54, n6, June 2012, p. 206

Telling, R. H. , Pickard, C. J., Payne, M. C., and Field, J. E. (2000), "Theoretical Strength and Cleavage of Diamond", *Phys. Rev. Lett.*, Vol. 84, pp. 5160–5163.

Termonia, Y. et al (1985), "Theoretical Study of the Influence of the Molecular Weight on the Maximum Tensile Strength of Polymer Fibers", *Macromol.*, Vol. 18, pp. 2246-2252.

Tsiolkovsky, K. E. (1959), "Speculations of Earth and Sky and On Vesta", Moscow, USSR Academy of Sciences, 1959 (in Russian – first published 1895).

TSM (2010), "Technological Strategy Zmap 2010 – Energy", Ministry of Economy, Trade and Industry. Available at:
http://www.meti.go.jp/policy/economy/gijutsu_kakushin/kenkyu_kaihatu/str2010download.ht ml

Tsuchida, Akira, "A Space Elevator Roadmap 2010," 2010 IAC, Prague, Oct 2010.

Tsuchida, Akira, et al. (2011), "Space Elevator Road Map 2011", 62nd International Astronautical Congress, Cape Town, Republic of South Africa, 2011

Tsuchida A. et al (2009), "New Space Transportation System-Space Train (Elevator) : World trends and Japanese Space Train Concept",
Technical report of IEICE. SANE 109(101), 93-98, 2009-06-18

Tsukiyama, Y. (2010). "Tribological properties of high-alignment carbon nanotube films", The Machine Design and Tribology Division meeting in JSME 2010 (10), 49-50, 2010-04-18

Tsyganenko, N., Fortran programs Geopack-2008,
http://geo.phys.spbu.ru/~tsyganenko/modeling.html

Tyc, G. and Han, R.P.S. (1995). Attitude Dynamics Investigation of the OEDIPUS: A Tethered Rocket Payload. Journal of Spacecraft and Rockets, Vol. 32, No. 1, p. 133□141, February 1995.

Uchiyama, K., Iijima, K., and Fujii, H. A., "Construction of Space Elevator Model Using Absolute Nodal Coordinate," Transactions on Advanced Research IPSI Bgd Internet Research Society, ISSN 1820-4511, Vol. 9, No. 2, pp.8-12, July 2013.

Umehara, N. (2007), "Tribology of Fullerane and Carbon Nano Tube as Advanced Materials Designed Nano-structures", *Shinku*, Vol. 50 No. 2, 2007. Pp. 76-81

USAF (2012), "Energy Horizons", United States Air Force, Energy S&T Vision 2011-2026, AF/ST TR 11-01 31 January 2012, Pgs. 21-24.

Vigneron, F.R., Jablonski, A.M. et al. (1997). Comparison of Analytical Modeling of OEDIPUS Tethers with Data from Tether Laboratory. Journal of Guidance, Control and Dynamics, Vol. 20, No. 3, pp.471-478, May-June, 1997.

Volland, H.J. Geophys. Res. 78, 171 (1973); & D.J. Stern, Geophys. Res. 80, 595 (1975).

VSO (Visual Satellite Observer's Homepage). http://www.satobs.org/noss.html, last accessed November 2010.

Wang, X. et al. (2009) "Fabrication of Ultralong and Electrically Uniform Single-Walled Carbon Nanotubes on Clean Substrates" *Nano Lett.* Vol. 9 no 9, pp. 3137-3141.

Wang, Z., Ciselli, P. & Peijs, T. (2007), "The extraordinary reinforcing efficiency of single-walled carbon nanotubes in oriented poly(vinyl alcohol) tapes", *IOP Nanotechnology*, Vol 18 No 45, 455709.

Weeden, B. (2009), Billiards in Space. The Space Review, Feb 23, 2009. Available at: www.thespacereview.com/article/1314/1

Wei, X. et al (2010) "Tensile Tests on Individual Multi-Walled Boron Nitride Nanotubes", *Adv. Mater.*, Vol 22 No 43, pp. 4895-4899.

Welch, J. (2012), http://thinkexist.com/quotation/good_business_leaders_create_a_vision-articulate/151585.html, June 2012.

Wen, Q. et al (2010) "Growing 20 cm Long DWNTs/TWNTs at a Rapid Growth Rate of 80−90 μm/s", *Chem. Mater.*, Vol 22 No 4, pp. 1294-1296.

Wen, Q. et al (2010b) "100-mm Long, Semiconducting Triple-Walled Carbon Nanotubes", *Adv. Mater.*, Vol 22 No 16, pp. 1867-1871.

Wertz, James R.(2011), "Space Mission Engineering: the New SMAD," Microcosm Press, Hawthorne Calif., 2011.

Westling, E. (2005), Personal communications, e-mail note, 2005.

Whitesides, G. (2004), "Panel Discussion," The Space Elevator 3rd Annual International Space Elevator Conference, 30 June 2004, Washington,D.C.

Williams, P., Blanksby, C., Trivailo, P., "Tetehred Planetary Capture Maneuvers," Journal of Spacecraft and Rockets, Vol. 41, No. 4, pp.603-613, 2004.

Williams, P., "Dynamics and Control of Spinning Tethers for Rendezvous in Elliptic Orbits," Journal of Vibration and Control, Vol. 12, No. 7, pp.737-771, 2006.

Williams, P., "Dynamic Multibody Modeling for Tethered Space Elevators," Acta Astronautica, Vol. 65, No. 3-4, pp.399-422, Aug-Sept. 2009.

Williams, P. and Ockels, W., "Climber motion optimization for the tethered space elevator, Acta Astronautica, doi:10.1016/ j.actaastro.2009.11.003, 2009.

Wright, D. "Electric Currents on the Space Elevator," International Space Elevator Conference, Seattle, August 2013.

Wong, S.S. et al. (1997) "Nanobeam Mechanics: Elasticity, Strength, and Toughness of Nanorods and Nanotubes", Science, Vol 277 No 5334, pp 1971-1975.

Woo,P. and Misra, A.K. "Dynamics of a partial space elevator withmultiple climbers," Acta Astronautica, doi:10.1016/j.actaastro.2010.04.023, 2010.

Xie, H. et al., "Growth of high-density parallel arrays of ultralong carbon nanotubes with catalysts pinned by silica nanospheres", Carbon, Vol. 52, pp. 535-540.

Yakobson, B.I., & Avouris, P. (2001), "Mechanical properties of carbon nanotubes" Carbon Nanotubes, Vol 80, pp. 287–327.

Yamada, T. et al (2008) "Revealing the Secret of Water-Assisted Carbon Nanotube Synthesis by Microscopic Observation of the Interaction of Water on the Catalysts", Nano Lett., Vol 8 No 12, pp. 4288-4292.

Yao, Y. et al (2007) "Raman Spectral Measuring of the Growth Rate of Individual Single-Walled Carbon Nanotubes", J. Phys. Chem. C, Vol 111 No 24, pp. 8407-8409.

Yu, M.-F. et al (2000) "Strength and Breaking Mechanism of Multiwalled Carbon Nanotubes Under Tensile Load", Science, Vol 287 No 5453, pp. 637-640.

Yuan, Q. et al (2011) "Threshold Barrier of Carbon Nanotube Growth", Phys. Rev. Lett., Vol. 107, 156101.

Yuan, Q. et al (2012) "Efficient Defect Healing in Catalytic Carbon Nanotube Growth", Phys. Rev. Lett., Vol. 108, 245505.

Zedd, M.F. (1998). Experiments in Tether Dynamics Planned for ATEx's Flight. Tether technology Interchange Meeting, NASA/CP-1998-206900, NASA Marshall, January 1998.

Zhang, M. et al (2004) "Multifunctional Carbon Nanotube Yarns by Downsizing an Ancient Technology", Science, Vol 306 No 5700, pp 1358-1361.

Zhang, X. et al (2007) "Ultrastrong, Stiff, and Lightweight Carbon-Nanotube Fibers", Adv. Mater., Vol 19, pp. 4198-4201.

Zhang, X. & Li, Q. (2010) "Enhancement of Friction between Carbon Nanotubes: An Efficient Strategy to Strengthen Fibers", ACS Nano, Vol 4 No 1, pp. 312-316.

Zhang, R. et al (2011) "Superstrong Ultralong Carbon Nanotubes for Mechanical Energy Storage", *Adv. Mater.*, Vol 23 No 30, pp. 3387-3391.

Zhao, Q. et al (2002) "Ultimate strength of carbon nanotubes: A theoretical study", *Phys. Rev. B*, Vol 65 No 14, 144105.

Zheng, L.X. et al (2004) "Ultralong single-wall carbon nanotubes", *Nature Mat.*, Vol 3 No 10, pp. 673-676.

Zheng, L. et al (2009) "Tuning Array Morphology for High-Strength Carbon-Nanotube Fibers", *Small* Vol 6 No 1, pp. 132-137.

Web Sites

[1] en.wikipedia.org/wiki/upper-atmospheric_lightning

[2] www.intercomms.net/AUG03/content/struzak1.php credited to COSPAR International Reference Atmosphere [3]

[3] nssdc.gsfc.nasa.gov/space/model/atmos/cospar1.html

[4] Wikipedia, Radioactive waste. Updated 1 Feb 2013. Available at: http://en.wikipedia.org/wiki/Radioactive_waste

[5] Wikipedia (2013), "Space Elevator". Available at: http://en.wikipedia.org/wiki/Space_elevator

[6] www.scribd.com/doc/67431324/ - US Army offshore oil operations safety # 04-2009.

Appendix A – Contributors

Name		Nation	Role-chapter	Organization
Swan	Peter	USA	Editor	IAA Commission III & VI, ISEC
Raitt	David	UK	Editor	IAA Commission VI
Penny	Robert	USA	Ed. 8, 9	Cholla Space Systems, ISEC
Swan	Cathy	USA	Editor	IAA Commission VI
Knapman	John	UK	Ed. 5, 7	Independent Researcher, ISEC, ESwA
Semon	Ted	USA	4	President ISEC
Shelef	Ben	USA	3, 4	Independent Researcher, ISEC
Chase	Frank	USA	Artist	Resident Artist for ISEC
Gassend	Blaise	USA	6, E5	Independent Researcher
Laubscher	Bryan	USA	3, E2	Independent Researcher, ISEC
Lades	Martin	Germany	E2	ISEC, ESwA
Fujii	Hironori	Japan	6	Kanagawa Institute of Technology
Uchiyama	Kenji	Japan	6	Nihon University
Takeichi	Noboru	Japan	6	Nagoya University
Watanabe	Takeo	Japan	6	Teikyo University
Perek	Lubos	Czech R.	review	Astronomical Inst. Czech Acad. Sci.
Mashayekhi	Mohammad	Iran	6	McGill University
Misra	Arun	Canada	6	McGill University
Williams	Paul	Australia	6	BAE Systems Australia
Laine	Michael	USA	4, 11	LiftPort, ISEC
Cohen	Stephen	Canada	6	Vanier College
Kai	Sunao	Japan	12	Nihon University, College of Law
Lofstrom	Keith	USA	5	Independent Researcher
Kruijff	Michiel	Netherlands	6, E3	Delta-Utec Space
Brambilla	Gilberto	Italy	3	University of Southampton
Tsuchida	Akira	Japan	10, 11	Earth-Track Corporation
Aoki	Yoshio	Japan	10, 11	Nihon University
Sato	Minoru	Japan	10, 11	Tokai University
Saito	Shigeo	Japan	10, 11	JSEA
Matsumoto	Takane	Japan	10, 11	JSEA
Nakadai	Kohei	Japan	10, 11	Nihon University
Takezawa	Yoshinori	Japan	10, 11	Nihon University
Natsume	Hideyuki	Japan	10, 11	JSEA
Ishimaru	Osamu	Japan	10, 11	JSEA
Hara	Emiko	Japan	10, 11	Nihon University
Sannomiya	Kotaro	Japan	10, 11	Nihon University
Yoshino	Nobuto	Japan	10, 11	Nihon University
Sasaki	Fumiki	Japan	10, 11	JSEA
Hanada	Takaki	Japan	10, 11	JSEA, kikyu.org
Akiyama	Ayano	Japan	10, 11	JSEA
Mimura	Kunihiko	Japan	10, 11	JSEA

IAA - International Academy of Astronautics; **ISEC** – International Space Elevator Consortium;
JSEA - Japanese Space Elevator Association, **ESwA** - EuroSpaceward Association

Appendix B – Glossary of Terms and Acronyms

Term	Description
ADCS	Attitude Determination and Control subsystem
AIAA	American Institute of Aeronautics and Astronautics
AMD	Archiving and Maintaining the Mission Database
AML	Aging material lift [part of FC calculations]
APD	Activity Planning and Development
ASAT	Anti-satellite system
BCC	Body centered cubic
BSS	Base Support Station
C&C	Command and communications
CADH	Command and Data Handling subsystem
CCS	Computers and Communications Support
CDP	Climber Data Processing
cf	Centrifugal force factor when calculating the effect of rotation on a long string
CMG	Control moment gyro's
CNT	Carbon Nano-Tubes
COC	Climber Operations Center
COMSAT	Communication Satellite Organization
CONOPS	Concept of operations
COPUOS	Committee on the Peaceful Uses of Outer Space
CPA	Climber Planning and Analysis
CPU	Central processing unit [on-board computer]
CSWI	Carbon Space-Way, Inc.
CTC	Characteristic time constant [part of FC calculations]
CVD	Chemical vapor deposition
DMS	Developing and Maintaining Software
DSP	Defense Support Program Satellite System
DTD	Data Transport and Delivery
EEZ	Exclusive Economic Zone
EOC	Enterprise Operations Center [Business Center]
ESA	European Space Agency
ESWA	European Spaceward Association
EUSPEC	European Space Elevator Challenge
FC	Feasibility Condition, operating region for space elevator parameters – discussed in chapter 3
FLTSATCOM	Fleet SatCom Satellite System
FMS	Financial Management
FOP	Floating operations platform
FS	Fraction Weight of the Spare in orbit [part of FC calculations]
g	Gravitational attractive standard – 1 "g" at Earth's surface
g/cc	Grams per cubic centi-meter
GEO	Geosynchronous Orbit [42,164 altitude]
GEONode OC	GEO Node Operations Center
GPa	Giga Pascal, a measure of strength for a material in tension
GPS	Global positioning satellite system
HQ	Headquarters
HSO	High stage one

IAA	International Academy of Astronautics
IADC	Inter Agency Space Debris Coordination Committee
INCOSE	International Council of Systems Engineers
IR&D	Internal Research and Development
ISEC	International Space Elevator Consortium
ISWC	International Space-Way Creators, Inc.
JAXA	Japan Aerospace Exploration Agency
JSEA	Japanese Space Elevator Association
JSETEC	Japan's Space Elevator Technical and Engineering Competition
JSTM	Japanese Technology Roadmap
ka, ku	High data rate communications frequencies above 15 GHz
kg, [also g]	1000 grams or kilogram
km, [also m]	1000 meters or a kilometer
kN	Kilo newton force
kWatt	Kilowatt power
LEO	Low Earth Orbit [200 – 2000 km altitude]
LIB	Lithium Ion Batteries
LL	Lessons learned
MC	Mission Control
MEO	Medium Earth Orbit [between LEO and GEO]
mm	Millimeter [one meter /1000]
MMH/NTO	Magnetoplasmadynamic and/or nitrogen tetroxide / monomethyl-hydrazine
MMO	Managing Mission Operations
MN	Mega newton force
MP	Mission Planning
MRL	Minimal required lift capacity [part of FC calculations]
MSFC	Marshall Spaceflight Center
MSO	Marine stage one
MT	Meteric ton [1,000 kg]
MWatt	Mega watt in power
MYuri	Mega Yuri, a measure of specific strength for tethers [see appendix for details]
NASA	National Aeronautics and Space Administration
NIB	Neodymium Iron Boron
NOAA	National Oceanographic and Atmospheric Administration
NPA	Navigation Planning and Analysis
NSS	National Space Society
NTRM	NASA Space Technology Roadmaps
O&M	Operations and Maintenance
OV	Operational View
P pos	Possible mass throughput [part of FC calculations]
P req	Required mass throughput in SMUs [part of FC calculations]
PD	Power density [part of FC calculations]
PMR	Payload mass ration [part of FC calculations]
PMT	Payload mass throughput [part of FC calculations]
POC	Primary Operations Center
PPA	Customer Payload Planning and Analysis
PV	Photo voltaic [solar cells]
R&D	Research and Development

Rpm	Revolutions per minute
S/C	Spacecraft
S&T	Science and technology
SEDS	Small Expendable Deployer System
SEIT	Systems Engineering, Integration and Test
SGL	Support growth lift [part of FC calculations]
SMU	Standard mass unit [part of FC calculations]
SOC	Satellite Operations Center [Customer's own site]
SPC	Satellite processing center
SSC	Space control center
SSN	Space Surveillance Network
SSP	Space Solar Power
STU	Standard throughput unit [part of FC calculations]
T-Rex	Electrodynamic Tape Tether
TD	Time to Double [part of FC calculations]
TiPS	A tether mission
TL	Material lifetime in service [part of FC calculations]
TMR	Tether mass ration [part of FC calculations]
TOC	Tether operations center
TR	Taper ratio
TRL	Technology Readiness Level [NASA's measure of being ready for space deployment]
TSL	Tether specific loading [part of FC calculations]
TSS	Tether satellite system [flew on the Space Shuttle #1 & 2]
TT&C	Tracking, Telemetry and Control [sometimes also includes communications]
UN	United Nations
UV	Ultraviolet
V & V	Verification and Validation
VASIMR	Variable Specific Impulse Magnetoplasma Rocket
YC	Yearly capacity [part of FC calculations]
YES2	Young Engineers Satellite
□	Dissociation energy

Proposal for Forming an IAA Study Group SG 3.11

Title of Study: Space Elevators: An Assessment of the Technological Feasibility and the Way Forward

Proposer(s): Peter Swan, Ph.D., David Raitt, Ph.D. & Cathy Swan, Ph.D.

Primary IAA Commission Preference: III, Space Technologies and Systems Development

Members of Study Team

Chairs: Peter Swan and David Raitt

Secretary: Cathy Swan

Other IAA Members: Robert Penny, John Knapman, Lubos Perek, Tetsuo Yasaka, Radu Rugescu, Hironari Fujii, Arun Misra, Stephen Cohen, Sunao Kai, Gilberto Brambilla, Akira Tsuchida.

Other Members: Frank Chase, Ben Shelef, Blaise Gassend, Bryan Laubscher, Martin Lades, Kenjhi Uchiyama, Nobaru Takeichi, Takeo Watanabe, Mohammad Mashayekhi, Paul Williams, Michael Laine, Michiel Kruijff, Yoshio Aoki, Minoru Sato, Shigeo Saito, Takane Matsumoto, Kohei Nakadai, Yoshinori Takezawa, Hideyuki Natsume, Osamu Ishimaru, Emiko Hara, Kataro Sannomiya, Nobuto Yoshino, Fumiki Sasaki, Takaki Hanada, Ayano Akiyama, Kunihiko Mimura.

Short Description of Scope of Study

####### Overall Goal:
1) Assessment of the Technologies [ribbon materials, dynamics of ribbon, base station infrastructure, ribbon rider motor/wheels, power to ribbon rider (lasers vs. sun), ribbon rider platform].
2) Systems design Issues [space debris, deployment, environmental elements]
3) Description of space elevator implementation [dynamics and control of long ribbon, buildup of 1-meter wide ribbon, power approach, payload carrying capacity, anchor design].
####### Intermediate Goals:
1) Conduct sessions at IAC's [South Africa, Naples] with the purpose of presenting technological aspects of the space elevator.
2) Conduct a mini-symposium co-sponsored by the Academy and the International Space Elevator Consortium presenting the results of this study.
3) Facilitate cooperative productive networking between organizations with common interests and programs.

Methodology: The initial step is to sponsor sessions inside the IAA D.4.4 Symposium {Symposium of the Far Future: Space Elevators and Tethers}. A parallel step is to create a study group, establish goals, objectives and timelines for a space elevator cosmic study. The last step would be to produce a report for the Academy that discussed the feasibility and a road forward.

Time Line:
1) Meeting 1 – Prague Oct 2010, establish study group.
2) Meeting 2 – Paris Mar 2011, establish timelines and break out responsibilities.
3) Meetings 3/4/5/6 – South Africa, Paris, Naples, Paris, progress reports
4) Meeting 7 – Turin Italy announces to press the completion of the report
5) Meeting 8 – Washington DC January 2014 – presentation of results.

Final Product (Report, Publication, etc.):
Study report in the form of a technical book [>400 pages].

Target Community:
IAA, Space Agencies, Academic Institutions, Space Policy Organizations (pubic & private), Professional Societies, Aerospace Industry, International Community.

Support Needed:
1) Use of IAA web site.
2) meeting rooms at different venues.

Potential Sponsors:
IAA, World Space Agencies (including ESA, NASA, CNES, JAXA, DLR), Private Industry (Boeing, Lockheed Martin, Shimizu Corporation), International Space Elevator Consortium, Japanese Space Elevator Association, Eurospaceward.

To be returned to IAA Secretariat Paris fax: 33 1 47 23 82 16 email: sgeneral@iaanet.org

Date: March 22, 2010   Signature: *Peter Swan*

For IAA Use Only:

Commission III Approved:	*27 June 2013*
Peer Review Approved:	*26 August 2013*
SAC Approval:	*22 September 2013*
BoT Approval:	*17 October 2013*

Appendix D
History of the Space Elevator

As this study has tried to demonstrate, the modern day space elevator, especially as described by Dr. Brad Edwards in his book "Space Elevators" (Edwards and Westling, 2003), is likely to be accomplished in the relatively near future; however, it was felt useful to summarize the history of the space elevator concept (Wikipedia, 2013) in order to afford a better understanding of the environment in which it will operate.

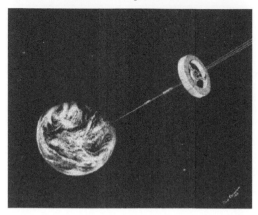

Figure D-1. Space Elevator, an Air Force Painting, 1975

The idea of a "stairway to heaven" is as old as the Bible, and includes the Tower of Babel, Jacob's Ladder and the children's fairy tale Jack and the Beanstalk which dates from the early 1400s (Raitt, 2005). Modern thought on space elevators goes back to 1895 when Konstantin Tsiolkovsky (Tsiolkovsky, 1959), a school teacher in St. Petersburg, Russia, who, inspired by the newly-constructed Eiffel Tower in Paris, considered a tower reaching all the way up into space. He thought of putting a "celestial castle" at the end of a spindle shaped cable, with the "castle" orbiting the earth in a geosynchronous orbit. Tsiolkovsky's tower would be able to launch objects into orbit without a rocket. Tsiolkovsky realized, because of their rotation, gravity would decrease as you ascended such a tower, reversing at the altitude where a satellite would have a period the same as the rotation period of the body. Here the gravitational and centrifugal forces on a body in geosynchronous orbit are in balance. Tsiolkovsky calculated the synchronous altitudes for the five visible planets and also the sun, but he concluded that building a real tower into orbit was impossible as there was no material in existence at the time with enough compressive strength to support its own weight under such conditions.

Some sixty years later another Russian scientist, Yuri N. Artsutanov, conceived of a more feasible scheme for building a space tower by using a geosynchronous satellite as the base from which to construct the tower. By using a counterweight, a cable would be lowered from geosynchronous orbit to the surface of the Earth while the counterweight was extended from the satellite away from Earth, keeping the center of gravity of the cable motionless relative to Earth. Artsutanov published his idea in the Sunday supplement of Komsomolskaya Pravda in 1960 (Artsutanov, 1967). He also proposed tapering the cable thickness so that the tension in the cable was constant. The significance of Artsutanov's ideas was not recognized in the West at the time.

Figure D-2. Space Elevator, an Air Force Painting, 1973

In 1966, a group of oceanographers led by John Isaacs at the Scripps Institute re-discovered the concept, but they proposed such a thin wire that it would be cut by micro-meteoroids almost instantly, and was therefore completely impractical (Isaacs *et al*, 1966). The four engineers determined what type of material would be required to build a space elevator, assuming it would be a straight cable with no variations in its cross section. They found that the strength required would be twice that of any existing material including graphite, quartz and diamond.

Then in 1975, Jerome Pearson, an aerospace engineer with the Air Force Research Lab near Dayton, Ohio, independently discovered the concept and published it in the international journal *Acta Astronautica* (Pearson, 1975). This technical article made the international aerospace community aware of the space elevator for the first time. An Air Force painting of Pearson's space elevator is shown in Figure D-2, with capsules moving up and down from the space complex in synchronous orbit. His discovery included using the space elevator for zero-net-energy space launching, and for launching payloads from the elevator tip to reach other planets without requiring rockets. He also was first to examine the dynamics of actually lifting payloads up the elevator, and found limitations on the speeds of ascent, akin to the critical velocities of a rotating shaft and the periodic loads from soldiers marching on a bridge.

A few years later in 1978, Arthur C. Clarke introduced the concept of a space elevator to a broader audience in his novel "The Fountains of Paradise" (Clarke, 1979). His main character built a space elevator close to the equator on a mountain top with similar engineering traits to today's concepts. Paul Penzo then extended the idea of space elevators and tethers to Phobos, the closest moon of Mars. He also proposed using a rotating tether to attach a spacecraft to asteroids, to change their orbits without rockets, like a gravitational assist.

One fundamental problem of building the space elevator is the phenomenal strength of materials required to support its mass over the 35,800-km height to geostationary orbit. Artsutanov and Pearson recognized that carbon "whiskers" representing perfect-crystal structures, might be one way to achieve the required strength. When carbon nanotube structures were discovered, it was realized immediately by Richard Smalley at Rice University in Houston, Texas and by Boris Yakobson at North Carolina State University that these super-strength materials would make the space elevator possible. The next big step was with the interest of NASA's Marshall's Advanced Projects Office in ideas such as the space elevator. David Smitherman of NASA completed a detailed study of the concept of space elevators in 1999 and concluded that in possibly 50 years or so, this method of cheap transportation to geostationary orbit could become a reality and dramatically lower the cost of getting into space. The plan was to capture a carbonaceous chondrite asteroid, drag it into a stable orbit around the Earth and mine it for the necessary material to make the cable, which would eventually reach down to the Earth's surface. His publication, "Space Elevators: An Advanced Earth-Space Infrastructure for the New Millennium" (Smitherman, 2006), is based on findings from a space infrastructure conference held at the Marshall Space Flight Center in 1999. The conference included scientists and engineers from government and industry representing various fields such as structures, space tethers, materials, and Earth/space environments.

It was using these older ideas and materials, that Bradley Edwards proposed a practical scheme for constructing a space elevator about the Earth, and received NASA funding for a study. His study resulted in a surprising conclusion: The space elevator could be developed within 15 years at a modest cost of less than $10 billion. His studies included calculations and analyses on fiber composed of epoxy-bonded carbon nanotubes, propulsion techniques, climber designs, location of base infrastructure, and cost/schedule estimates. "In 1999, we began examining what was a science fiction concept from a new direction, what is possible in the near future. At the time if we began a search of the internet we would have returned roughly 200 references to the space elevator. Last week it was well over 150,000. Part of this growing interest is the book that was published in 2003, as a result of a NIAC-funded study, "The Space Elevator". There are now hundreds of people working on some aspect or other of the space elevator (Edwards, 2004)." It is with this historical background that this present IAA study has been carried out.

Appendix E-1

Mega-Yuri Definition

The reason the Space Elevator community talks about Mega-Yuri is because it measures THE critical attribute for a material capable of constructing one. This is because most of the tension of an SE is caused by its own mass. Mass which has weight below geosynchronous orbit, increasingly as you get closer to the Earth's surface, and mass which has centrifugal force into space above GEO, increasingly as you get further away. In both cases, those forces are creating tension on the ribbon at the "center." More mass means more tension, so the material has to be strong enough to withstand inherent tension – but the less dense it is, the less mass involved, and thus lower tension forces. This required attribute - being very strong yet very light - is why carbon nanotubes (CNTs) are the leading contender for the material with which to build a feasible space elevator.

Specific Strength is measured in stress/density, or Pascal/(kg/m3) in the SI system. For tether materials, it is convenient to measure strength in GPa and density in g/cc, so the everyday unit used is GPa-cc/g, which is equal to 1E6 Pascal/(kg/m3). In another system, the measuring force is Newtons and linear density in g/km (a.k.a Tex) which gives the equivalent form of the unit - N/Tex. As if this wasn't enough, reducing the unit of Pascal/(kg/m3) to its basic units yields (m/s)2 - velocity squared! Rather than choosing between GPa-cc/g, N/tex, or Mega-(m/s)2, we propose to simply give all of them a name - a derived SI unit -- 1 Yuri = 1 (m/s)2, and thus 1 Mega-Yuri = 1 N/Tex = 1 GPa-cc/g. The traditional symbol used in engineering to denote stress is σ. We propose using τ as the symbol for Specific Strength or Tenacity. $\tau = \sigma/\rho$. This leads to the short version: a Mega-Yuri (or MYuri) is a measure of how strong (in tension) a material is relative to how dense (mass per volume) the material is. The technical version is:

> 1 Mega-Yuri = 1 GPa-cc/g, with
> Specific Strength or Tenacity (τ) = stress (σ) / density (ρ)
> Breaking length = $\tau / g = \sigma / \rho g$ where g is mean acceleration

The "Yuri" is named after Yuri Artsutanov, co-inventor of the SE. It has not yet been adopted as an officially named unit.

Table G1-I below gives some insight into why the potential for CNTs to have very high strength with low density is so critical to the feasibility of a Space Elevator. As noted above, the center of the ribbon [at GEO] has to be strong enough to hold the two Earth-ward and space-ward halves together, which can be thought of as how wide that point has to be compared to the bottom end at the Earth's surface, which only has to be wide enough to hold your payload. Thus the ribbon tapers from the middle out. The lower the MYuri of your favorite material, the higher the taper - dramatically so. The higher the taper, the larger the mass of the Space Elevator. At around 30 MYuri, we begin to enter feasibility, as a starter ribbon would weigh about 955 tons - for comparison, the Space Station masses 417 tons. At even higher MYuri materials, things get much better, such that a starter ribbon only weighs 44 tons - for comparison, the Space Shuttle could carry a 24 ton payload to LEO. Note that 10^{54} is
1,000,000,000,000,000,000,000,000,000,000,000,000,000,000,00 0,000.

	Steel	Zylon	Graphite Whiskers	CNT (low)	CNT (high)
Strength (GPa)	4.1	5.8	42	40*	130*
Density (g/cc)	7.8	1.5	2	.1.3*..	1.3*
MYuri	0.5	3.9	21	30.8	100
Taper	10^{52}.	14 billion	100	22	2.6
Tons of ribbon needed to lift 1 ton	10^{54}	2 trillion	5,000	955	44

Table G1-I. Comparison of properties of CNTs

Note: Much of this was paraphrased from Ben Shelef's work on space elevator development. His complete analysis is available at: http://www.isec.org/sec/index.php/about-the-space-elevator/terminology http://keithcu.com/wiki/index.php/Specific_Strength_in_Yuris

Appendix E-2
The Complexities of High Power Lasers for
Space Elevator Climb to GEO & Beyond

The baseline provided by Dr. Edwards and Eric Westling (2003) in their book "The Space Elevator" based the ascent of the climbers on being powered by large lasers on the surface of the ocean in the vicinity of the Marine Node. This has been the baseline for the last ten years as the idea has basic merit in that the energy did not originate on the tether climber, but on the surface of the Earth where energy is available and relatively inexpensive. Their conclusion was that taking the energy on the tether climber, as fuel in tanks, was a non-starter and could hinder the development of the concept. They are correct in their desire to not carry fuel; however, current analyses provide a new answer. The last ten years of discussions, conference papers, cosmic studies, and interest around the globe has lead to two conclusions:

- Solar Array technology is improving rapidly and will enable sufficient energy for climbing with very light-weight structures/arrays
- Laser power is too complex and difficult

The difficulty of using high-energy lasers covers many different engineering and physics arenas. The beauty of high-energy lasers is that there is definitely enough spare energy delivered to climb and conduct operations as the system rises above the surface of the ocean. However, the difficulties become overwhelming and are shown below.

Safety Issues
- Personnel on the ground [around high energy, nuclear or other]
- Personnel on the ground [pointing at climber on Marine Node at start]
- Laser platforms [one per climber, or 7 simultaneously] coordination and operations
- Over-flight of aircraft and operations of ships in area
- Over-flight of space systems

Reliability Issues
- Extremely high power needs to operate 24/7 365 days [none exist today at needed powers]
- Operations through rain and thunderstorms [clouds limit path]
- Pointing stability requires major equipment co-operations
- Pointing through the atmosphere requires adaptive optics, which would have to be extremely reliable to ensure proper energy on target, continuously.

Power Generation Needs
- Extremely high demands, Mega-watts needed
- Potential demand for nuclear when multiple lasers radiate
- Continuous irradiation of high energy for multiple climbers at long ranges creates tremendous heat problems locally, as well as extremely large energy demands
- Probably need one high energy laser for each tether climber plus spares for reliability needs
- Facilities require large laboratory like equipment with tremendous support equipment with the appropriate logistics tail, located in the middle of the ocean

Laser Clearinghouse Demands
- MUST have permission to radiate 24/7 365 – very difficult to obtain
- Risk damage to ALL satellites with their downward sensors such as; Earth Resources main telescopes, attitude sensors [Earth looking], science sensors. The energy impingement on satellite components has not been designed for. [it is high energy to climber at 60,000km distance, so at 400km, imagine the strength]
- In addition, GEO satellites are stationary with respect to the space elevator and will be in the beam [spill-off] of the high-energy laser for long periods of time. As most GEO satellites point at the Earth, the laser is impacting their sensitive side. This could lead to never receiving permission to radiate towards the tether climbers.

Solar Array Baseline
As a result of this conclusion – not to use high-energy lasers as a power source – the space elevator design team has concluded that the advancements in solar array's reduced mass and power efficiency will enable this source of energy to provide climbing power. The global space community is actively pursuing extremely lightweight solar arrays with remarkable efficiencies for future spacecraft. The projected numbers, in many cases using carbon nano-tube innovations, are impressive. As a result, the design team believes there will be sufficient advances to provide power during the daylight hours to climb to GEO and beyond. During the eclipse, the tether climber will go into hibernation and be prepared to climb at dawn. This is only significant during the first night of climb as the angle to the sun improves rapidly as the shadow of the Earth recedes. To enhance this approach, the team has pulled together a systems approach to provide energy to tether climbers with ubiquitous solar energy:

- **Step One**: Launch at dawn above the atmosphere [currently estimated to be 40km high]
- **Step Two**: Use fragile solar arrays for tether climber power with large arrays strung out below the climber with pointing capability for sun searching.
- **Step Three**: Hibernate during eclipse [maximum is around 4 to 6 hours for first night and rapidly goes down from there to continuous solar impingement soon after second day – depending on solar season]

Baseline Assumption: Must be placed at 30 or 40km altitude for sunrise start. There are four approaches being considered at this time to place the tether climber at 40km altitude [see chapters 4 and 6]:

- *High Stage One*: A permanent base station at 40km altitude capable of supporting 400 metric tons without impacting the space elevator tether.
- *Extension Cord to Altitude*: This alternative is one that protects the tether climber inside a CNT box during the ascent in the atmosphere and then releases the deployed tether climber at daybreak. The extension cord runs the climbing motor and drive train and is extremely light with CNT materials for strength and even conduction of power.
- *Spring Forward*: This alternative takes advantage of the elastic properties of the space elevator tether. The tether is pulled down 40km, the tether climber is attached in a protective box, and the tether pulls the package up to 40km with strain induced. The package is released for deployment and initiation of climb at daylight and the protective box is pulled down again for the next climber.
- *Laser Power to Altitude*: This is an alternative that would have a lower power laser working in the range of zero to forty kilometers on a one-on-one relationship for nighttime

movement from the surface of the ocean to the starting point. The tether climber would be enclosed in a protective shield for the environment and deployed at altitude.

Figure G2-1 below is an image by Frank Chase showing tether climber, tether climber solar arrays stored to get to 40km altitude and then the deployed solar arrays for ascending to GEO and beyond.

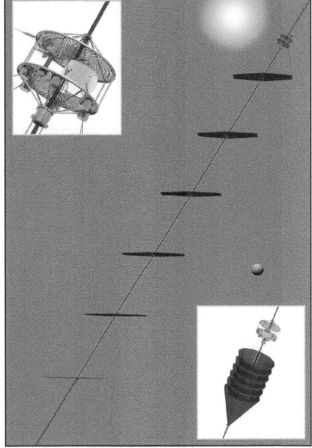

Figure G2-1. Tether and array [Chase]

Appendix E-3
Summary of Space Tethers

The earliest experiments on space tethers took place in the 1960s. In two separate experiments in 1966, the Gemini 11 and 12 manned capsules were connected by a 36m cable to their respective Agena upper stage. With considerable difficulty the astronauts manually controlled the tethered system they were a part of using cold gas thrusters, in order to bring the system first in a gravity gradient stabilized position and then in rotation. The Gemini 12 crew succeeded to achieve a somewhat stabilized vertical orientation. The complex dynamics encountered during these bold trials with short tethers may have been the reason it took 14 years before tethers were deployed in space again. Tether experimentation in the eighties and early nineties was dominated by modest short suborbital flights. Japanese, U.S. and later also Canadian sounding rocket experiments used conducting tethers to investigate their interaction with the Earth ionosphere. The first Tethered Payload Experiments (TPE) suffered from deployment problems, but with assistance from cold gas thrusters the various CHARGE (Cooperative High Altitude Rocket Gun Experiment) and OEDIPUS (Observations of Electric-field Distribution in the Ionospheric Plasma – a Unique Strategy) missions were completed successfully, with tether lengths ranging from 400m to 1174m. Table I provides an overview of the major suborbital and orbital tether experiments that have been built and (in most cases) flown to date, as well as relevant references for each.

From these technically modest experiments it was a large step to the 19.6km, 2mm thick and layered electric cable that was deployed from the Space Shuttle in 1992 as part of the American-Italian Tethered Satellite System (TSS). The objective was to deploy the tether upward out of the Shuttle, collect electrons at the far end using a 1.6m diameter endmass as anode and study the tether electrodynamics as a result of the current flowing through the tether. The complex, actively controlled reel system got stuck after 268m of deployment, but the tethered satellite could be successfully retrieved and returned to Earth. In 1996, during the TSS-1R reflight of the same equipment, 19.6km of tether was deployed exposing the endmass to an emf of as much as 3500V. A current of several amperes caused significant dynamics in the tether, and a significant Lorentz drag force must have acted on the Space Shuttle. A clear skip-rope motion was observed in the tether. The experiment also provided a wealth of information concerning the electron collection behavior of large charged spheres in a plasma. Unfortunately, the tether was severed near the Shuttle end due to sparking after damage due to debris or meteoroid impact (Chobotov, 1999).

A less ambitious orbital electrodynamic tether experiment was performed in 1993, the Plasma Motor Generator (PMG), a 500m tether attached to a Delta upper stage. PMG succeeded in demonstrating that the Lorentz drag force can be turned around into a thrust force, by actively sending electrons upward through the cable. Highly successful mechanical tether experiments were NASA's Small Expendable Deployer System missions, SEDS-1 and SEDS-2. They each deployed downward 20km of a 0.78mm line braided from a special polyethylene fiber material, Spectra, again from a Delta upperstage. A small subsatellite as endmass transmitted dynamics data to the ground whereas the deployed length and tension were measured on the Delta side. SEDS-1 deployed the tether with an open-loop control and ended in a swing and subsequent release and re-entry of the tether and subsatellite. SEDS-2 took a step further with a closed-loop controlled deployment to a stable vertical position of the tether. Unexpectedly, the SEDS-2 tether was severed just 3.7 days after successful completion of the mission, most probably by a debris particle.

Recent data indicates however that the SEDS-2 cut must have been an anomaly. The Naval Research Lab's 4km long, 2mm thick tether of TiPS (Tether Physics and Survivability) was unwound in May 1996, using also SEDS deployer technology. It was orbiting for over a decade in vertical orientation, with a slight oscillation, to be cut only in July 2006 (VSO, 2010), providing evidence that many tether lifetime estimations that are based on ground-based impact testing are too conservative. Nevertheless, especially the TSS-1R and SEDS-2 tether severings have resulted in the evidently false, but widely-held belief that tethers in space are severely prone to failure. Only recently, nearly a decade after ATeX, new tether experiments have been launched, all developed in educational context, and with mixed results. In 2007, the European Space Agency's 2nd Young Engineers' Satellite (YES2) deployed a 32km tether, the first controlled deployment in two stages as part of a SpaceMail demonstration (accurate capsule re-entry).

Year	Experiment	Length [km]	Technology	Objective	Success	Remark	Ref.
1966	Gemini 11	0.036	Mechanical link between Gemini	Artificial gravity	YES	Spin stable 0.15 rpm Manned with manual	NASA 1967
1966	Gemini 12	0.04	and Athena upper stage	Gravity gradient stabilization	MOSTLY	control	
1980	TPE-1	0.04 of 0.4	Conductive	Plasma interaction and VHF wave generation	PARTLY	Suborbital	
1981	TPE-2	0.07 of 0.4			PARTLY		Sasaki 1987
1983	Charge-1	0.418	Cold gas assisted		MOSTLY		Sasaki 1994
1985	Charge-2	0.426			YES		
1992	Charge-2B	0.4			YES		
1989	Oedipus-A	0.959	Conductive Cold gas assisted	Ionospheric science	YES	Suborbital	Tyc 1995
1995	Oedipus-C	1.174	Passive reel		YES		Vigneron 1997
1992	TSS-1	0.268 of 19.6	Conductive, active reel deployment	Electrodynamic Power generation	NO	Shuttle missions. Tether jammed	Dobrowolny 1994
1996	TSS-1R	19.6			MOSTLY	Tether broke after science success	Gilchrist 1998
1993	PMG	0.5	Conductive insulated tether, passive spool	Power and thrust	YES	7 hrs experiment piggyback on Delta	McCoy 1995
1993	SEDS-1	20	Mechanical, brake + spool	Swing & cut	YES	SEDS-2 probably cut	Carroll 1993
1994	SEDS-2	19.7		Controlled deployment	YES	by debris after mission completion	Carroll 1995.I
1996	TiPS	4	Mechanical, passive spool	Study survival and stability	YES	Cut after 1 decade in orbit	Barnds 1998
2005	ProSEDS	(13.1)	Bare conductive/ mechanical, brake + spool	Thrust	-	Cancelled for ISS safety	Johnson 2003
1997	YES	(35)	Mechanical, double-strand, brake + spool	Rotation, re-entry	-	GTO. Not deployed due to unsafe orbit	Kruijff 1999.II
2007	YES2	31.7	Mechanical, brake + spool	Accurate re-entry of a scientific capsule	MOSTLY	Full two-stage deployment. Overdeployed.	Kruijff 2009.I, II
1998	ATeX	0.02 of 6.2	Mechanical, tape, reel, active	Stability & control	NO	S/W stopped deployment	Zedd 1998
2000	METS	(5)	Bare conductive tape/mechanical, passive reel	Thrust (Mir station)	-	Cancelled as Mir was deorbited	Levin 2007
2007	MAST	0? of 1.0	Multistrand plus inspector crawler	Study tether survivability	NO	Minimal deployment	Hoyt 2003
2010	T-REX	0.14 of 0.3	Conductive bare tether tape, passive folded	Deployment and current collection demonstrator	MOSTLY	Suborbital Successfully deployed, video	Fujii 2009

Table I. Overview of major tether experiments to date, by chronology of experiment family. Experiments with length between brackets were not launched or deployment was not started. In addition, from 2000 onward, a number of picosat missions have been performed: e.g. Picosats 21/23 (2000), Picosats 7/8 (2001), MEPSI-1 (2002), MEPSI-2 (2006) and Aerocube-3 (2009). These missions aimed to connect two cubesat endmasses by a tether of 15-60m length.

Acknowledgement
Based upon Ph.D. Dissertation by Michiel Kruijff entitled, "Tethers in Space," Uitgeverij BoxPress, Oisterwijk, 2011.

Appendix E-4
Selection of Factor of Safety: 1.4 for Tether

For the initial unmanned version of the space elevator, the factor of safety should be 1.4. The rationale is:

Factor of Safety = Material Strength/Design Load or
$$FS = MS/DL$$

- The investment to initiate a space elevator will be large, driving exhaustive modeling of the space elevator tether. The calculations will be complex in order to precisely estimate maximum stress loads within the tether vs. the mass of the space elevator tether [+climbers, +wind loads, etc.]. In addition to the computer modeling, there will be extensive proof testing of materials leading up to the "flight tether."
- The safety factor for aerospace ranges from 1.2 to 1.5 as a result of the demanding requirement for saving mass coupled with modeling techniques to estimate actual loading forces. In addition, the aerospace industry conducts quality control checks and frequent inspections during production to ensure safety factors are maintained.
- Mass savings in the tether will be one of the principle drivers in this calculation. The cost of the system will be driven by the complexity and stress demands of the space elevator tether.

It seems that the appropriate quotes would be...

"who can design and build machines that are sufficiently strong but not too strong."

"For some reason, lost in time, the standard FS for human space flight is 1.4, just slightly less than that for aviation."

"Expendable launch vehicles are generally built to even lower factors of safety: 1.25 being commonplace and 1.1 also used at times. These lower factors of safety are a recognition of the additional risk that is allowed for cargo but not humans and the extreme importance of light weight."

Should we go to a safety factor of 1.25 and do even more calculations? Probably not. The safety factor should be 1.4 for the space elevator tether.
Note: Ben Shelef (2011) in his Feasibility Condition paper used 33% safety factor.
It is worth quoting a few lines from a blog entry by Wayne Hale entitled "Factors of Safety" which provides some additional perspective
(http://blogs.nasa.gov/cm/blog/waynehalesblog/posts/post_1229459081779.html)

"It's a dry passage but I'd like to quote from one of my old college textbooks on this subject (Phelan, 1970):

" . . . the choice of an appropriate factor of safety is one of the most important decisions the designer must make. Since the penalty for choosing too small a factor of safety is obvious, the tendency is to make sure that the design is safe by using an arbitrarily large value and overdesigning the part. (Using an extra-large factor of safety to avoid more exacting calculations or developmental testing might well be considered a case of "under-designing" rather than "overdesigning.") In many instances, where only one or very few parts are to be made, overdesigning may well prove to be the most economical as well as the safest solution. For large-scale production, however, the increased material and manufacturing costs associated with overdesigned parts result in a favorable competitive position for the manufacturer who can design and build machines that are sufficiently strong but not too strong."

As will be evident, the cost involved in the design, research, and development necessary to give the lightest possible machine will be too great in most situations to justify the selection of a low factor of safety. An exception is in the aerospace industry, where the necessity for the lightest possible construction justifies the extra expense.

Some general considerations in choosing a factor of safety are . . . the extent to which human life and property may be endangered by the failure of the machine . . . the reliability required of the machine . . . the price class of the machine.

Standards for factors of safety are all over the place. Most famously, the standard factor of safety for the cables in elevators is 11. So you could, if space allowed, pack eleven times as many people into an elevator as the placard says and possibly survive the ride. For many applications, 4 is considered to be a good number. In the shuttle program the standard factor of safety for all the ground equipment and tools is 4.

In the aircraft industry, a factor of safety standard is 1.5. Think about that when you get on a commercial airliner some time. The slim factor of safety represents the importance of weight in aviation. It also means that much more time, engineering analysis, and testing has gone into the determination of maximum load and the properties of the parts on the plane.

For some reason, lost in time, the standard FS for human space flight is 1.4, just slightly less than that for aviation. That extra 0.1 on the FS costs a huge amount of engineering work, but pays dividends in weight savings. This FS is codified in the NASA Human Ratings Requirements for Space Systems, NPR 8705.2. Well, actually, that requirements document only references the detailed engineering design requirements where the 1.4 FS lives.

Expendable launch vehicles are generally built to even lower factors of safety: 1.25 being commonplace and 1.1 also used at times. These lower factors of safety are a recognition of the additional risk that is allowed for cargo but not humans and the extreme importance of light weight.""

Appendix E-5
Tether Substantiation Methods

The baseline approach in this report for going from a weak initial tether light enough to launch to one that is thick enough for the desired payloads has been to deploy a uniform stress tether, and build it up progressively while maintaining the uniform stress profile using climbers, as in Chapter 4. While the uniform stress profile is optimal when the goal is to transport mass up a static tether, it is not necessarily the optimal profile for getting tether mass up as quickly as possible. In this section, we consider the use of tethers that have an exponential taper. For more details, the reader is referred to "Exponential tethers for accelerated space elevator deployment"(Gassend, 2004).

Exponentially Tapered Tether Basics

With an exponentially tapered tether, the cross section of the tether goes like $exp(z/a)$, where z is altitude, and a is the characteristic height of the taper. If a is positive, then the tether is skinny at the surface of the Earth, and increases in cross section with altitude, which we shall call normal taper. If a is negative, then the tether is widest at the surface of the Earth, and decreases with altitude, which we shall call inverse taper. For a given material, there are structural limits on an exponential tether. If it is to reach the surface of the Earth, the characteristic height a must be above some limit. Moreover, there will be a limit to how far the tether can reach beyond GEO. As we shall see, inverse taper tethers are best suited to space elevator deployment. Unfortunately, they can only exist for tethers that have a working strength greater than 48.5 MYuri, the critical strength beyond which an un-tapered tether can support itself. Exponentially tapered tethers have the useful property that if you pull the tether up or down, its taper profile remains unchanged. This property will be used by the various buildup methods described below.

Reel to Reel Elevator Buildup

If the tether is stronger than 48.5 MYuri, then it is possible to deploy an initial tether with inverse taper, and an apex anchor containing a large reel. Once the tether is anchored, the reel at the apex anchor starts to reel up tether material while new material is fed from the surface of the Earth. Because of the inverse taper profile, the elevator's cross section increases with time. The apex anchor's mass also increases as it reels in tether material keeping the elevator in equilibrium. The key metric for characterizing space elevator buildup is growth rate, which characterizes how much time it takes for the elevator cross-section to be multiplied by some amount. As shown in "Exponential tethers for accelerated space elevator deployment" (Gassend, 2004), the Reel-to-Reel buildup method's growth rate surpasses the optimal climber-based method for tethers with working strength greater than 55.4 MYuri. For practical climber-based methods (climber not 100% tether material, non-zero spacing between climbers), the Reel-to-Reel approach surpasses the climber approach at somewhat lower tether strengths. Intuitively, the improved buildup rate for the Reel-to-Reel approach compared with climber-based approaches can be understood as follows. In the climber-based approach, a small amount of mass is lifted along a static elevator. The only mass going up at any given point in time is the climber and its payload. With the Reel-to-Reel approach (and the other exponentially tapered tether approaches considered below), the whole tether is moving up, so the amount of mass going up per unit time is greater. However, lifting a lot of mass per unit time is only useful for elevator buildup if the negative taper is sufficient to allow the tether's cross section to grow at a significant rate. If the negative taper is not sufficient then the mass all ends up going into the apex anchor, where it does not help substantiate the tether. This explains why the Reel-to-Reel approach is not very effective as the critical 55.4 MYuri strength for an un-tapered tether is approached. The Redeploy-and-Splice method considered below is able to extend the benefits of exponentially tapered tethers at the cost of increased complexity.

Pull Down Elevator
The Reel-to-Reel deployment method has the advantage over climber-based approaches that it avoids any tether splicing in space. However, it moves the energy expenditure from the climbers to the apex anchor, which can be problematic. First, the already difficult power-beaming problem becomes even more difficult, since the full power must now be delivered all the way out to the apex anchor. An alternative could be solar cells at the apex anchor to ensure continuous power. Second, the machinery at the apex anchor must be scaled so that it can deliver the power necessary for the final elevator, or it must be replaced/expanded as buildup progresses.

An improved approach is for the apex anchor to simply be an inert mass with a pulley. The exponential tether goes from the surface of the Earth up to the pulley, and then back down to Earth. On one side of the pulley, the taper is inverse, on the other it is normal. Now deployment progresses by reeling in tether at the base of the normal taper side of the tether, and reeling it out at the base of the inverse taper side of the tether. The deployment is now directly powered from the ground, with the machinery needed for the deployment all on the ground where it can be easily maintained or scaled with tether growth. In this approach, the apex anchor mass can be grown by splitting the tether at the apex anchor, with one portion being reeled up at the apex anchor to be used as mass, and the other returning to Earth. It should be note that this approach has some structural constraints that limit taper ratio in addition to the ones that apply for the Reel-to-Reel approach.

Slice Off Approach
Another variant of the reel-to-reel approach is to use centrifugal force to drive tether deployment "Segment Based Ribbon Architecture" (Shelef, 2004). In this approach, the tether is made long enough that it will support itself without any apex anchor. If the tether is made slightly longer than this, then centrifugal force will pull more tether material from the Earth. The top of the tether is then periodically broken to keep the amount of centrifugal force, and hence the stress in the tether, bounded.

Redeploy and Splice Approach
The major drawback of the approaches described above is that they require a negative taper tether, and hence only work with materials having a working stress greater than 55.4 MYuri, significantly greater than the strengths assumed in the rest of this report. With the Redeploy-and-Splice approach, it is possible to grow the tether using normal taper tethers allowing the benefits of exponential tethers to be extended to weaker tether materials. In this method, the apex anchor reels up one earth-to-apex-anchor length of tether onto a spool at the apex anchor. Then it cuts the tether at the apex-anchor, and reels up a second earth-apex-anchor length of tether onto a second spool. Then the tethers from the two spools are pulled back down to Earth. As they are being pulled down, machinery at the apex anchor splices the two tethers into a single thicker tether. When the pull-down phase completes, the tether has grown by a factor $1+exp(-a/L)$, where L is the length of the elevator. This approach is slower and more complex than the previously described methods as material must be pulled up and then back down. It also places more complexity and power use at the apex anchor, including some splicing (though less than in climber-based buildup). It never beats the optimal climber-based method's growth rate, but, for example, it does beat climber methods with one launch every

three days down to 32.3 MYuri. Below about 30 MYuri, the growth rate rapidly becomes very low and this method is not practical.

Breeder Elevator
Exponentially tapered tethers can also be useful for creating multiple space elevators from a single one. Applying the Redeploy-and-Splice method without splicing the two tethers as they are reeled back down yields two tethers that can be split apart and used as separate elevators. This approach is beneficial as long as it is faster to get the elevator mass into space this way than it would be using climbers.

Conclusions
Exponential taper buildup methods are the fastest and simplest way to build up an elevator with materials well above the untapered taper limit. However, for the lower strength tethers considered in this report, the case is much less clear. At worst, at 27 MYuri, exponential tethers are not practical. Above about 30 MYuri they start being able to compete with climber-based methods, depending on the details of how the climber-based method is implemented, and the difficulty of powering reeling operations in space, and splicing tethers in space.

Finding: "Exponentially tapered tether approaches deserve careful evaluation in the future for both tether buildup and subsequent tether deployment."

Appendix F – International Space Elevator Organizations

At the present time, the following key international organizations are studying and developing the space elevator concept with EuroSpaceward sponsoring international conferences:

Name	Goal	Approach	Location
International Space Elevator Consortium	"... ISEC promotes the development, construction and operation of a space elevator as a revolutionary and efficient way into space for all humanity ..."	ISEC's plan of action is based upon yearly themes.. The results are a Conference focus, a year-long study effort resulting in a report, and a theme for the yearly Journal, Climb. 2010 was Space Debris survivability with 2011 focusing on CNT's. 2012 resulted in a Space Elevator Concept of Operations while 2013 is looking at tether climbers.	www.isec.org Holds yearly conference in Seattle, co-sponsored by Microsoft and the Museum of Flight.
Euro Spaceward Association	EuroSpaceward's mission – preserving and improving life on Earth by going into space	The fate of humanity depends very much on its ability to harness all planetary energy and develop a sustainable ecology, economy, and biosphere. Hence EuroSpaceward envisions to: lastingly contribute to the technical development of mankind in order to enable its evolvement to a type I civilization which masters planetary survival by harnessing all planetary energy and having developed a sustainable ecology, economy and biosphere. Organizes EUSEC – European Space Elevator Challenge; and conference on Space Elevator Systems	www.eurospaceward.org
Japan Space Elevator Association	JSEA's objectives: - Accumulate knowledge and develop the technology for constructing Space Elevator. - Enlighten widely people on the importance of Space Elevator. - Make the construction of Space Elevator socially meaningful.	JSEA's activities: - Annual conference about Space Elevator - Annual technology challenge about climber and tethered balloon system - Outreach program for students - Supervising books, movies and events about Space Elevator - Media exposure and exhibitions	http://jsea.jp/
International Academy of Astronautics	Foster the development of astronautics for peaceful purposes; Recognize individuals who have distinguished themselves in a related branch of science or technology; Provide a program through which members may contribute to international endeavors; Encourage international cooperation in advancement of aerospace science.	The Space Elevator Study Group, consisting of 40 authors and editors from around the globe, addressed the feasibility of the concept and proposed a roadmap. The study group reports to the Commissions and are groups of experts in charge of producing an Academy report within a timeframe of 3 years or less. Many are Academy elected members and some are invited to assist in the study from an area of specialty. Sessions on Space Elevator topics are included every year in the International Astronautical Congress under the auspices of the IAA.	www.iaaweb.org

Appendix G
Consolidated Study Findings

This appendix pulls together, in one convenient place, the various findings from the different chapters. The findings reflect the analysis accomplished over the study period and are the contributions of the authors and the editors.

G.1   Findings

Chapter 1 - Introduction

Finding 1-1:   The space elevator will improve the human environment. The characteristics of a routine, on schedule (7 times a week), $500/kg fee, non-explosive service, without major pollution or launch shake-rattle-roll and without major restrictions on packaging of the payload, will lead to robust demand for space elevators.

Chapter 3 - Tether Material

Finding 3-1:   Space elevators can be developed with 30 MYuri tethers, as explained in the feasibility condition (Shelef, 2011).

Finding 3-2:   If growth in specific strength continues at the same pace, it is possible that yarns with specific strengths in the range of 20 MYuri can be demonstrated as early as 2015. Scaling up the process to lengths in excess of 1000km might take a couple of years, meaning that a space elevator tether could be available before 2025.

Finding 3-3:   CNTs are not the only available material. Multiple alternatives exist, ranging from polymers (polyethylene, polyborazylene, etc) to boron nitride nanotubes and diamonds.

Finding 3-4: The design of the tether has a taper ratio to compensate for the greater tensions near the GEO node. With the current strength projections, the expected taper ratio will be less than eight.

Finding 3-5: The macro design of the space elevator tether is a sparsely filled, one-meter wide, curved, woven tether that is designed for winds under 100kms altitude and debris between 200 and 2,000kms altitude.

Chapter 4 - Tether Climbers

Finding 4-1:   CNT materials will be incorporated into the structural design and will substantially lessen the mass of components and structures through-out future space elevator satellites, including all varieties of tether climbers.

Finding 4-2:   The strongest concept for tether climbers is solar only from 40km altitude based upon projection of technology. There are three viable concepts to move the climber from the Marine Node to the appropriate starting altitude: box satellite with extension cord, spring forward, and High Stage One.

Finding 4-3: Large, light-weight, deployable, advanced solar arrays will power the tether climbers above 40km altitude.

Finding 4-4: Operations are to launch at daybreak from above the atmosphere, climb using solar during the first day, rest during the first night, and then solar during the rest of the trip [with small eclipses outage]

Finding 4-5: Although massive at 86.5 metric tons, the movement from LEO to the GEO node of the deployment satellite is not technologically challenging. Improvements in mass to GEO could be gained with significant improvement in thruster performance by demanding development of massive ion engines or equivalent efficiency improvements.

Chapter 5 - End Station Infrastructure (Base & Apex Anchor)

Finding 5-1: The Apex Anchor will be at roughly 100,000km altitude and will provide significant tension in the ribbon to adapt to the various forces on the tether dynamics, including tidal forces and tether climber motion.

Finding 5-2: The Apex Anchor will do far more than "just be a mass at the end of the space elevator."

Finding 5-3: There are many good locations for the terrestrial stage, but the most obvious ones are near the equator in the middle of the ocean. The preferred option is 1000km west of Galapagos.

Finding 5-4: Stage One will either be on the surface of the ocean or at a reasonable altitude [30-50km] escaping the Earth's atmosphere. This trade is being undertaken and clearer choices will be available in the near future.

Finding 5-5: Marine Stage One has tremendous operational advantages. Its primary advantage is that ocean-going operations are routine with international delivery of materials and cargo becoming less expensive and more reliable every year. This is based upon thousands of years of ocean transportation of goods and over 120 years of ocean drilling platforms.

Finding 5-6: The High Stage One has tremendous operational advantages. However, as technological maturity is less than optimum, there must be a risk reduction program with significant early prototype testing.

Finding 5-7: The strongest concept for space elevator climber is solar only from 40km altitude based on projection of technology. As such, there are three viable concepts that will move the climber from the Marine Node to the appropriate starting altitude: extension cord, spring forward, and High Stage One.

Chapter 6 - Dynamics & Deployment

Finding 6-1: If the necessary tether to apex anchor mass ratio is not maintained, the structure will not maintain nominal equilibrium: it will find a slightly modified equilibrium configuration – one where the stress profile is no longer constant.

Finding 6-2: The nominal space elevator system consisting of a deployed tether and Apex Anchor is a stable one for linearized stationary vibrational modes.

Finding 6-3: The space elevator dynamics due to ascending or descending tether climbers are well-behaved.

Chapter 7 - Systems Design for Environment

Finding 7-1: The environmental threats to a space elevator are not significantly different from historical threats to orbiting spacecraft, reflecting on the differences in motion – orbiting around the Earth vs. rotating with the Earth. Similarities will be obvious for Human transportation and when designing for the atmospheric portions of the space elevator. The large scale of the space elevator crosses many environment regions which increases complexity.

Finding 7-2: Incorporating the concept of initiating the tether climber at altitude enables the tether operators to successfully monitor, move and adjust the space elevator tether depending upon the environment, including winds. As such, winds aloft become an operational planning challenge, not a risk to the program.

Finding 7-3: Electromagnetic effects on the space elevator tether must be studied in detail in the near future. The estimate is that the electric and magnetic fields and currents will not affect operations, but could enhance them.

Finding 7-4: This large transportation infrastructure must be valued and protected as airports around the world are currently. Physical protection, personnel monitoring, and active sensors should ensure that the human element does not affect operations of the space elevator.

Finding 7-5: Radiation is not a problem for tether climbers, as the designers will incorporate this threat into the design requirements and ensure operational success through any radiation environment. Historic precedence supports this conclusion as the space community runs spacecraft in all the regions where the space elevator will be operating. However, when people are included in the tether climb [after some years of robotic success], the radiation problem becomes an order of magnitude more difficult. There are many ways to reduce the radiation and shorten the trip, which will have to be incorporated when the human element is added.

Finding 7-6: Design for thermal control has been a major element in space system survival in this hostile environment. The tether climber will leverage 50 years of historic lessons learned over 50 years and successfully manage its thermal characteristics in the long climb from the surface of the ocean to the Apex Anchor.

Finding 7-7: Spacecraft charging will need to be addressed by the design engineer, who will leverage 50 years of experience with this issue. Spacecraft charging will need to be designed for, but is not a risk for tether climbers.

Chapter 8 - Systems Design for Space Debris

Finding 8-1: In the GEO altitude region space debris is not a problem.

Finding 8-2: In the MEO altitude region space debris is not a problem.

Finding 8-3: Untracked, small [<10cm] debris will, on the average, impact a space elevator tether in the LEO altitude region [200-2000km] once every ten days. Therefore, the tether must be designed for impact velocities and energies. Putting this into perspective, there are 1,800,000 one-meter by one-meter squares as targets for an impact every ten days.

Finding 8-4: Tracked debris will impact the total LEO segment [200 – 2000km] once every 100 days or multiple times a year if no action is taken. Once again, tracked debris lends itself to mitigation through long range planning and operational movement of the space elevator tether at the correct altitude and time. This threat then becomes manageable.

Finding 8-5: Tracked debris will, on average, impact a single 60km stretch of a LEO space elevator every 18 years and every five years in the peak regions if no avoidance action is taken. In addition, there are some operational satellites that might choose to lessen their risks by planning their orbit maneuvers to coincide with the prediction of conjunctions with the tether.

Finding 8-6: The threat from LEO Space Debris is manageable with relatively modest design and operational procedures. For small debris, tether design will enable survivability while for tracked debris, movement will prevent collision.

Chapter 9 - Operations Concept

Finding 9-1: Operation of the space elevator will leverage over 50 years of experience in operating satellite systems. The tether climber, Apex Anchor, and GEO node are essentially satellites. Space elevator operations will be an easy extension of today's practices. Operations centers will look very much like today's satellite operations centers.

Finding 9-2: Operation of the space elevator will leverage more than a hundred years of experience in off-shore drilling operations. The Floating Operations Platform will likely be a modified drilling platform. Support to off-shore drilling platforms is a mature industry.

Finding 9-3: The operation and maintenance costs appear to be reasonable.

Chapter 10 - Summary of Technological Assessment

Finding 10.1: In all technological endeavors there are projections into the future. In the case of the space elevator, this study has recognized that there are two thrusts that must be taken:

Thrust ONE: Assume tether material is space qualified by 2030.
Thrust TWO: Assume tether material is available two decades later.

Each of these two thrusts has valid research projects leading to their estimates; however, no one can predict the future reliably, so this study will present both cases.

Finding 10.2: Based upon Thrust ONE, the space elevator should be available during the middle of the 2030 decade. Based upon Thrust TWO, the space elevator should be available after 2060. This is principally due to the availability of a tether material sufficiently strong to handle the longitudinal stresses inherent in a 100,000km long tether.

Finding 10.3: The remaining components of the space elevator have historical precedent and can be constructed as soon as needed with sufficient investment in design and production capability. The NASA Space Technology Roadmaps cover much of these major segments of the space elevator such as solar power, materials manufacturing, and nanotechnology.

Chapter 11 - Developmental Roadmaps

Finding 11-1: The development of a space elevator infrastructure will cross many timelines and require parallel tasking of activities. Future roadmaps will lead to space elevators around the world, identifying and lowering risks, as well as moving technologies up the maturity hierarchy.

Finding 11-2: Parallel prototype developmental programs must be established to lower risk and raise technology readiness levels (TRLs). The successful program will then enable a construction company to initiate development of a space elevator infrastructure in the 2035 time frame.

Finding 11-3: A parallel prototype testing environment should lead to a full up, in-orbit, flight demonstration by 2023–25.

Finding 11-4: The CNT material development is pacing the prototype testing activities.

Finding 11-5: There are three activities that should be initiated as soon as possible: initiate a program office; establish a process for identifying requirements; and develop and validate a simulation of the space elevator dynamics.

Chapter 12 - Legal and Regulatory Frameworks

Finding 12-1: The risk to the space elevator infrastructure from placing the base station inside a nation state's is too high to be acceptable.

Finding 12-2: The Marine Node of the space elevator will be in the ocean beyond the continental shelf and beyond any exclusive economic zone (EEZ) of individual countries. In addition, the Marine Node must be flexible enough to not infringe upon any nation's rights of movement.

Finding 12-3: As the space elevator is to be established stretching upward from the high seas on the equator, the undefined boundary between airspace and outer space is not a major problem.

Finding 12-4: The treaty, as the "Charter of Outer Space", established the principles governing the activities of states in the exploration and use of "Outer Space." As the treaty has been ratified by 100 countries to date, it can be said to have attained the status of an established law of nations [international customary law].

Finding 12-5: Multiple space elevator companies will require the support and sponsorship of sovereign nation state's.

Chapter 13 - Market Projections

Finding 13-1: Market projections show robust customers demand for multiple space elevators as soon as they are available. This is not surprising as the expected fee is $500 per kg or three orders of magnitude less than today's fees.

Finding 13-2: The traditional GEO and LEO markets could be satisfied with a fraction of a space elevator capacity.

Finding 13-3: Space Solar Power will drive the demand for space elevator infrastructure for safe, reliable, inexpensive and routine delivery of mass to GEO. One pair, and even three pairs, of space elevators will only minimally satisfy the needs of the SunSat Corporation.

Finding 13-4: The future demand from innovative businesses will exceed the initial supply.

Chapter 14 - Financial Perspective

Finding 14-1: Space elevators will make major profits in the long run. As in most transportation infrastructures, the initial investments are massive and will require flexibility and creative funding; however, as the profit potential is so great, there will be money to be invested.

G.2   Category Findings

Finding C-1, Technological Benefit: A space elevator with its mode of operations will dramatically lower the tremendous amount of pollutants resulting from rocket launches and reduce the debris creation.

- Space Elevator operations will open up human spaceflight.
- A space elevator, launching once per day for 365 days, will deliver significantly more to orbit than can be dreamed up today with rockets. One of the big advantages is that there would be no pollution from the chemical burning of thruster fuel as the rockets went from the surface of the Earth to the LEO environment.
- Once the space elevator was in operation, the debris in space would start being reduced by natural attrition as the creation of space debris would have been dramatically reduced. The space elevator does not leave major components, nor little pieces, as it ascends to its mission orbit.

Finding C-2. R&D Needs: Developing a space elevator infrastructure will require targeted research and development leading to:

- A space elevator that will be entirely doable by the decade of the 2030s! Materials are advancing steadily – solar power vs. lasers is safer, easier, and with less risk.
- Projections based upon progress to date, mainly with carbon nanotubes (CNTs), indicate that a suitable material is likely to become available in the 2020s. The required specific strength of tether material is 27 MYuri ($27MPa/(kg/m^3)$) plus a

safety margin of 40%. There is already a great deal of research on CNTs and other strong, lightweight, materials because of their many terrestrial applications. For the space elevator, research needs to focus on methods for achieving the necessary tether length.

- Prototype development of major segments of the space elevator during the next ten years in parallel with the tether material development.
- Recognition that the environmental threats are manageable [debris, radiation, charging, etc] to include human shielding for future travel.

Finding C-3, Business – Fifty Years of Experience: This study has lead the authors and editors to recognize that the past 50 years of space design and development will enable major components of the space elevator to be accomplished. Leveraging the last 50 years of space development will:

- Provide jobs, jobs, jobs.
- Encourage investors to chase large profits with new businesses.
- Enhance the tether climber design leveraging spacecraft design and production to ensure required power [from solar arrays], stiffness/ lightness [from graphic carbon composites – future with CNTs], and survivability [radiation hardness].
- Recognize that operations for a space elevator will be merely an extension of what we've accomplished throughout the solar system. In addition, the operations will present no risk, have reasonable costs, and could be accomplished today.

Finding C-4, Cultural – Opening up the Solar System: A single space elevator has the capacity to launch much more than the total payloads currently launched into space. Just as railways and railroads greatly increased the volume of freight and travel in the 19th century, space elevators are expected to stimulate rapid growth in space travel and exploitation, leading to greater prosperity and more options for solving existing problems. Opening up of the solar system with inexpensive, routine, safe, and massive avenues to GEO and beyond will:

- Open a new era in human progress which becomes possible as escape from Earth's gravity well becomes routine.
- Enable new missions to improve the human condition such as space solar power and disposal of nuclear waste.
- Drive new research and development.
- Encourage international cooperation.
- Create a cultural renaissance around the world.

International Academy of Astronautics

A Brief Description

Founded:
16 August 1960, Stockholm, Sweden, by Theodore Von Karman. Independent non-governmental organization recognized by the United Nations in 1996.

Aims:
Foster the development of astronautics for peaceful purposes;
Recognize individuals who have distinguished themselves in space science or technology;
Provide a program through which members may contribute to international endeavors; Promote international cooperation in the advancement of aerospace science.

Structure:
Regular Meeting (every two years). Board of Trustees (meets twice a year), consisting of: President; four Vice-Presidents and twenty-eight Trustees, seven from each Section: Basic Sciences, Engineering Sciences, Life Sciences and Social Sciences. Current President: Dr Madhavan G. Nair, Past-President: Prof. Edward C. Stone, USA, Vice-Presidents: Mr. Yannick d'Escatha, France; Prof Liu Jiyuan, China ; Dr. Hiroki Matsuo, Japan; Prof. Anatoly Perminov, Russia, Secretary General Dr. Jean-Michel Contant, France.

Activities:
Encourage international scientific cooperation through scientific symposia and meetings in the area of: - Space Physical Sciences, - Space Life Sciences, - Space Technology and System Development, - Space Systems Operations and Utilization, - Space Policy Law and Economy, - Space and Society Culture and Education. A major initiative of the Academy is the development of a series of "Cosmic Studies" and "Position Papers" dealing with the many aspects of international cooperation endeavors in: - The exploration and habitation of the solar system and beyond; - The space debris, - The small satellites, - Declaration of Principles Concerning Activities Following the Detection of Extraterrestrial Intelligence, - EVA Safety and Space Suit Interoperability, - Inexpensive Scientific Satellite Missions, - Lunar and Martian Exploration, - Next Steps in Exploring Deep Space, - Space to promote Peace, - Space Traffic Management, - Knowledge Management in Space Activities, - Cost Effective Earth Observation Missions.

Events:
Establishment of cooperation with national academies: The Royal Swedish Academy of Sciences (1985), the Austrian Academy of Sciences (1986, 1993), the Academy of Sciences of the Institute of France (1988, 2001), The Academy of Finland (1988), Indian Academy of Sciences (1990, 2007), The Royal Spanish Academy of Sciences (1989), German Academy of Sciences (1990), The Kingdom of Netherlands (1990), RSC: The Academies of Arts, Humanities and Sciences of Canada (1991), the U.S. National Academy of Sciences (1992, 2002), the U.S. National Academy of Engineering (1992, 2002), the Israel Academy of Sciences and Humanities (1994), Norwegian Academy of Science and Letters (1995), Chinese Academy of Sciences (1996, 2013), the Academy of Sciences of Turin (1997), the Australian Academy of Sciences (1998), The Royal Netherlands Academy of Arts and Sciences (1999), the Brazilian Academy of Sciences (2000), the U.S. National Institute of Medicine (2002) the Academy of Sciences of South Africa (ASSAf) (2011), the Royal Society of South Africa (2011), the Pontificia Academia Scientiarum (2012).

Publications:
The journal of the Academy, Acta Astronautica (elevating to impact factor 4th position upon 64 scientific journals); IAA e-newsletter; Yearbook, Dictionaries and CD-ROM in 24 languages (last languages added Afrikaner and Swahili), Position Papers and Cosmic Studies (https://shop.iaaweb.org/), IAA Book Series on Small Satellite - Programs, Missions; IAA Book Series on Conference and Symposium Proceedings; IAA Book Series on Remote Sensing of the Earth System - Science, Technologies and Applications; Scientific Papers Data Base on the IAA Web site.

Members:
Full and Corresponding Members (active: 1123) in four Trustee Sections; Honorary members (3); members in 81 countries.
- Africa: Algeria, Burkina Faso, Cameroon, Egypt, Ethiopia, Ivory Coast, Kenya, Libya, Morocco, Nigeria, Senegal, South Africa, Tunisia.
- Americas: Argentina, Bolivia, Brazil, Canada, Chile, Columbia, Cuba, Guatemala, Mexico, Peru, Uruguay, USA, Venezuela.
- Asia: Bahrain, Burma, China, India, Indonesia, Israel, Japan, Kazakhstan, Korea, Kuwait, Kyrgyz Republic, Malaysia, Mongolia, Pakistan, Saudi Arabia, Singapore, Sri Lanka, Syria, Thailand, Turkey, Vietnam.
- Europe: Armenia, Austria, Belarus, Belgium, Bulgaria, Croatia, Czech Rep., Denmark, Estonia, Finland, France, Germany, Greece, Hungary, Ireland, Italy, Latvia, Macedonia, Netherlands, Norway, Poland, Portugal, Romania, Russia, Serbia, Slovakia, Slovenia, Spain, Sweden, Switzerland, United Kingdom, Ukraine.
- Oceania: Australia, New Zealand.

Headquarters in Bern, Switzerland, **Secretariat:** 6 rue Galilée, 75116 Paris, France; Branches of Secretariat in Bangalore (India) and IAA Study Center in Beijing (China); Regional offices in Abuja (Nigeria), Tunis (Tunisia), Buea (Cameroon) and Nairobi (Kenya).
Mailing Address: IAA, PO Box 1268-16, F-75766 Paris Cedex 16, France
Telephone: 33 1 47 23 82 15, **Fax:** 33 1 47 23 82 16, email sgeneral@iaamail.org
Web Site: http://www.iaaweb.org https://shop.iaaweb.org/